CRIMINAL RESPONSIBILITY AND MENTAL DISEASE

CRIMINAL RESPONSIBILITY AND MENTAL DISEASE

By

C. R. JEFFERY

Director of Delinquency Research
Washington School of Psychiatry

Visiting Lecturer in Criminology
New York University Law School

With a Foreword by

Henry H. Foster, Jr.

Director, Law-Psychiatry Project
Professor of Law
New York University Law School

CHARLES C THOMAS • PUBLISHER
Springfield • Illinois • U.S.A.

Published and Distributed Throughout the World by

CHARLES C THOMAS • PUBLISHER

BANNERSTONE HOUSE

301-327 East Lawrence Avenue, Springfield, Illinois, U.S.A.

NATCHEZ PLANTATION HOUSE

735 North Atlantic Boulevard, Fort Lauderdale, Florida, U.S.A.

With THOMAS BOOKS *careful attention is given to all details of
manufacturing and design. It is the Publisher's desire to present books
that are satisfactory as to their physical qualities and artistic possibilities
and appropriate for their particular use.* THOMAS BOOKS *will be true
to those laws of quality that assure a good name and good will.*

To my wife
For whom dogma is heresy
And wisdom is skepticism

FOREWORD

THE CONFLUENCE of law, morality, science, and medicine is the general subject of this provocative study. The *Durham* rule, as it has been applied by the courts, is the focal point. A critical examination and evaluation is given law, psychiatry, and the behavioral sciences as to the treatment and processing of criminal offenders.

The author is well equipped by training and experience to undertake such a controversial task. Doctor Jeffery studied sociology under Sutherland, sat in on a criminal law course given by Jerome Hall, completed a freshman year at law school, achieved a doctorate in sociology, and has specialized in criminology for a number of years. Currently, he is teaching seminars in criminology and juvenile delinquency at the Law School of New York University and directing a project for "dropouts" in Washington, D. C. In his spare time, he writes books and serves as the Book Review Editor of the *Journal of Criminal Law, Criminology and Police Science.* He is a co-author of *Society and the Law* (1962). In other words, he is a busy man.

Lawyers and judges perhaps will find the chapters on the post-*Durham* cases of greatest interest, while behavioral scientists will better appreciate the second part of the book. Both parts merit careful reading but the last two chapters present the greatest challenge to law and psychiatry. Doctor Jeffery presents a strong case for an approach to crime and criminality in terms of experimental psychology, and depending upon whether or not one adopts his definition of "scientific," he makes a devastating attack upon psychiatrists as competent expert witnesses.

One need not accept the conclusions of this book nor the opinions of its author. If one disagrees, however, he may find it extremely difficult to formulate a convincing rebuttal. The premises of the criminal law are shaken, if not undermined.

Faith in what he calls the "religion" of psychiatry is impaired. If one agrees with Doctor Jeffery, a complete overhaul of our jurisprudence and the treatment of criminal offenders is imperative.

The sophisticated reader may find that he accepts some but not all of Doctor Jeffery's conclusions. For him, the addition of the dimension of experimental psychology and the affirmative case for such an approach may take precedence over the attacks upon psychiatry, and in a spirit of compromise such a reader may decide that we need both experimental psychology and psychiatry if we would begin to ameliorate the problem of crime and criminals in modern society. All too often the specialists, as the legendary blind men of Afghanistan, have seen but a portion of the problem. There are excellent summaries of such points of view.

The gist of the psychological approach to crime recommended by Doctor Jeffery is taken from B. F. Skinner and is summarized in the argument that, "If we are interested not only in predicting but also in controlling human behavior, we must search for stimulus-response laws." In other words, in order to control behavior, we must control the stimuli, and we cannot control one response with another response. Of course, it may be impossible to control the stimuli. As long as there are women, some males will be stimulated to seduction or rape unless there is a counter aversive stimuli. However, Jeffery's emphasis upon the control of behavior by environmental contingencies and his exposition of the experimental method are most welcome and convincing, and should find increasing acceptance in legal circles.

Since man, human behavior, and law cannot be analyzed or evaluated only in scientific terms, an acceptance of the premises of experimental psychology provides only partial answers or one method of approach to complex problems.

The corpus of the criminal law constitutes an expression of social values, religious dogma, superstition, moral sentiment, and state concern. Historically, religion and morality, rather than science or medicine, have been the fonts for the criminal law. As a matter of fact, when the law has too eagerly followed current scientific fads. such as it did in the case of so-called sex psychopath laws and in laws permitting the sterilization of habitual criminals, the results were far from efficacious. Public support, resources, personnel, adequate facilities, all must co-exist or specialized treatment of sex offenders becomes an euphomism for incarceration. So too, the juvenile delinquent or the alleged mental incompetent is imprisoned rather than "treated" if, in fact, the institution where he is committed lacks adequate resources and personnel.

It is hoped that this volume will receive a wide audience and will provoke fruitful discussion. There are many dimensions to the problems here raised, and support should be forthcoming for projects that will test the thesis of the prime importance of environmental control in the regulation of criminal behavior.

HENRY H. FOSTER, JR.

PREFACE

THOUGH the issues discussed in this report are related to one jurisdiction, namely, the District of Columbia, the issues themselves are general and are to be found embodied in the criminal law both in this country and abroad. The insanity defense raises the issue of the purpose of criminal law—treatment and rehabilitation versus punishment and revenge. The protection of society issue can be defended in terms of either a treatment or a punitive philosophy of criminal law.

Also basic to the insanity defense is the issue of free will versus determinism. The defense of insanity rests upon the assumption that insanity negates free will, and the law does not punish people who lack the capacity for free choice; whereas a person who of his own free will commits a crime is legally responsible and should be punished.

The law is based on social policy and ethics. The law, however, also admits expert testimony as to why the defendant committed a criminal act. Such testimony is based not on a philosophical position of free will, but on a scientific position of determinism. The issue is thus shifted from "Did the defendant's act result from free will?" to "Did the defendant have a mental disease and did the mental disease cause the criminal act?" Scientific explanations of behavior often conflict with philosophical notions concerning human nature, and in the insanity defense, we see this conflict as it has been institutionalized in our legal structures.

To add to the difficulty, the expert testimony given in court concerning human behavior is itself subject to careful analysis, since in many ways such testimony is not based upon scientific evidence. Psychiatric and psychological testimony is often contradictory and subject to question by both scientists and lawyers. The insanity defense portrays crime as a *medical* problem, whereas evidence can be introduced which indicates it is more fruitful perhaps to regard crime as a *social* problem. The experts on crime in our courtrooms are experts on medicine, and not experts on social problems and social behavior.

Sociologists, criminologists, and experimental psychologists do not testify in court as to the reasons people become criminals, though it is generally agreed that criminal behavior is learned behavior involving group processes.

These several issues will be discussed and developed in terms of the new definition of criminal responsibility contained in the *Durham* rule.

C. R. JEFFERY

INTRODUCTION

IN 1954, David L. Bazelon, Chief Judge, United States Court of Appeals, Washington, D. C., put forth the case of *United States vs. Durham*, 214 F. 2d 862, a new legal doctrine concerning the meaning of insanity and responsibility. What would otherwise have been a routine criminal case (Monte Durham was charged with housebreaking) now stands out in criminal law as a twentieth century landmark in the legal definition of crime and insanity. Not since the famous case of *Daniel M'Nagten* in 1843, 8 Eng. Rep. 718, has a case caused so much comment and discussion in legal and psychiatric circles.

In order to gain knowledge of the actual operation of the *Durham* rule in the District of Columbia, a research project was undertaken entitled "Criminal Law and Psychiatry in the District of Columbia." Richard Arens, Attorney-at-Law, was appointed director of the project. In 1962, the author of this report was added to the project staff as senior social scientist and co-investigator.

This document is divided into two parts: The first is concerned with the methodology and findings of the research project; and the second, with an analysis of these findings in the light of contemporary behavioral science. Alternative explanations of criminal behavior are examined in the light of new evidence. A review of the literature is not attempted, since these materials are readily available to the interested reader.

Likewise, this is not a review of the legal doctrine involved in the District of Columbia, although major doctrines and cases are discussed. The materials used in this work are research materials, and the emphasis throughout is placed upon the implications of a science of behavior for law. The writer is a sociologist, with training in law, who recently has become interested in experimental psychology.

This investigation was supported in whole by United States

Public Health Service Grant No. M-5009 from the National Institute of Mental Health. The writer wishes to acknowledge the advice and help of the Washington School of Psychiatry and its Executive Director, Robert G. Kvarnes. It would not be possible to mention here all the individuals who have aided the writer in developing his thinking on this subject. Included among them, however, would be Jerome Hall of the Indiana University Law School, Francis A. Allen of the University of Chicago Law School; the late E. H. Sutherland of Indiana University; and Henry H. Foster, Jr., of New York University Law School. For his efforts in establishing scientific research in the area of human behavior, David McK. Rioch, Director of the Division of Neuropsychiatry, Walter Reed Army Institute of Research, deserves special mention. And to my secretary, Sonia Cohen, a special acknowledgment of appreciation.

The statements and conclusions made in this report are the sole responsibility of the author, and in no way reflect the opinions of the personnel of the National Institutes of Health, the Washington School of Psychiatry, or of any of the other individuals involved in the project. Other conclusions can and will be reached by other students of the problem.

C.R.J.

CONTENTS

CRIMINAL RESPONSIBILITY AND MENTAL DISEASE

PART I

THE LAW, CRIME, AND MENTAL DISEASE

Chapter 1

CRIMINAL INTENT AND INSANITY

CRIMINAL INTENT

THE PHILOSOPHICAL tradition of Western civilization has included as an important aspect of it the doctrine of duality—mind and body. Plato gave expression to this position when he differentiated the ideal world from the material world. Descartes posited a dualistic world of mind and body: "I think, therefore I am."

This dualistic position has forced philosophers to account for the interaction of mind and body. Some have solved the issue through the doctrine of parallelism, the notion that interaction between mind and body does not occur, and the two systems operate independently but in parallel fashion as if mind influenced body. The manner in which mind influences body is still a major philosophical problem with which psychologists and philosophers are wrestling.

The lawyer follows this philosophical tradition when he distinguishes between the act and the mental element which is related to the act. The mental element is referred to as intent.

Some writers, such as Wigmore and Sayre, have argued that early primitive law was based on strict liability where intent was not an element of the crime. "The doer of the deed was responsible whether he acted innocently or inadvertently, because he was the doer."[1] The act was judged according to its consequences rather than in terms of a mental element of intent. Sayre argues that strict liability existed in order to stop the

---

[1] Wigmore, John: Responsibility for tortious acts. *Harvard Law Review*, Vol. 7, p. 317.

blood feud. A system of payments or tariffs existed at this stage of legal development.[2]

On the other hand, Professor G. O. W. Mueller has argued that even in early primitive law the mental element of an act was considered to be an important aspect of the definition of torts and crimes.[2A]

The Christian moralists, or early Christian philosophers, introduced the notion of a mental element to an act. The early Christion theologians listed seven deadly sins: pride, covetousness, lust, anger, gluttony, envy, and sloth. Deadly sins are evil states of mind that can lead to the commission of offenses against God. A mortal sin is a freely willed, deliberate offense against God. Thus the Christian moralists regarded mental states by themselves as sins. This view was never completely accepted by the legal system, since a basic legal requirement is an act as well as a mental state. Moral culpability became an important aspect of legal liability.[3]

The common law rule was "No crime without an evil intent."[4] The laws of Henry I mentioned the rule as *reum non facit nisi mens rea*. Radin credits the Christian theologian Saint Augustine with this rule. The general rule is that the accused is responsible for the consequences of his intentional acts.

The doctrine of *mens rea* has created several serious problems. The law requires proof of intent—intent must be present in the act. Then the proposition is reversed, and if the act occurs, the act itself is proof of intent. The proof of intent is of an inferential nature; intent is present if the criminal act occurred. The doctrine of *dolus indirectus* stated that all foreseeable conse-

---

[2]Sayre, Francis B.: Mens rea. *Harvard Law Review*, Vol. 45, p. 974 ff. See also Radin, Max: Intent, criminal. *Encyclopedia of the Social Sciences*. New York, Macmillian, *Vol. 8*, p. 126 ff., 1932.

[2A]Mueller, Gerhard O. W.: Tort, crime and the primitive. *Journal of Criminal Law, Criminology, and Police Science*, September-October, 1955, pp. 302-32.

[3]Ames, James B.: Law and morals. *Harvard Law Review*, Vol. 22, p. 97 ff.

[4]Sayre: *op. cit.* p. 974 ff.

quences of behavior are regarded as willed.[5] The law often assumes that an actor intends the natural and probable consequences of his act.[6] Professor Jerome Hall quotes several legal opinions concerning the difficulties involved in determining the internal mental state of a defendant:[7] ". . . now man is competent to judge only of outward acts, because man seeth those things that appear, while God alone is competent to judge the inward movement of wills. The thought of man shall not be tried, for the devil himself knoweth not the thought of man." On the other hand, Justice Bowen stated, "The state of man's mind is as much a fact as the state of his digestion."

A second major problem is that the mental element of a crime is related to two, not one, physical events. One is the act itself: the intent to pull the trigger of a gun is proven by the movement of the finger. There is also involved here the "intent" to produce the consequences of the act: to kill a man or an animal, or to shoot at a can. The law has never satisfactorily answered the question whether the intent required refers to the act, its consequences, or both.

Justice Lord Devlin declared that *mens rea* consists of two elements: (1) the intent to commit an act, and (2) knowledge of the circumstances that make an act a criminal offense. On the other hand, Justice Shearman limited *mens rea* to the intention to commit the act which is made penal by statute.[8] Intent can refer to the objective, knowable consequences of behavior, or to the mental state which accompanied the behavior and which is not knowable but always exists at an inferential level. The dictionary defines intent as "to have in mind, as a design or purpose." The same act may produce different consequences. Firing a gun, for example, may kill a deer or it may kill a man.

---

[5]Radin: *op. cit.* p. 127.

[6]Donnelly, Richard C., Goldstein, Joseph, and Schwartz, Richard D.: *Criminal Law.* New York, Free Press, 1962, p. 573.

[7]Hall, Jerome: *General Principles of Criminal Law.* 2nd ed., Indianapolis, Bobbs-Merrill, 1960, pp. 153-54.

[8]*Ibid.,* p. 71.

Did the defendant intend to shoot a deer or to kill a man? Diagrammed, it would look like this:

Response	Consequence	Legal Status
Firing a gun	killing a deer	no crime
Firing a gun	killing a man	murder
Firing a gun	killing a man	no crime, because actor intended to kill a deer

How do we know the actor intended to kill a deer and not a man? We *infer* the intent from the behavior, and from the consequences of the behavior.

Professor G. O. W. Mueller has attempted to handle this problem, stating that the act is always a psychophysical event in which the effect has been caused by conscious interaction of mind and body, a mental process called voluntariness and a physical movement.[9] He then notes that intent is not *mens rea*, and cites the case of *United States vs. Gris*, 247 F. 2d 860 (1957), in which Judge Medina held that the act and the intent to do the act (wire tapping in this case) were all that were necessary for a crime. According to Mueller, many thousands of legal cases have been decided on this basis. He argues, however, that this is not *mens rea*, since if we followed this doctrine, we could consider a man guilty of murder if he intended to shoot a deer but, on firing his rifle, killed a man. Mueller distinguishes between the act (*actus reus*) and the evil mind (*mens rea*). The act is a fusion of mental and physical processes, a rational movement involving consciousness of a willed movement. The act involves cognition and volition, knowing and willing.

> . . . in the sphere of legally relevant act, we mean by "act" always a psychophysical event in which a perceptible effect has been caused by conscious interaction of the mind and body, i.e., a mental process—frequently and popularly referred to as an intention or voluntariness—and a physical movement.

---

[9]Mueller, Gerhard O. W.: On common law mens rea. *Minnesota Law Review*, Vol. 42, No. 6, p. 1050.

Mens rea refers to a moral decision—doing something that one ought not do, and knowing that it is wrong to do it. It involves both cognition and volition; recognition of wrongfulness and the decision to act despite such recognition. It is not the mental element required in the *actus reus*. "*Mens rea* is not the mere psychic relation between act and action; it is rather the ethico-legal negative value of the deed."

In the case of *Morrissette vs. United States*, 342 U. S. 246 (1952), the defendant was charged with stealing spent bomb casings from a government firing range. His defense was that he thought the casings were abandoned. The trial court held that, "If the defendant took the property, he is guilty. The question of intent is whether or not he intended to take the property." Upon appeal, the Supreme Court held that an *evil state of mind (mens rea)* is necessary, described as intentional, knowing, or malicious. Stealing involves the intention to keep wrongfully the item stolen. The Supreme Court then went on to state that the lower court had erred when it assumed the only question was "Did the defendant intend to take the property? But that isolated fact is not an adequate basis on which the jury should find the criminal intent to steal or knowingly covet; that is, *wrongfully* to deprive another of possession of property." In the *Morrissette* case, the Supreme Court held that the intent necessary in a criminal act must be an evil intent.

In *Lambert vs. California*, 355 U. S. 255 (1957), the defendant was charged with failure to register as a convicted felon as required by a Los Angeles city ordinance. Mrs. Lambert stated she lacked knowledge of the ordinance. The Attorney General, in defending the conviction of Mrs. Lambert, noted that the intent required is the intention to commit the unlawful act. Upon an appeal, the Supreme Court of the United States reversed the conviction, and Justice Douglas noted in the majority opinion that knowledge of wrongdoing *(mens rea)* was necessary for conviction in a criminal case. Unjust conviction of the blameless is not valid. This does not destroy all absolute liability, however—for example, in cases where there is a duty to be informed of legislation. In both *Morrissette* and *Lambert,* the Supreme Court held that wrongful intent was necessary; that is, the defendant must both commit the act and intend its unlawful consequences.

> Pound's statement concerning *mens rea* is: Historically, our substantive criminal law is based upon a theory of punishing a vicious will. It postulates a free agent confronted with a choice between doing right and doing wrong, and choosing freely to do wrong.[10]

In *Carter vs. United States,* 252 F. 2d 608 (1957), the court stated:

> If a man is *amens sine mente* in respect to an act to such an extent that in doing the act he is not a free agent, or not making a choice, or unknowing of the difference between right and wrong, or not choosing freely, or not acting freely, he is outside the postulate of the law of punishment.

The crucial place of the mental element in crime is summarized by Professor Mueller when he writes:

> The more we learn scientifically about the human psyche, the more insecure we become in the matter of proper alignment of our criminal law along those newly won recognitions . . . Everyone will agree that a criminal law that disregards human psyche is as useful for society as a police force of deaf, dumb, blind, and lame. . . .[11]
>
> In the field of criminal law, no question occupies today's scholars, reformers, and legislators as much as that of the mental element of crime, *mens rea.*[12]

Professor Radin has stated:

> As long as in popular belief intention and the freedom of the will are taken as axiomatic, no penal system that negates the mental element can find general acceptance.[13]

---

[10]*Donnelly et al.: op. cit.,* p. 565.

[11]Mueller: On common law mens rea. *op. cit.,* p. 1046.

[12]*Ibid.,* p. 1045.

[13]Radin: *op. cit.,* p. 130.

Legal scholars disagree on whether there is one mental state called *mens rea* or whether each crime has its own particular mental state. Stephens, in *Regina vs. Tolson*, states that, "The mental elements of different crimes differ widely." Professor Sayre expressed this view in this country when he stated:

> The truth is that there is no single precise state of mind common to all crime. The old concept of *mens rea* must be discarded, and in its place must be substituted the new concept of *mentes reae*.[14]

Hall and Mueller, on the other hand, defend the notion that the mental element required should be the same for all crimes.

LEGAL DEFENSES

Because intent is required as an essential element of a crime, there exist in legal doctrine certain defenses based on the absence of the necessary intent. If a man did not intend the consequences of his act, he is not guilty of a crime even though he behaved in a manner so as to produce the forbidden consequences.

The law recognizes that some acts are independent of intent, such as heart beat, digestion, and circulation. Often the consequences of volitional and nonvolitional behavior are identical and difficult if not impossible to distinguish. A knee-jerk is a knee-jerk whether the knee has been jerked intentionally by the subject or whether someone has tapped the patellar tendon with a rubber mallet.

The *Model Penal Code* of the American Law Institute states that the following are not voluntary acts:

1. A reflex or convulsion.
2. A bodily movement during unconsciousness or sleep.
3. Conduct during hypnosis.
4. A bodily movement that otherwise is not a product of the effort of determination of the actor, either conscious or habitual.

The *Model Penal Code* states that liability is based on conduct

---

[14]Hall: *op. cit.*, p. 75.

which includes a voluntary act. The Code further states that a person is not guilty of an offense unless he acted purposely, knowingly, recklessly, or negligently. A person acts purposely when it is his conscious object to engage in conduct of that nature or to cause such a result, and he knows the existence of the circumstances that are elements of the crime. A person acts recklessly when he consciously disregards a substantial risk that will result from his conduct.[15] The requirement of intent is satisfied by recklessness or negligence since a natural and probable consequence of reckless or negligent behavior is harm to another person or his property.

Infancy

The common law includes infancy as a defense against a criminal charge. An infant under the age of seven is assumed to be incapable of forming the necessary intent. Today, due to the growth of the juvenile court movement, most juvenile offenders under the age of eighteen are treated as wards of the state rather than as criminals. The concept of intent may be disregarded in the case of the juvenile offender because the issue is one of treatment and rehabilitation rather than punishment.

Necessity and Coercion

Necessity and coercion are also recognized as legal defenses. The general rule is that the necessity or coercion must constitute a threat of death or serious bodily harm. In two leading cases, both involving cannibalism by shipwrecked sailors, the court held that the killing of one of the members of the party by others constituted murder, even though it was absolutely necessary for survival. *Rex vs. Dudley and Stephens,* 14 Q. B. 273 (1884), *Holmes vs. United States,* 26 Fed. Case 360 (1842). The legal position is that necessity always exists in any human act, but yet an element of freedom of choice must also exist if the act is to be considered moral and subject to legal liability.[16]

---

[15]Donnelly *et al.: op cit.,* pp. 525-26.
[16]Hall: *op. cit.,* pp. 446-48.

Ignorance and Mistake

A mistake of fact is a defense if the mistake is such as to exclude *mens rea*, and if *mens rea* is a necessary element in the crime charged. The mistake must be a reasonable one, and it does not apply to strict liability offenses such as bigamy or statutory rape.

Ignorance of the law is not a defense in many cases. A justification of the ignorance-of-the-law doctrine is difficult in light of the element of *mens rea*, e.g., knowledge of wrongdoing. How can the law hold someone responsible if he did not "know" that what he did was against the law? Professor Hall defends *mens rea*, the intentional doing of a morally wrong act.[17] He also defends the ignorance-of-the-law doctrine in a most interesting manner. He notes that the law can never be known with certainty. The subjective opinions and interpretations of individuals or lawyers are not the standards to be used in determining the law. A person acting on the advice of legal counsel is still guilty of an offense if he violates the law. The law is the interpretation which coincides with the later relevant interpretation by authorized officials.[18] This statement by Hall certainly is a direct contradiction of his position concerning *mens rea*. How can an offender intend to commit an unlawful act if he does not know it is unlawful? If knowledge of the law cannot be subjective, and must depend on an objective criterion—that is, the actual behavior of judges—the requirement of *mens rea* is eliminated. Hall compromises these contradictions by stating that the criminal law represents an objective ethics which must oppose individual convictions of right and wrong. The established ethical judgments of the community must be applied.[19]

Accident

It has been legal doctrine since early Anglo-Saxon times that an accidental harm by itself does not constitute a crime. If we

---

[17]*Ibid.*, p. 103.
[18]*Ibid.*, pp. 409 ff.
[19]*Ibid.*, p. 385.

look only at the act itself and its consequences, then shooting at a deer and killing a man would constitute murder. If we look at the intention of the actor, and if we are satisfied he intended to kill a deer and not a man, then the necessary element of *mens rea* is lacking for the crime of murder. The actor did not knowingly commit an act he knew was wrong.

Some offenses, usually called strict liability or public welfare offenses, do not require the establishment of intent. These offenses include such acts as possession of adulterated tobacco, selling adulterated milk, or selling diseased meat.

Professor Hall states that strict liability also exists in the felony-murder rule, the use of negligence as intent, the objective test (reasonable man test) of liability, and in cases of bigamy and statutory rape.[20] He concludes that strict liability cannot be brought within the scope of a penal law based on culpability and *mens rea*.

Insanity

Insanity is one of the ways in which *mens rea* or criminal intent can be negated. A diseased or disordered mind cannot entertain or formulate a criminal purpose, or know that the act is wrongful.

Many tests of legal insanity have been used: the count-to-twenty test; the know-his-father test; the child-of-fourteen test; the wild-beast test; the good-and-evil test; and the right-and-wrong test.[21]

The *M'Naghten* case, 8 Eng. Rep 718 (1843), is the famous landmark in the legal definition of insanity. M'Naghten shot and killed Edward Drummond, under the delusion he was killing Sir Robert Peel. Because of the political implications of the case (the Anti-Corn laws were involved in the assassination attempt), the House of Lords asked the judges for the legal definition of the insanity defense. The answer given was that the defendant was not legally responsible (1) if, at the time of

---

[20]*Ibid.*, pp. 326 ff.

[21]Michael, Jerome, and Wechsler, Herbert: *Criminal Law and Its Administration.* Chicago, Foundation Press, 1940, pp. 807 ff.

the act, he was laboring under such defect of reason, from disease of mind, as not to know the nature and quality of the act he was doing; or (2) if he did know it, he did not know what he was doing was wrong.

The *M'Naghten* test is established legal precedence in the United States. It is sometimes supplemented by the irresistible-impulse test. Today, because of advances in psychiatry, psychology, and sociology, many behavioral experts are advocating overruling the *M'Naghten* test in favor of a more modern, more scientific concept of insanity. The case against M'Naghten has been the subject of hundreds of books and articles. Judge Bazelon has written:

> The main criticism of the right-wrong test are fourfold. First, it misses the point entirely, because whatever "insanity" means, the term refers to abnormal conditions of the mind that cannot all be gathered under the rubrics "know" and "wrong." Second, the test is based on an outmoded theory of faculty psychology—derived from phrenology—that divided the topography of the mind into separate compartments. Modern psychology views a man as an integrated personality, and reason as only one element of that personality and not the sole determinant of conduct. Third, the test poses to the expert an ultimate question involving legal and moral as well as medical issues. Fourth, the test has so straitjacketed psychiatric testimony that insanity is defined exclusively in terms of extreme psychosis and patent organic deterioration.[22]

The *Durham* decision was an attempt on the part of the Court of Appeals of the District of Columbia to meet the criticisms leveled against the *M'Naghten* rule.

SUMMARY

The legal definition of crimes includes a mental element, which some writers have divided into intent and *mens rea,* the purpose of the act and knowledge that the act is wrong. The insanity defense exists as a legal defense because it negates

---

[22]Bazelon, David L.: The awesome decision. *Saturday Evening Post,* January 23, 1960, pp. 32 ff.

either intent or *mens rea*. The *M'Naghten* rule gave expression to this doctrine when it defined intent in terms of the nature and quality of the act, and *mens rea* in terms of knowledge of right and wrong.

The *Durham* rule was put forth in an effort to bring the insanity defense more in line with twentieth century psychiatry and behavioral science, and to allow psychiatrists to testify in medical terms rather than legal or moral terms. The *Durham* rule rejected the legal position that insanity had to be defined exclusively in terms of psychosis.

Chapter 2

RESEARCH PROCEDURE

THE DURHAM DECISION changed the legal doctrine concerning mental illness and legal responsibility in the District of Columbia. The *Durham* rule broadened the meaning of insanity so that, within a legal framework, nonpsychotic psychopathology could be considered as insanity. The purpose of the research was to determine what factors other than those specified by the law are important in the insanity defense.[1]

The major variables involved in the insanity defense are: (1) the defendant; (2) the defense counsel; (3) the government (prosecution); (4) jurors, if used; (5) psychiatrists; (6) the public; and (7) community facilities such as mental hospitals, jails, prisons, and social welfare agencies. The influence of these several variables is very much interrelated and interdependent; that is, what a defense attorney does is dependent on what a judge, jury, psychiatrist, or prosecuting attorney is going to do.

In the trial of a criminal, there are three positions that can be discussed in terms of desired goals:

1. The defense attorney and the defendant behave in such a manner as to minimize the punishment of the defendant; that is, they are seeking the defendant's freedom or a short prison sentence. The defendant wishes to avoid conviction because conviction means (a) execution, (b) incarceration, (c) a fine, (d) social disgrace, etc. The rewards for acquittal are several and varied. For the defense counsel they include: (a) monetary payment or fees; (b) reputation and hence more criminal cases in the future; (c) social or humanitarian service, and (d) win-

---

[1]The present writer was not a part of the project during the planning or interviewing stage, and the data were gathered by other members of the project staff.

ning the game. A defense attorney is not rewarded if he loses cases. His behavior, therefore, is governed by his desire to win cases. Other factors influencing the behavior of the defense attorney are the rate of compensation, the time available, experience, the possibility of a compromise, etc. In 90 per cent or more of the criminal cases, a plea of guilty is entered because the defendant has neither the money nor the grounds to go to court and plead not guilty, and by pleading guilty he may receive a reduced charge and/or a reduced sentence.

2. The government lawyer is hired to secure the conviction of the defendant: he views his job as one of securing convictions. The environment within which the prosecutor operates is so structured that he is rewarded for convictions, not for losing cases. If he loses cases, the press attacks him for releasing dangerous criminals into the community. Occasionally, he is hailed as a great defender of liberty if he corrects an obvious error in justice; but in 99 per cent of the cases, the public wants criminals detected, arrested, convicted, and imprisoned.

3. The judge and the jury are theoretically neutral in this battle of litigants. They are assigned the task of listening to the evidence and bringing in a verdict. As the legal realists have pointed out in forceful ways, judges and jurors often come to trials with preconceived or predetermined responses to issues raised at the trial. Lawyers capitalize on this fact when they select certain individuals for jury duty in a given type of case. Theoretically, however, the judge and jurors are neutrals, regardless of the fact that they are not in reality neutral.

The courtroom drama that unfolds, therefore, is one in which the defense is attempting to gain an acquittal, whereas the prosecution is attempting to get a conviction of the defendant. Some of the most interesting behavioral processes available for observation in our society are those in the courtroom, where behavior is manipulated and altered in very systematic ways by the several parties to the lawsuit.

RESEARCH METHOD

Lawyers and psychiatrists were interviewed concerning their

experiences under the *Durham* rule. The results of the interviews are discussed below.

The most exciting and rewarding aspect of the project has been the actual trial of real legal issues in a real judicial setting. One of the complaints usually leveled against such current social science research is that it is artificial, e.g., it deals with artificial juries, artificial trials, and so forth. The usual approach, and the one utilized by the University of Chicago Jury Project, is to ask subjects: "How would you respond to a given set of facts, e.g., the *M'Naghten* rule versus the *Durham* rule?" Such an approach tells us how people answer questionnaires, or how verbal behavior can be shaped in a given interview situation.

In contrast to the above-mentioned type of research, the experimental approach is a valuable tool in establishing causal relationships. The basic paradigm or model for an experiment is the manipulation of an independent variable by the investigator, under carefully controlled conditions. Observations and measurements are then made of changes occurring in the dependent variable. In the trial materials, we have a rare example of the manipulation of these variables. The consequences of introducing an insanity plea for a condition less than psychotic, such as alcoholism, homosexuality, drug addiction, or sociopathy, are different for the government, for defense counsel, for psychiatrists for the government, for psychiatrists for the defense, for the Bench, the jurors, and the defendant. The responses of these individuals involved in the judicial process are now analyzable in terms of the direction and type of change manifest under a new set of conditions.

The project handled more than twenty cases involving the insanity defense. The trials of cases were conducted by Mr. Richard Arens, an attorney, with the aid of additional legal counsel as needed in any given case. Mr. Arens also had available, out of project funds, money to hire psychiatrists for the purpose of giving mental examinations and evaluating the mental state of defendants.

The problems involved in doing human research in an area as sensitive as criminal law are extremely difficult and hazardous at best. The data from the trial cases are most valuable and revealing and they will be analyzed in detail in the following chapters in order that some light may be shed on the operation of the insanity plea.

PSYCHIATRIC INTERVIEWS

Thirty-six general interviews with psychiatrists were conducted (see appendix). These psychiatrists varied from young men with no courtroom experience to administrative staff members of Saint Elizabeth's Hospital and the District of Columbia General Hospital with twenty or more years experience in forensic psychiatry.

The interviews focused on general problems encountered by psychiatrists in the courts where the insanity plea was an issue. There was a wide diversity of opinion on crucial issues relating to the insanity defense. It is difficult if not impossible to summarize these interview materials in any statistical way, since the answers given were not in the form of agree or disagree, but rather answers to open-end questions. The variety of responses elicited from the questions was such that no attempt was made to tabulate them in any form, for to do so would create an artificial sense of preciseness which the data did not reveal. If anything, the wide variety of responses indicated a basic disagreement among lawyers and psychiatrists as to the issues involved in the insanity defense.

Roughly half of the psychiatrists interviewed expressed the opinion that the *Durham* rule removed the handcuffs from psychiatrists; under the *Durham* rule psychiatrists are given greater latitude in their courtroom testimony than was the case under the *M'Naghten* rule. Half the psychiatrists objected to the *Durham* rule, basically because it allowed too many criminals to plead insanity and to escape punishment. The psychiatrists who support the *Durham* rule usually are men who feel that criminals ought to be rehabilitated and, for that reason, belong in hospitals, not in prisons. The psychiatrists who oppose the *Durham* rule do so either because they feel that criminals ought to be punished or because they believe that adequate medical facilities are not now available to handle antisocial behaviors, homosexuality, drug addiction, alcoholism, etc. They noted that all criminals may be considered insane and not guilty if the meaning of mental illness is extended. Several psychiatrists pointed out that the *Durham* rule assumed knowledge on the part of the psychiatrist that he did not possess. Some claimed that in many cases criminals are better off in prison than in a mental institution. One psychiatrist complained that the Bench and the Bar are now busy playing psychiatrist, trying to be experts in psychiatry—a movement he viewed with alarm. It might be said, in order to make the record complete, that the legal materials also suggest that psychiatrists are now busily playing lawyer, an equally dangerous development. It is not at all uncommon to find psychiatrists expounding on the more technical requirements of the criminal law, whereas lawyers are now quoting medical journal and textbook materials to psychiatrists and asking, for example: "Is it not true, Doctor Brown, that this condition is caused by imperfect ego-formation, in conjunction with an unresolved Oedipus complex, leading to a very high state of unresolved neurotic anxiety?"

When asked what constitutes a mental disease or illness, the psychiatrists answered with a mixture of legal-medical terminology. The answers ranged all the way from "All diagnostic categories in the APA Manual constitute an insanity defense" to "Only schizophrenics with paranoia are mentally ill." If asked to distinguish legal insanity from mental illness, many psychiatrists replied that only major psychoses, and perhaps severe neuroses, constituted legal insanity. This is, of course, a reflection of legal doctrine and court practice. The criterion used was whether or not the individual was responsible; e.g., could he control his behavior, or "Does he have sufficient ego strength to control dangerous impulses," or "Does he have impaired reality testing." Several psychiatrists defined responsibility in terms of free will. If the unconscious mind has taken over the conscious mind, then no free will exists, and therefore no responsibility exists.

The psychiatrist is aware of the fact that, in the courtroom, the problem is a moral and legal issue, and not a medical issue.

The difficulty of relating a medical concept to a legal definition was apparent from the interviews. Several psychiatrists stated that only at the appellate level did the *Durham* rule apply, while at the trial court level the *M'Naghten* rule was still used.

Very few psychiatrists regarded sociopaths as mentally ill, within the legal framework or even within a medical framework. "If psychopaths are mentally ill, then all criminals are mentally ill," was a reply often received. One psychiatrist stated that if a man wanted treatment, then he was mentally ill.

Treatability is an important criterion in diagnostic classification. Sociopaths are often regarded as not treatable, and therefore are not classified as mentally ill. A member of the administrative staff at Saint Elizabeth's told an interviewer that sociopaths are not mentally ill, although the official policy of the hospital is to certify them as with mental disease. The policy of certifying sociopaths as mentally ill conflicts with the statement that they are not treatable. Many psychiatrists feel that sociopaths are better off in prison than in mental hospitals, for they may stay in a mental hospital for life.

Several psychiatrists expressed the view that everyone in prison has a psychopathology, so only those who are treatable should be in hospitals. Sociopaths should be imprisoned for life since they are not treatable.

To the question about the causation requirement—the relationship between the criminal act and the mental state necessary to constitute a defense—the usual reply was that the presence of psychosis or severe neurosis would constitute a causal relationship between crime and mental illness. This is, of course, a statement of the general legal doctrine concerning causation. One psychiatrist, when informed of the *Carter* case, which states that an indirect causal relationship is sufficient, responded that now he would include many more cases in his court testimony than he did before. This is an excellent example of the way legal concepts shape the behavior of psychiatrists.

Most psychiatrists express an opinion that it is very difficult or impossible to establish a direct causal relationship between crime and mental illness if less than a severe psychotic or severe neurotic condition exists. They also point out that the psychiatric examination of the defendant usually occurs three to six months or more after the criminal act, and that it is almost impossible to establish a mental condition at the time of the crime. One psychiatrist expressed the opinion that all criminals are mentally ill, that criminality is in itself a symptom of mental illness, and therefore criminal behavior is always a product of mental illness. This position has been under attack by the Bench and the Bar, and it is the usual practice of a prosecutor to ask the defense psychiatrist if he believes all criminal behavior is a mental illness.[2] If the answer is yes, then the testimony is discredited because the obvious implication is that all criminals are sick people and should be hospitalized. If the answer is no, then the psychiatrist is again put on the spot, for he must now defend the proposition that some crimes are caused by mental illness and others are not.

The diagnostic and therapeutic facilities at Saint Elizabeth's Hospital and the District of Columbia General Hospital were regarded as inadequate by all but one of the psychiatrists interviewed. Overcrowding and understaffing were often mentioned as major difficulties facing these two medical facilities. The quality and availability of facilities are important factors in the willingness of a lawyer to use the insanity defense in the disposition of a case, since if facilities are not available, there is no sense in sending a man to a mental hospital. Sociopaths are in this group, for most hospital administrators do not wish to have such antisocial characters in their wards. Sociopaths create disciplinary problems which can be avoided if they are not in hospitals; otherwise, hospitals tend to become prisons. A local institutional psychiatrist responded as follows:

> Sure, the man is sick. Under the *Carter* case I would say that his crime is a product of mental illness. But I choose to accept a stricter legal standard because, if I did not, we would be flooded with undesirables who are not acutely ill and who

---

[2]Flannery, Thomas: Meeting the insanity defense. *Journal of Criminal Law, Criminology, and Police Science*, September-October, 1960, p. 316.

would clutter up our facilities which are already strained to a breaking point.

The psychiatric examination usually lasts for one to two hours at Saint Elizabeths or at D. C. General Hospital. Social case histories or psychological tests are not used in most cases. Psychiatric examinations are routine and usually a mere formality. Neurological examinations are ordered whenever a physical problem is suspected. Many of the defendants are examined in jail—a situation which in itself suggests questioning the results of such examinations.

Lawyers repeatedly use certain psychiatrists who appear in criminal court on the side of the defense. A question often asked a defense psychiatrist by the prosecutor is: "Have you ever appeared in a criminal case in opposition to the defense?" If the answer is no, then it is implied to the judge and jurors that this man has been purchased.[3] Another way of broaching the topic is to ask the psychiatrist by whom he is being paid. It should be noted, in this respect, that government psychiatrists are also paid, and that the same psychiatrists for the government are also used repeatedly.

The government has a major advantage in this respect because it can call upon Saint Elizabeths or the D. C. General Hospital for psychiatric help at any time, whereas the vast majority of defendants are too poor to hire psychiatrists to aid in their defense.

A large majority of the psychiatrists interviewed felt that lawyers and judges are very hostile to psychiatric testimony. Judges were singled out as a group opposed to the extension of the *Durham* rule to include nonpsychotic psychopathology. One psychiatrist related a case he participated in where, after the government attorney had conceded the insanity of the defendant, the judge took it upon himself to ask a personal friend, a psychiatrist, to examine the accused. The hostility between Bench, Bar, and psychiatry is found in many places in criminal proceedings.

---

[3] *Ibid.*, p. 314.

Most psychiatrists stated they felt that judges and jurors were more sympathetic to clinical descriptions than to psychodynamic descriptions of behavior, though the psychiatrist favors a psychodynamic interpretation in many instances.

LAWYER INTERVIEWS

Twenty-six lawyers were interviewed concerning their opinions on the insanity defense (see appendix). Both government and defense lawyers were interviewed. These men ranged from the very inexperienced in criminal trial work to those who had spent many years in the trial of criminal cases.

The lawyers were quite diverse in their opinions concerning the *Durham* decision. One claimed that 99 per cent of the cases could be handled under the *M'Naghten* rule. Others indicated they were with *Durham* "all the way." Approximately 80 per cent of those interviewed were opposed to the *Durham* rule for one reason or another. It was pointed out by several lawyers that 90 per cent of all criminals qualified for acquittal under the *Durham* rule. One of the major objections to *Durham* is exactly this point. Several lawyers objected to the rule because it negates responsibility and free will.

Those lawyers who support the *Durham* rule do not use the insanity defense except in case of severe psychosis. This behavior is a reflection of the fact that the courts will often reject nonpsychotic psychopathology as mental illness, and therefore it is a dangerous legal maneuver in cases of neurosis, character disorders, homosexuality, drug addiction, and alcoholism. This disparity between interview and courtroom behavior can be explained. Verbal behavior is under the control of a set of contingencies that differ from those controlling the lawyer's action in the courtroom. A lawyer being interviewed by a defense attorney is likely to make verbal statements generally in support of the *Durham* rule. Such verbal behavior is reinforced in the interview situation. Unless, however, this behavior is reinforced in the courtroom, it will not occur during the trial. A lawyer will express one opinion about the *Durham* rule in an interview situation, while in court he will behave in an entirely

different manner. It is dangerous to generalize or make inferences from verbal behavior to other behaviors. "Talk is
cheap" is an expression that conveys this problem in popular
form.

Another important factor is the availability of treatment facilities for mental patients. Most lawyers interviewed have little
confidence in Saint Elizabeths or the D. C. General Hospital.
The problem of overcrowding and understaffing, again, are often
mentioned. Insufficient examination of the patients at the government hospitals is also mentioned. Lawyers complain that
government psychiatrists are prosecution-minded, that too often
they stamp reports "without mental disease or defect." Many
point out that an insanity defense, if successful, means that the
defendant is placed in a mental institution for an indeterminate
period—perhaps for life. They feel that prison is a better place
for serving time than a hospital. In the case of a misdemeanor,
a man, if convicted, might receive probation or at most a
one-year sentence in a jail or a reformatory. This is viewed as
preferable to a commitment to Saint Elizabeths. Most lawyers
state that they use the insanity plea only in capital cases, or
if the defendant faces a long period in prison. A lawyer who is
faced with two alternatives will select the least aversive course
of action. If the alternatives are probation or confinement to
Saint Elizabeths, under these circumstances, probation is the
obvious choice. If the alternatives are execution or life imprisonment, then confinement to Saint Elizabeths is a desirable
alternative.

Some lawyers feel that psychiatric examinations should be
divorced from government sponsorship because of the prosecution bias of institutional psychiatrists. They would favor routine
psychological screening of all felons if these examinations are
removed from government control and placed under private
auspices. Most lawyers complain that they are unable to secure
free psychiatric services, and most defendants are too poor to
pay for private psychiatric help. Several lawyers mentioned the
fact that, in misdemeanor cases involving upper or middle-class
clients, usually sex offenses, the customary arrangement was to

have the case dismissed in return for placing the defendant under private psychiatric care. Private out-patient treatment is preferred to institutionalization, if the defendant can pay for it. Commitment to a mental hospital is avoided at all cost.

Many lawyers stated they used psychiatric pools that consist of defense-minded psychiatrists. "If a man doesn't testify the right way he is not rehired," one attorney said. Although lawyers complain about government-biased psychiatrists, they readily admit to making use of defense-biased psychiatrists. The psychiatrist is placed in an impossible situation so long as he has to testify as an expert witness for the government or for the defense.

Most of the lawyers stated a preference for jury trials rather than waiving a jury trial in favor of a judge. Without exception, they stated that judges are opposed to the insanity plea and convey their opposition in facial expression, mannerisms, questions asked of expert witnesses for both sides, and so forth. One case cited occurred when a jury returned a verdict of not guilty by reason of insanity. The judge informed psychiatrists from Saint Elizabeths that had the defendant been convicted, he could have been sentenced to fifteen years in prison; therefore the judge would object to a premature release of the defendant from Saint Elizabeths. These judicial opinions may have an effect upon the release procedures of institutions such as Saint Elizabeths, whereas it might be very desirable that such releases be based on medical grounds rather than on legal pressures.

Lawyers, unlike psychiatrists, prefer clinical descriptions to psychodynamic case histories—this despite the fact that the Court of Appeals had used language to the contrary. Again, if we question lawyers on the use of these clinical categories, we learn that, at the trial court level, the judges and lawyers want this kind of testimony. Court procedure in an insanity defense is still basically one of fitting a psychiatric category into a legal pigeonhole. A defendant must be diagnosed as psychotic before many members of the Bench will have sympathy with an insanity defense.

Most lawyers do not systematically interview a client to determine whether he is mentally ill. Since lawyers are not trained in behavioral science, it is difficult to imagine what sort of interview they would conduct to determine if a client has a mental disease. If the client is behaving in an obviously bizarre manner, and if he has a history of behavioral problems, then the lawyer may impose the insanity defense. The impression gained from project data—and it is only an impression—is that the decision to use an insanity defense is based on factors such as the economic position of the defendant, the nature of the criminal charges, the medical facilities in the community, the legal status of the insanity plea in the local courts, etc. In other words, the actual psychological state of the defendant may be a rather minor factor in determining whether a lawyer will use the insanity defense.

Psychiatric knowledge on the part of lawyers is very meager and confused. Several of them indicated they did not know the meaning of "psychosis." Communication between lawyer and psychiatrist in the courtroom is poor at best. The quality of interaction is not much better when a lawyer hires a psychiatrist to examine his client. Often lawyers do not inform psychiatrists of important legal cases that might help the psychiatrist in his preparation of a case for the lawyer. For example, the *Carter* case liberalizes the causal relationship needed between the criminal act and the mental state, yet lawyers often neglect to inform psychiatrists of the implications of this legal doctrine. Several of the lawyers interviewed did not know the *Carter* case themselves, so this would also be a factor in the situation.

Lawyers do not have any clear concept of what is meant by "causation," as used in the *Durham* and *Carter* cases. Many say this is a medical, not a legal, problem. Others will cite the language of the courts in defining causation in legal terms.

SUMMARY

In general, the lawyers and psychiatrists interviewed were divided on the basic principles of the *Durham* rule. At least 50 per cent of the psychiatrists and 80 per cent of the lawyers found fault with the *Durham* rule. There was obvious difficulty in both professions in defining mental disease or productivity. A confusion of legal and medical concepts is found in the answers given by lawyers and psychiatrists. Even those who regard the *Durham* rule as a step in the right direction indicate that their courtroom behavior is based on a concept of insanity which is close to the medical term "psychosis." Only a major mental disease is defined in practice as constituting legal insanity. This is close to the legal meaning of insanity as found under the *M'Naghten* rule.

Both lawyers and psychiatrists are concerned about the lack of adequate medical facilities for mental patients. Many lawyers and psychiatrists expressed the opinion that a defendant is often better off in prison than in a mental hospital. Psychiatric facilities are an important variable in determining the way in which the insanity defense is used by a defense attorney.

Many lawyers and psychiatrists feel that judges at the trial court level are opposed to the *Durham* rule.

Chapter 3

MENTAL DISEASE AND THE COURTS

JUDICIAL BEHAVIOR

THE FACT that the *Durham* decision has not appreciably altered the ideology of the criminal law in the District of Columbia[1] or in the United States is due in no small respect to the Bench. Judges in general oppose the extension of the concept of mental illness to nonpsychotic psychopathology.

Liberal Position

Isaac Ray, a psychiatrist, expressed his dissatisfaction with the law in his *Treatise on the Medical Jurisprudence of Insanity* in 1838. This was five years before the *M'Naghten* case. The state of New Hampshire, in *State vs. Pike*, 49 NH 399 (1870), and *State vs. Jones,* 50 NH 319 (1871), followed Ray's treatise and stated that a defendant was not criminally responsible if his unlawful act was the product of mental disease or mental defect.

In 1954, in *United States vs. Durham,* the Court of Appeals adopted the product test for the District of Columbia. The test used in the U. S. Court of Appeals for the District of Columbia is: "The accused is not criminally responsible if his unlawful act was the product of mental disease or mental defect." Durham had been charged with housebreaking. His criminal record dated back to the age of sixteen. At the time of his trial, he was diagnosed variously as "psychopathic personality" and "without mental disorder but with psychopathic personality."

Judge Bazelon stated two basic purposes in the *Durham*

---

[1]Krash, Abe: The Durham rule and judicial administration of the insanity defense in the District of Columbia. *Yale Law Journal, Vol. 70,* No. 6, May, 1961, p. 952.

decision: (1) to free the psychiatrist from having to make moral and legal determinations of right and wrong for which he had no special qualifications; and (2) to restore to the jury its traditional function of applying our inherited ideas of moral responsibility to individuals prosecuted for crime under the historically sanctioned precept that our collective conscience does not allow punishment where it cannot impose blame.[2]

The major criticisms that have emerged from the product rule are these:

1. The term "mental disease" cannot be defined.
2. The basic function of the insanity defense is to deny free will and to apply determinism to human behavior. This position stands in direct opposition to the philosophy of criminal law. If criminals are mentally ill, then we must abandon *mens rea* and its corollary principle, punishment.
3. Psychiatry does not have the facilities for diagnosing, treating, or reforming criminals.
4. The meaning of "product of" has not been determined. When is a given criminal act a "product of" a mental disease? This is a problem in causation and behavior.

The reader should bear in mind that Judge Bazelon has written:

> Many psychiatrists who admit their inability to answer the right-wrong question follow the mechanical practice of testifying that a psychotic cannot distinguish right from wrong, while an individual suffering from a nonpsychotic mental illness can. They so testify even though such an artificial demarcation has neither a medical nor a legal basis. Under *Durham*, there will not be the same compulsion to dispose of the issue by means so deviously mechanical—a practice that also wrongly relieves the jury of its duty to decide the case.[3]

The basic issue raised by Judge Bazelon in *Durham vs. United*

---

[2]Bazelon, David L.: The awesome decision. *Saturday Evening Post*, January 23, 1960, p. 54.

[3]*Ibid.*, p. 54.

States is contained in the question: "Are psychosis and insanity the same thing?" The basic purpose of the "product" rule is to expand the legal meaning of the insanity defense. According to Judge Bazelon, nonpsychotic psychopathology would qualify as insanity within the meaning of mental disease or mental defect. The court thus expanded upon the meaning of the term "insanity." The purpose of the research project on "Criminal Law and Psychiatry in the District of Columbia" was to determine whether the courts did, in practice, extend the insanity pleas to include nonpsychotic psychopathology.

As Judge Bazelon has written, if a person is insane, he is treated; if guilty of a crime, he is punished. The issue of retribution or reform is the central theoretical question in criminal law. The theory of deterrence compromises these other two positions by stating that punishment protects society. Underlying this argument is the free will-determinism controversy.

> If we consider the issue of criminal responsibility on spiritual rather than practical or ideological grounds, we discover an ancient philosophical conflict at the heart of the problem— free will versus determinism.[4]

Darwin made man a part of nature. Freud applied scientific determinism to behavior. Freud's concept of unconscious motivation has compelled us to reconsider the question of criminal responsibility. There are also social and economic determinants to behavior. The *Durham* decision also perpetuates the Freudian interpretation of behavior, a psychological system now fifty years old.

Judge Bazelon strongly suggests that the purpose of the *Durham* decision was to extend the notion of determinism beyond what the law had done prior to *Durham*. However, the *Durham* decision continues to perpetuate that dualistic nature of man: one part *determined;* one part *free will.*

> The legal and moral traditions of the Western world require that those who, of their own free will and with evil intent or *mens rea,* commit acts which violate the law, shall be criminally

---

[4]*Ibid.*, p. 56.

responsible for those acts. Our traditions also require that where such acts stem from and are the product of a mental disease or defect as those terms which are used herein, moral blame shall not attach, and hence there will not be criminal responsibility. *Durham vs. United States,* 214 F. 2d 862 (1954)

The issue of legal responsibility and insanity is created by (1) the philosophical view of human nature incorporated into law; and (2) the psychological view of human nature, a Freudian interpretation of behavior, which has been made a part of our legal process.

In *Holloway vs. United States,* 148 F. 2d 665 (1945), the Circuit Court of Appeals said: "Our collective conscience does not allow punishment where it cannot impose blame." In *Douglas vs. United States,* 239 F. 2d 52 (1956), the court states that for criminal behavior there was punishment; for mental disease there was treatment. In *Blunt vs. United States,* 244 F. 2d 355 (1957), the court used this language:

> That one who commits a wrong by reason of insanity must be acquitted is so well settled that no one questions it. Only the guilty are to be punished. For the merely dangerous, society provides other treatment.

In *Williams vs. United States,* 250 F. 2d 19 (1957), the court said:

> Under our criminal jurisprudence, mentally responsible lawbreakers are sent to prison; those who are not mentally responsible are sent to hospitals. It is both wrong and foolish to punish where there is no blame and where punishment cannot correct. The community's security may be better protected by hospitalization than by imprisonment.

In *Lynch vs. Overholser,* 288 F. 2d 388 (1961), the court stated:

> The cases cited above establish almost a positive duty on the part of the trial judge not to impose a criminal sentence on a mentally ill person . . . By its very nature, a jail sentence is for a specified period of time, while, by its very nature, hospitalization, to be effective, must be initially for an indeterminate period. This difference is not fatal because of

the overriding interest of the community in protecting itself and its interest in rehabilitating the defendant himself.

The liberal point of view expressed in the above-quoted judicial opinions can be summarized as one that draws a distinction between punishment and treatment; deterrence and reform; behavior for which a person can be held responsible (free will), and behavior for which a person cannot be held responsible (determinism). Whether or not these distinctions can be maintained and justified in the light of modern psychological findings is something we shall consider in due time.

Conservative Position

The conservative position is basically opposed to the extension of the insanity plea in criminal cases. In *Wright vs. United States*, 215 F. 2d 498 (1954), in a minority opinion a judge stated:

> For the reasons stated I cannot concur in the majority's disposition of the case, which seems to me to be a usurpation of the jury's function and another example of what I regard as an alarming judicial tendency to magnify the rights of criminals at the expense of the public interest in the strict enforcement of the criminal laws, particularly in cases where the defense of insanity is interposed. This reversal allows a murderer to go unpunished and, in all probability, will result in his almost immediate release from any custodial restraint.

In *Gilleo vs. United States*, Criminal No. 583-59, District Court for the District of Columbia, the judge, in sentencing the defendant Gilleo, stated:

> There has developed a practice among lawyers representing defendants that I think is detrimental in some cases to the defendant's best interest. The practice of pleading insanity in cases in which the defendant has a chance for probation or risks a fairly short sentence is very unwise from the defendant's standpoint because he is locked up for a lengthy examination and, even if he is acquitted on the ground of

insanity, while insanity is medically only an illness, nevertheless society's attitude toward it puts a black mark on a person who is declared insane. It is more difficult for a person who has been acquitted on the ground of insanity to get a job than for a man who is an ex-convict. It is undesirable to plead insanity except in capital cases or in cases where a long prison sentence stares the defendant in the face.

In the case of *United States vs. Melchior,* No. 5689-60, Municipal Court for the District of Columbia, the defendant was charged with cashing two small bad checks. The government wanted to raise the insanity issue. The judge, however, allowed the defendant to plead guilty, commenting that once before he had had a case of this type, and the woman who was acquitted by reason of insanity was still in a mental hospital, twelve years after the trial.

In the case of *Blunt vs. United States,* 244 F. 2d 355 (1957), the Court of Appeals reversed the trial court finding in which the jury had returned a verdict of guilty. Among the errors committed by the trial judge was a question directed by the judge to a psychiatrist: "Then it would be dangerous to the community, in your opinion, to turn him loose, would it not?" In this case, the Court of Appeals stated, concerning the behavior of the trial judge: "His assertions were not within the judicial privilege to analyze and comment upon evidence. What the judge did here took on the aspect of advocacy."

In several cases, the trial judges asked psychiatrists if they believed in free will. In the *Watson* case, the judge asked: "Suppose I want to go to a movie, or buy a suit of clothes, or go to a football game, I could do so if I chose to, couldn't I?" *United States vs. Watson,* Criminal No. 907-60, District Court for the District of Columbia.

In another case, the trial judge asked a psychiatrist: "Did the defendant have freedom of will when he pushed his way into an apartment to attack a woman? Did he have freedom to walk by 1611 21st Street, N. W.? Could he have entered Apartment 1 instead of Apartment 2?" *Jenkins vs. United States,* No. 16,306, U. S. Court of Appeals for the District of Columbia.

The opposition to the insanity plea can be summarized as follows:

1. The insanity defense is often more detrimental to the defendant than a conviction for a criminal offense.
2. The insanity defense allows dangerous individuals to be released to the community.
3. The insanity defense denies the basic notion of free will that exists in the criminal law.

The first point is a most valid one, as will be seen in the detailed discussion of the *Lynch* case. The other two points involve issues that cannot be justified scientifically. The behavior of judges is governed by the fact that if all nonpsychotic psychopathology is viewed as mental illness, then many criminals will be acquitted by reason of insanity. By redefining criminal behavior as mental illness, we do not solve the problem of criminality. By sending criminals to hospitals rather than to prisons, we do not solve the problem of criminality.

THE LEGAL MEANING OF MENTAL ILLNESS
Burden of Proof

A man charged with a crime is presumed to be sane according to the *M'Naghten* rule. "The jurors ought to be told in all cases that every man is presumed to be sane and to possess a sufficient degree of reason to be responsible for his crimes, until the contrary is proven. . ." *M'Naghten's Case*, 8 Eng. Rep. 718 (1843).

The mental state of the defendant is an issue in a criminal trial at three points of time:

1. At the time of the trial.
2. At the time of the offense.
3. At the time of the release or execution of the defendant.

In the first and third situations, a direct examination of the defendant by the psychiatrist is possible. In the second situation, the defendant's mental state must be inferred from a later examination, or from the facts surrounding the criminal act itself. Since the psychiatrist cannot testify as to the mental state of the defendant at the time of the crime, the hypothetical question is often used; that is, a series of facts resembling the case at trial are presented to the expert witness, and he is asked whether the defendant knew right from wrong (the *M'Naghten* rule), or whether he had a mental illness or defect (the *Durham* rule), at the time of the crime. The issue is the mental state of the defendant at the time the alleged crime was committed, not his mental state at the time of the trial. If the defendant is insane at the time of the trial, he cannot be tried because of the competency-to-stand-trial doctrine (situation 1). However, at a later date he can be tried for his criminal behavior, if and when he recovers his rational abilities to the point needed to be declared competent to stand trial. The standard for such competency, as set forth in Section 24-301(a) of the D. C. Code, is an ability to understand the nature of the proceedings against him, and the ability to cooperate with counsel in his defense. The motion to determine competency to stand trial must be supported by *prima facie* evidence that the defendant is of unsound mind.[5] Whenever the competency issue is raised, the judge can order a psychiatric examination, after which the defendant is either declared competent to stand trial or committed to a mental institution until such time as he is declared competent. Serious civil rights issues are raised by the question of competency. Ezra Pound, before he was released as incurable and not dangerous, was a patient at Saint Elizabeths for fourteen years under such a commitment.[6] Theoretically, it is possible for a man to be institutionalized for life under a competency proceedings.

The major issue, however, is situation 2: The mental state of the defendant at the time of the alleged crime. At this point the *M'Naghten* rule or the *Durham* rule is the standard used, depending on the jurisdiction within which the defendant is

---

[5]Krash: *op. cit.,* p. 909.

[6]*Ibid.,* pp. 916-17.

being tried. Once the issue of insanity is raised, the burden of proof shifts to the government. The standard needed to raise the issue of insanity is unclear. In *Tatum vs. United States*, 190 F. 2d 612 (1951), the Court of Appeals stated that the standard was "some evidence of mental disease relevant to the issue of manslaughter." In the *Tatum* case, the defense of insanity rested solely on the defendant's statement that he remembered nothing of what happened at the time the offense was committed. The Court of Appeals held this statement was enough to introduce the issue of insanity. The defendant is not required to show that the crime was a product of mental illness. Once the issue of sanity is raised, the jury must return a verdict of not guilty by reason of insanity if they believe that there is some doubt as to the sanity of the defendant at the time of the offense. The prosecution has the burden of proving beyond a reasonable doubt that the accused is sane. See *Davis vs. United States*, 160 U. S. 469 (1895); *Carter vs. United States*, 252 F. 2d 608 (1957). However, it is more realistic as a matter of practice to state that the defense must prove that the mental illness exists, and that the crime is a product of such disease or illness.

In *Clark vs. United States*, 259 F. 2d 184 (1958), the defendant declared: "I must have been insane." Defense counsel did not use the insanity defense. The trial judge held that the defendant's statement was sufficient to raise the issue of insanity, and the Court of Appeals upheld the trial court's ruling.

In *Goforth vs. United States*, 269 F. 2d 778 (1959), the defendant was charged with taking immoral liberties with a female child. He was convicted and he appealed, alleging that the trial judge erred in not instructing the jury on the issue of insanity. Testimony by the defendant indicated that he heard voices and had delusions, and established the fact that he was an alcoholic. The trial judge instructed that if the state of alcoholism was such that the accused could not distinguish right from wrong and was incapable of forming the specific intent needed for the crime, then he was not guilty as charged. The Court of Appeals reversed the District Court, holding that the instruction on insanity should have been given where evidence of delusions and hallucinations was offered. This is, of course, evidence of schizophrenia—a psychosis.

In a dissenting opinion in the *Goforth* case, a judge of the Court of Appeals argued that the evidence indicated that the accused was an alcoholic, and that he had been hospitalized for alcoholism, not for a mental condition. "At most there was only his own testimony as to the imaginings of his intoxicant-befuddled mind, a not unusual phenomenon of continued and continuous drinking, and a far cry from mental disease or defect."

In *Smith vs. United States*, 272 F. 2d 547 (1959), the defendant was charged with assault on his wife with a knife. He was convicted, and he appealed, alleging that "some evidence" of mental illness had been introduced. The defense introduced evidence that there had been a deterioration of the accused's family and social relationships, and in his work habits. He had a history of violent outbursts of temper in which he would fly into a rage. The arresting officer had testified that Smith was not coherent when he was arrested, but later this testimony was changed to state that the defendant had been coherent at the time of his arrest.

The Court of Appeals affirmed the conviction, stating that:

> To hold that the insanity issue is presented in a criminal case merely because the accused has become increasingly violent, has a violent temper, and then makes an unprovoked and violent attack upon another because of some concocted grievance, would be tantamount to holding, as many psychiatrists profess to believe, that any person who commits a crime is mentally ill and should receive treatment instead of punishment. We are not prepared to make such a ruling.

Judge Bazelon dissented, holding that the evidence introduced satisfied the "some evidence of mental illness" requirement.

It is obvious that the concept of mental disease is important in respect to the burden-of-proof doctrine. If one holds that delusions and hallucinations are evidence of alcoholism and not psychosis as in the *Goforth* case, then there can be no such thing as mental illness, for nothing in the psychiatric nomenclature is left. It is also to be remembered that alcoholism is a personality disorder, according to the *APA Diagnostic and Statistical Manual*. On the other hand, if temper, violence, and poor interpersonal relations are symptoms of mental disease, then every crime committed involving anger, violence, or poor social relationships automatically raises the issue of insanity. In the *Goforth* case, a judge in a dissenting opinion refused to recognize psychosis as a mental disease, whereas in the *Smith* case, a judge in another dissenting opinion recognized poor social relationships, anger, and violence as evidence of mental disease. Violence thus becomes a symptom of mental disease: the defendant has a mental disease because he behaves violently. In the *Tatum* case, the defendant's statement that he did not remember what had happened was held to be evidence of mental disease; and in the *Clark* case, the defendant's statement, "I must have been insane," was held to be evidence of mental disease. Thus, on the one hand, some judges have stated that psychotic symptoms are not evidence of mental disease, whereas, on the other hand, other judges have said that anger, poor social relationships, and verbal statements are evidence of mental disease.

In commenting on *Tatum, Clark* and *Goforth,* a judge of the United States Court of Appeals stated:

> A person who chooses to do what he knows is a criminal act, when he is mentally able to control his conduct and refrain from doing the criminal act, is sane in the legal sense even though he has some aberration or emotional disturbance which psychiatrists classify as a mental disease or defect. *McDonald vs. United States,* No. 16,304, United States Court of Appeals for the District of Columbia, 1962.

The third situation, the mental state of the defendant at the time of release, will be discussed under the heading of release procedures.

Examination Required

The court has recently held that the psychiatric examination to determine competency can be extended to include the state of the defendant's mind at the time of the crime. In *Winn vs. United States*, 270 F. 2d 326 (1959), the court held that a prosecutor who knew:

> . . . that the accused's mental state at the time of the crime will be a critical issue at the trial has an obligation to see to it that any pretrial mental examination of the accused that may be ordered be broad enough to cast light on that issue. . . In addition to the psychological and neurological tests which may be indicated, a proper psychiatric examination addressed to the mental state of the accused at the time of the crime requires adequate knowledge and a proper expert evaluation of the accused's personal history and the circumstances surrounding the crime. [See also *Calloway vs. United States*, 270 F. 2d 334 (1959)]

In another case the court held:

> If the Government feels that psychiatric opinions which come into evidence ought to be based on examinations of greater scope and intensity than has been the practice heretofore, it can and should arrange to have such examinations made. [*Wright vs. United States*, 215 F. 2d 498 (1954)]

This judicial admonition was in response to a government attack on psychiatric examinations as being too remote in time from the date of the alleged crime. In *Blunt vs. United States*, 244 F. 2d 355 (1957), the trial judge in his instructions to the jury, stated:

> The doctor's opinion was not based on actual observation or on actual fact, but on conclusions drawn from examination held considerably after the commission of the offenses.

The Court of Appeals again used language indicating an obligation on the part of the prosecutor to secure an adequate pretrial mental examination.

In *Carter vs. United States*, 252 F. 2d 608, 617 (1957), the court stated:

> Unexplained medical labels—schizophrenia, paranoia, psy-

chosis, neurosis, psychopathy—are not enough. Description and explanation of the origin, development, and manifestations of the alleged disease are the chief function of the expert witness. The chief value of an expert's testimony in this field, as in all other fields, rests upon the material from which his opinion is fashioned and the reasoning by which he progresses from his material to his conclusion; in the explanation of the disease and its dynamics, that is, how it occurred, developed, and affected the mental and emotional processes of the defendant; it does not lie in his mere expression of conclusion. The ultimate inferences *vel non* of relationship, of cause and effect, are for the trier of the facts.

This statement by the Court of Appeals would appear to call for a psychodynamic, rather than a clinical classificatory, approach by psychiatrists to mental illness. As has been mentioned, however, this judicial statement has not found its way into the day-by-day operation of the insanity defense.

Mental Disease

The *Durham* decision stated that any mental disease or defect would qualify to negate responsibility if causation is present. In that decision, the court defined mental disease as a condition capable of either improving or deteriorating. The court defined mental defect as a condition that is considered incapable of either improving or deteriorating, and which may be congenital, the result of injury, or the residual effect of a physical or mental disease. *Durham vs. United States*, 214 F. 2d 862 (1954). One of the major difficulties growing out of the *Durham* decision is the meaning of mental disease or mental illness.

The *Durham* decision does not replace or upset either the right-and-wrong rule or the irresistible-impulse test. *Douglas vs. United States*, 239 F. 2d 52 (1956). It merely extends the meaning of insanity to include any mental disease or mental defect.

In the trial of a pyromaniac, the trial judge refused to order a psychiatric examination because a probation officer decided the defendant was mentally defective, but not psychotic. The

Court of Appeals reversed. Judge Bazelon stated that "the assumption that psychosis is a legally sufficient mental disease and other illnesses are not is erroneous." *Briscoe vs. United States*, 243 F. 2d 640 (1957).

In *Wright vs. United States*, 250 F. 2d 4 (1957), the Court of Appeals held it to be a reversible error for the trial court to refuse to answer the jurors' questions whether, in determining insanity, any condition other than schizophrenia might be included, and to refuse to give further instructions where jurors might have understood that schizophrenia was the only form of mental disease amounting to insanity.

In *Stewart vs. United States*, 214 F. 2d 879 (1954), the trial judge stated in his instructions to the jury:

> There are many people who are psychopathic to one degree or another; they are maladjusted; emotionally unstable; resentful, for one reason or another, of society; of low intelligence, indifferent towards the rights of others, and so on. That is a psychopath. He is not insane within the meaning of the law; he is simply an abnormal, maladjusted person, or subnormal, as the case may be; he is a misfit; he does not care about others; indifferent to them, and so on. You must distinguish in your mind between that kind of mental disorder, because it is obviously a mental disorder, and a real mental disease.

The Court of Appeals reversed this decision and left it to the jury to decide whether or not a psychopathic personality was a mental disease. It is interesting to note that five years after the *Stewart* case, the court again considered the issue of the psychopathic personality as a mental disease, this time in light of the fact that Saint Elizabeths was now certifying psychopaths as mentally ill. *Blocker vs. United States*, 274 F. 2d 572 (1959).

In *Gilleo vs. United States*, Criminal No. 583-59, United States District Court for the District of Columbia, the trial judge asked a psychiatrist if a psychosis is the same as insanity. The psychiatrist answered, "No, insanity is a legal term and psychosis is a medical term." The judge then asked, "Can there be a mental disease without insanity?" "Yes," the psychiatrist replied. The judge then asked, "Didn't William Alanson White in the

1920's use the term 'insanity'?" When the psychiatrist labeled the defendant as a dependent type personality, the judge asked, "Is a clinging vine a mental disease? Is indecisiveness a mental disease? Is alcoholism or chain-smoking a mental disease?"

In his instructions to the jury, the judge in the *Gilleo* case stated that it is not in every case in which the defendant is suffering from a mental abnormality or mental deficiency or defect that he is to be free from liability for his acts. The law holds many abnormal persons responsible for their crimes. The defendant must be suffering from a mental disease or defect, and the criminal act must be a product of this disease or defect in order for an insanity plea to prevail. In the *Gilleo* case, the trial judge was attempting to limit the legal meaning of insanity to psychosis.

In *Watson vs. United States*, Criminal No. 907-60, United States District Court for the District of Columbia, the judge asked a psychiatrist, "If mental illness is not psychosis, what is it?" The psychiatrist stated that it would include emotionally unstable personalities, and that many psychiatrists at Saint Elizabeths felt that all criminals are mentally ill.

In *Jenkins vs. United States*, Criminal No. 16,306 (1951), United States Court of Appeals for the District of Columbia, the judge in his charge to the jury stated:

> Insanity is a condition of mind which renders the affected person unfit to enjoy freedom of action . . . a disease of the mind and a breaking down of the mental faculties so that a person lacks the power to reason correctly. . . It is not every kind of mental derangement or mental deficiency which is sufficient to relieve a person of responsibility for his acts. The fact that the defendant's IQ is borderline is not in itself sufficient to relieve him from criminal responsibility. He must be suffering from a mental disease or defect, and the act must be a product of disease or defect.

Jury Decision

Even under the *Durham* ruling, the issue of insanity is still a matter for the jury to decide. Judge Bazelon has noted that one of the basic rationales of the *Durham* decision is to restore to the jury its traditional function of applying our ideas of moral responsibility to individuals prosecuted for crimes. In *Durham vs. United States,* 214 F. 2d 862 (1954), the court stated:

> Under the rule now announced, any instruction should in some way convey to the jury the sense and substance of the following: If you, the jury, believe beyond a reasonable doubt that the accused was not suffering from a diseased or defective mental condition when he committed the act, but believe beyond a reasonable doubt that the act was not a product of such mental abnormality, you may find him guilty. Unless you believe beyond a reasonable doubt either that he was not suffering from a diseased or defective mental condition, or that the act was not the product of such abnormality, you must find the accused not guilty by reason of insanity.

In *Holloway vs. United States,* 148 F. 2d 665 (1945), the court states that the psychiatrist will be permitted to carry out his principal court function, which is to inform the jury of the character of the accused's mental disease or defect. The court held in *Holloway* that the jury's decision should not be disturbed on the ground that it is contrary to expert psychiatric opinion.

In this respect the court has said:

> The reports of the psychiatrists do not reveal the basis for their conclusions and there is no way of knowing whether they used the terms "sound mind" or "mental disease" or "mental defect" in their legal or medical sense. At the trial, however, whether petitioner was suffering from such "mental disease" or "mental defect" when he lit the fire, as to discharge him of criminal responsibility, would be determined by the trier of the facts, not by psychiatric witnesses. [*Briscoe vs. United States,* 243 F. 2d 640 (1957). See also *Carter vs. United States,* 252 F. 2d 608 (1957).]

In *Lyles vs. United States,* 254 F. 2d 725 (1957), the Court of Appeals held that the jury must be informed that, if acquitted by reason of insanity, the appellant would be confined to a mental hospital until it was determined he was not dangerous to himself or others. This instruction is required unless it appears affirmatively on the record that the appellant did not wish that instruction. The point arises under the doctrine that the jury has no concern with the consequences of the verdict. Jurors have a general awareness of the meaning of verdicts of guilty or not guilty. They do not have an awareness of the consequences of a verdict of not guilty by reason of insanity, and therefore they must be so informed. [From the point of view of behavioral psychology, the behavior of jurors is governed by its consequences; therefore, the court is following good psychological principles when it informs the jurors of the consequences of a verdict of not guilty by reason of insanity.]

McDonald was charged with second-degree murder, and convicted of manslaughter. He appealed on the basis of two alleged errors in trial court procedure. *McDonald vs. United States*, No. 16,304, United States Court of Appeals for the District of Columbia, 1962. One error alleged in this case was that the trial court failed to inform the jury that, if acquitted by reason of insanity, the appellant would be confined in a mental hospital until it was determined he was no longer dangerous to himself or to others (as required in the *Lyles* case discussed above).

A psychiatrist and a psychologist testified that McDonald was mentally defective, with an IQ of 68. The psychiatrist further testified that there may have been organic pathology. The court stated that evidence of an IQ of 68, by itself and without more, is not evidence of mental defect, thus invoking the *Durham* charge. Where there is other evidence of mental abnormality, however, as in *McDonald*, the *Davis* case would control.

> What psychiatrists may consider a "mental disease or defect" for clinical purposes may or may not be the same as mental disease or defect for the jury's purpose in determining criminal responsibility. Consequently, for that purpose, the jury should be told that a mental disease or defect includes any abnormal condition of the mind which substantially affects mental or emotional processes and substantially impairs behavior con-

trols. . . . We emphasize that, since the question of whether or not the defendant has a disease or defect is ultimately for the trier of facts, obviously its resolution cannot be controlled by expert opinion.

In a dissenting opinion in the *McDonald* case, a Circuit Court judge stated that the majority opinion is important, for it means that the jury will know it is not bound by what experts say is mental disease, if the abnormal condition does not affect the defendant's capacity to control his conduct in relation to the law. This judge felt that the court should go even further in affirming this position. The ruling is necessary, he said, because the experts have expanded the definition of mental disease, reclassifying sociopathic personality, for example, to be included as a mental disease. He noted other such reclassifications: emotionally unstable personality as mental disease in *Campbell vs. United States,* No. 16,414, United States Court of Appeals for the District of Columbia, 1962; and narcotics addiction as mental disease in *United States vs. Carroll,* Criminal No. 383-62, United States District Court for the District of Columbia, likewise in *United States vs. Horton,* Criminal No. 59-62, United States District Court for the District of Columbia. The judge said, "It is plain these conditions newly called mental diseases are not such in a legal sense."

In the light of this discussion, it might be appropriate to quote from *The Criminal Mind* by Philip Roche, who said the following concerning mental illness:

What agreement can be reached on the meaning of the terms "insanity" and "mental illness?" Goodwin expressed the despair of those who pursue the circle of verbal definitions. He wrote, "Neither the lawyers or the doctors have been able to evolve, either separately or conjointly, any rigid definition of insanity for the simple reason that there is none." In so far as verbal definitions apply, this statement is equally applicable to "mental illness." This probable truth does not deter either lawyers or psychiatrists from acting as if the terms themselves have a "natural" and "proper" meaning, and one hears the recurrent complaint by lawyers that psychiatrists find lawyers troublesome in their insistence that "mental illness" is not invariably "insanity." Beyond this, some psychiatrists are given to calling mental illness insanity (which is not a medical term), and occasionally one hears the term "medical insanity," which is surely a bad marriage. If lawyers and psychiatrists will agree to regard "mental illness" and "insanity" less as they are verbally defined and more as what we do to people to whom we attach such terms, we will be nearer the sharing of behavioral reality, not only that of others but of ourselves.[7]

Summary

Psychiatrists disagree on the meaning of mental illness. Some use the term "mental illness" as synonymous with "psychosis," whereas others include neurotic disorders and personality disorders under the rubric "mental illness."

The *Durham* rule did not redefine insanity to include behavioral disorders other than psychoses. It did free the jury to hear testimony concerning nonpsychotic psychopathology, and to decide whether such psychopathology was insanity within the legal context. The meaning of mental disease or defect is still a matter left to laymen to decide.

By expanding the meaning of mental illness, sociopaths, alcoholics, and drug addicts are now included in the category of "mentally ill."

---

[7]Roche, Philip: *The Criminal Mind*, New York, Grove Press, 1958, pp. 14-15.

Chapter 4

CRIME, MENTAL DISEASE, AND CAUSATION

THE DURHAM decision stated that the criminal act must be a *product of* mental disease or defect; the mere presence of a disease or defect is not enough to excuse the defendant from responsibility for his acts unless these behaviors were a product of the alleged disease or defect.

Since 1954, the courts have attempted to give some meaning to the phrase "product of." In *Douglas vs. United States,* 239 M. 2d 52 (1956), the court stated that the criminal act alleged would not have occurred "except for" the mental abnormality of the accused, in order for an acquittal by reason of insanity to prevail.

The most liberal and loosely-constructed statement concerning causation appears in *Carter vs. United States,* 252 F. 2d 608 (1957):

> When we say the defense of insanity requires that the act be a "product of" a disease, we do not mean that it must be a direct emission or a proximate creation, or an immediate issue of the disease in the sense of Hadfield's delusion that the Almighty had directed him to shoot George III. We do not mean to restrict the defense to such cases; many mental diseases so affect areas of the mind that some or all of the mental elements requisite to criminal liability under the law are lacking. We mean to include such cases.
> When we say the defense of insanity requires that the act be a "product of" a disease, we mean that the facts on the record are such that the trier of the facts is enabled to draw a reasonable inference that the accused would not have committed the act he did commit if he had not been diseased as he was. There must be a relationship between the disease and the act, and that relationship . . . must be critical in its

effect in respect to the act. By "critical" we mean decisive, determinative, causal; we mean to convey the idea inherent in the phrases "because of," "except for," "without which," "but for," "effect of," "result of," "causative factor;" the disease made the effective or decisive difference between doing and not doing the act. . . But for this disease the act would not have been committed.

Causation is one of the problems created by the *Durham* decision remaining to be solved. This chapter will include a discussion of some actual cases in terms of the testimony of psychiatrists and psychologists concerning this issue. Whether a person has a mental illness is one problem. If he has such an illness, whether it produced the criminal act is another problem.

SCHIZOPHRENIA

In *United States vs. Ray*, Criminal No. 250-61, United States District Court for the District of Columbia, we have a case wherein schizophrenia is related to criminality.

Oscar Ray was charged with larceny, forgery, and housebreaking. His defense was insanity. The defendant's wife testified that her husband was argumentative and nervous; that he threw clothes in the hall, nailed his door closed, called his wife a devil after he ran out of a church during a Sunday morning service, talked to God, told God his wife was pregnant, talked to his dead mother, and tore up his marriage license. Ray's employer and supervisor testified that he appeared to be very nervous; that he thought other employees were persecuting him, and that he talked to God.

A psychiatrist, called as an expert witness for the defense, testified that Ray was a schizophrenic, paranoid type, suffering from a derangement of logical thinking characterized by withdrawal from reality and by apathy and autistic behavior (interest in or preoccupation with self). He said that Ray had delusions about Russian spies attempting to bomb him and hallucinations concerning conversations he had with God—that is, voices that give him instructions on how to behave.

This diagnosis was based on conversations with the defendant, with the family and friends, and on hospital records. Upon cross-examination, the defense psychiatrist admitted that Ray had been released from the D. C. General Hospital in 1960 as free from acute mental symptoms.

On the issue of causality, the psychiatrist stated that Ray wrote the checks in order to get revenge against society. He felt bitter and mistreated, and by committing these crimes he was able to get back at society, which in his mind was responsible for his plight. It was brought out in testimony that the defendant spent the money for liquor. The issue of causality can thus be stated: "Did the defendant commit the offense in order to secure money and liquor, or did he do it in order to get back at society?"

Another defense psychiatrist testified that there was a remission of symptoms when he examined the defendant; that is, he exhibited no psychotic symptoms during the examination. The diagnosis of schizophrenia was based, therefore, on the case history secured from relatives and friends. From his history of marital and employment difficulties, and from statements concerning his hallucinatory and delusional behaviors, the psychiatrist concluded this was psychotic behavior. This expert witness testified that he did not know whether revenge was the motive, but that he believed a causal relationship between schizophrenia and forgery did exist.

A Saint Elizabeths psychiatrist testified for the government that he did not find a mental disease or defect in the defendant. Upon cross-examination, the government psychiatrist testified he spent a great deal of time in court and that his diagnosis was based on a forty-minute interview with the accused and on records made available to him.

The first trial ended in a hung jury: the jury could not reach a verdict. The second trial resulted in an acquittal by reason of insanity, and Ray was committed to a mental hospital.

The *Kent* case also involved the issue of schizophrenia and crime. This case is reported in detail in Chapter 5.

NEUROSES

The insanity defense is seldom used for defendants diagnosed as neurotic. In *United States vs. Strickland*, Criminal No. 255-61,

District Court for the District of Columbia, the defendant had been in and out of mental hospitals over a period of five years. He was variously diagnosed as a psychotic with a psychopathic personality and as psychoneurotic. For a period of approximately nine months, Strickland was declared incompetent to stand trial. At the time of the trial, a defense psychiatrist testified that the defendant was classified as a psychoneurotic, with dissociative reaction and further that the criminal act (unauthorized use of a motor vehicle) was a product of the dissociative reaction.

In the *Strickland* case, one must assume that the verdict, not guilty by reason of insanity, was probably a reflection of the defendant's long history of mental and emotional disturbances.

In the case of *United States vs. Nelson,* Criminal No. 278-62, United States District Court for the District of Columbia, the defendant was charged with transporting a stolen car across a state line. He was diagnosed as having depressive reaction, with anxiety features, although the psychiatrist testified he could not form an opinion regarding a causal relationship between the act and the depressive reaction (neurosis) of this defendant. Nelson was acquitted by reason of insanity. This case is of interest because here mental depression is classified and accepted by the court as mental disease. The verdict may have been based on the fact that several years earlier, in another case, Nelson had been acquitted by reason of insanity and had spent time at Saint Elizabeths Hospital.

William Sutherland was charged with grand larceny and embezzlement. His defense was insanity. *United States vs. Sutherland,* No. 16,160, United States Court of Appeals for the District of Columbia.

The defendant was diagnosed as an alcoholic. Underlying his alcoholism was a psychoneurotic structure of anxiety and compulsion; this was dealt with through the use of alcohol, which made it possible to avoid anxiety at a conscious level. One psychiatrist testified that alcoholism was "a result of anxiety and the alleged criminal offense was the result of alcoholism. . . A neurosis is a condition that exists as a result of internal conflict within the individual." Upon cross-examination by the government, a staff member from Saint Elizabeths stated that he (the psychiatrist) spent 50 per cent of his time in court; that he had 350 to 375 patients under his care, and that he saw them once every two or three months. He agreed that the psychiatric examination of the defendant was not as thorough as it should have been.

It is of utmost interest that defense counsel, in his appellant brief, after noting the language of *Blunt, Winn, Williams, Calloway,* and *Lynch,* stated:

> . . . the implementation of such a policy, it is submitted, puts the burden of seeing to it that an indigent accused gets an adequate mental examination on the courts as well as on the prosecutor and defendants' counsel.

The brief then asked for a new trial based upon an adequate psychiatric examination. The government and the defense both rely on the inadequacy of diagnostic facilities, but for different purposes. The prosecutor raises the issue in order to discredit any testimony that might be regarded as favorable to an acquittal by reason of insanity; the defense raises the issue in order to argue that a thorough examination would show the defendant to be mentally diseased. The jury found Sutherland guilty of embezzlement.

PERSONALITY DISORDERS

In *United States vs. Gilleo,* Criminal No. 583-59, United States District Court for the District of Columbia, the defendant was charged with embezzlement of funds. He was diagnosed as a passive-aggressive personality, passive dependent type. Gilleo had a long history of bad check charges, alcoholism, and drug addiction. He would turn to alcohol whenever confronted with a serious problem. The last act of embezzlement for which he was in court came about when his wife became pregnant. Gilleo was very upset by his wife's pregnancy and the accompanying responsibility. For these reasons he was diagnosed as a dependent type. One psychiatrist testified that the act of embezzlement was product of his passive-dependent personality;

another testified there was no productivity in this case; still another testified as to the oral needs of the defendant which led to his drinking and the related problem of embezzlement.

The jury found Gilleo guilty, at which time the judge made the remarks quoted in Chapter 3 concerning the disadvantages to a defendant of the insanity plea. The judge placed him on probation.

George Watson was charged with manslaughter. *United States vs. Watson, Criminal* No. 907-60, United States District Court for the District of Columbia. Watson had been driving a stolen car and, when approached by a police car, he attempted to flee. In the process he struck another car, killing four of its occupants.

After the accident, the defendant was hospitalized for observation, during which time he attempted to commit suicide and threatened to kill a nurse. While in jail, he would sit rocking backing and forth in his cell. He also engaged in such behavior during the course of the trial. At the age of fifteen, he had been hospitalized for what was then diagnosed as a psychotic condition. One psychiatrist testified that Watson was schizophrenic with a paranoid reaction.

> I believe the fatal accident was the consequence of a panic reaction brought on by his being stopped by the police which precipitated his 100-mile-per-hour flight from the police. He has had a paranoid system centering on the police for a long time, and self-destructive activities which resulted in the fatal accident to four innocent bystanders seemed to be in response to his delusional fear of police. Consequently, it is my opinion that Mr. W. is suffering from a mental illness, with the diagnosis of schizophrenia paranoid type, and that his accident was undoubtedly the result of this illness.[1]

[The writer fails to appreciate the conclusion drawn here concerning paranoia. If one is driving a stolen car, the normal

---

[1]Salzman, Leon: Psychiatric interviews as evidence: the role of the psychiatrist in court—some suggestions and case histories, *George Washington Law Review*, June, 1962, p. 864.

reaction would be the expectation that the police were out to get him.]

The staff at Saint Elizabeths could not agree that Watson was schizophrenic. They classified him as emotionally unstable, a type of personality disorder but not a mental illness. No hallucinations or delusions were observed in the defendant. The Saint Elizabeths staff limited mental illness to psychotic behavior in this case. Watson became so behaviorally disorganized that the trial could not continue, and a mistrial was declared because the defendant was found to be incompetent to stand trial. At a second trial, the government did not contest the insanity defense. The court entered a judgment of not guilty by reason of insanity and Watson was committed to Saint Elizabeths.

In *Blocker vs. United States,* 274 F. 2d 572, United States Court of Appeals for the District of Columbia, a defense psychiatrist testified that a sociopath personality is:

> ... a longstanding personality disturbance characterized by a lack of moral responsibility and inability to profit from experience. These people are frequently in antisocial difficulties, and chronic alcoholics also fall within this group. The two diagnoses are really one, the chronic alcoholism being the kind of sociopathic personality disturbance that this man represented.

This statement argues that the symptom, alcoholism, is also the diagnosis; that is, the man is sociopathic because he is alcoholic, and he is alcoholic because he is a sociopath.

In *United States vs. Jackson,* Criminal No. 980-61, United States District Court for the District of Columbia, the defendant was charged with the murder of his Chinese employer. Jackson was classified as a schizoid personality, with psychopathic characteristics. He expressed feelings that people were against him. He came from a poor family environment, with a mother who was an emotionally unstable alcoholic. He suffered from feelings of depression. He felt rejected, especially by his parents. He expressed the desire to commit suicide, to "get it over with."

Jackson killed his employer while attempting a robbery.

Psychiatric testimony indicated that the defendant was explosive and violent under stress. Under the pressures of debt and family problems, he attempted to rob, and in the process killed his employer. Robbery was given as the motive for the crime. Jackson was found guilty of murder.

Robert King was charged with molesting a ten-year-old girl, the daughter of a woman with whom he was living. *United States vs. King*, Criminal No. 169-62, United States District Court for the District of Columbia. He was diagnosed to be a sociopath, a man devoid of any concept of responsibility. The defense psychiatrist stated in his report: "He appears to come from a cultural setting where such behavior would be widespread and acceptable." The writer finds it difficult to see how behavior, originating in the social setting described here and considered by that society to be normal, can be regarded as mental disease or mental defect. A psychiatrist for the government testified that King was free from mental disease or defect. The defendant was found guilty as charged and sentenced to six years each on two counts.

In *United States vs. Marocco*, Criminal No. 208-62, United States District Court for the District of Columbia, the defendant was charged with housebreaking and petty larceny. He was diagnosed as a sociopathic personality with an antisocial reaction. His juvenile record dated back to the age of twelve. He had been dishonorably discharged from the Army, and had served time in prison in Indiana, Illinois, and New Mexico. In all these cases, he had been paroled, and in several instances there had been a revocation of parole. He also had a history of homosexuality.

Marocco was described by a psychiatrist as quiet, soft-spoken, good-humored, and charming. Although he was caught repeatedly, he continued to commit crimes. He claimed he didn't care because he found life in prison better than "on the streets." In prison he was a bigshot, a privileged character.

The defendant showed no anxiety, no guilt feelings. He felt he was exempted from the usual, conventional norms of society. He seemed untouched by punishment; he wanted something for nothing. No delusions or hallucinations were present. "His mental illness reflects itself in the profound incapacity to adjust to the moral obligations of his culture." Marocco was found not guilty by reason of insanity.

DRUG ADDICTION

The issue of insanity in connection with drug addiction has been raised in the District of Columbia. In this respect the important case is *United States vs. Horton,* Criminal No. 59-62, United States District Court for the District of Columbia.

Horton, an illegitimate child, had been abandoned by his mother. He was reared by a woman who, according to psychiatric testimony, apparently overprotected him. At the age of twelve, he was in an industrial school because of truancy and behavior problems. He left school at the age of sixteen, at the fourth-grade level. He was drafted into the Army a year or so later, from which he received a medical discharge for psychoneurotic reasons.

In 1947, Horton married. The marriage was never successful and of short duration. He was not adequately trained in any trade and did menial work for a living. He had few friends. As an innocent bystander in a shooting, he was shot in the leg, which later had to be amputated because of gangrene. Hobbling about in parks at night, he met a dope peddler, and his addiction began at this point. He found the tranquilizing effect of drugs satisfying to his physical and emotional pains.

Horton was described by psychiatrists as a man of ambivalence and inertia. A great gap existed between his potential and his actual functioning. On projective tests he revealed an infantile, narcissistic pattern. Self-satisfying experiences were rare in this man's background. He was unable to meet the demands of everyday life, so he turned to a world of fantasy by way of morphine.

Each of the four psychiatrists called by the defense to testify classified Horton differently. One testified that the defendant was an inadequate personality; another claimed he was a sociopathic personality with drug addiction; a third said he was a neurotic depressive with sociopathic features; and the last expert testified that Horton was mentally defective because he scored 62 on the Army Alpha. Horton had a fourth-grade education and could not read or write, so the issue of his intellectual level— that is, the diagnosis of mental defectiveness—is certainly subject to question.

One of the defense psychiatrists stated that all drug addicts are mentally ill. Another testified on Horton's behalf without ever having interviewed the man. His testimony was based on the Saint Elizabeths record, and it consisted of showing how inadequate the hospital's record and examination were. The defense relied heavily on a book by Lawrence Kolb, *Drug Addiction: A Medical Problem,* in which it is stated that "chronic addiction is associated with emotional instability and immaturity."

Two psychiatrists for the government testified that Horton was free of mental disease or defect. They did find sociopathic tendencies in his life history. They both testified that there were addicts who were not mentally ill, citing the case of a cancer patient who received narcotics in order to ease the pain of severe illness. One of the psychiatrists for the government stated that he knew of no literature in which it was claimed that all addicts are mentally ill. He testified that the APA manual does not classify drug addiction by itself as a mental illness; rather, addiction must be present with another personality disorder for it to be considered mental illness. He went on to describe the causation aspect of addiction:

> The drug addict can postpone his immediate act, a temporary postponement, because drug addicts, in general, if on drugs, have a craving, a tremendous urge, to obtain the medication that they are receiving, and I think they can postpone temporarily this desire, but they eventually have a tremendous urge and a desire to satisfy both the physiological and psychological need to obtain narcotics.

The *Horton* case caused such a furor that the trial of cases by the NIH project was temporarily halted. The issue of drug addiction is so controversial and emotion-laden that any attempt to deal with it rationally is difficult, if not impossible. At several points, the judge questioned the defense attorney concerning the relationship between NIH funds and the psychiatric testimony. The defense attorney asked a staff member of Saint Elizabeths if it were not true that the hospital failed to meet the standards of the APA in terms of doctor-patient ratio. There were altercations between lawyers and witnesses. The government referred to one of the defense psychiatrists as "unworthy . . . a shame on the psychiatric profession." The judge asked eleven questions of government witnesses, and 108 questions of the defense psychiatrists. [See *United States vs. Horton*, No. 17,261, United States Court of Appeals for the District of Columbia; see also the Brief for Amici Curiae filed in the *Horton* case.]

A jury found Horton guilty, and he was sentenced to ten years in prison. On appeal, the Court of Appeals reversed the District Court. The court cited 18 U.S.C. 4244, which provides that:

> . . . a finding by the judge that the accused is mentally competent to stand trial shall in no way prejudice the accused in a plea of insanity as a defense to the crime charged; such a finding shall not be introduced in evidence on that issue nor otherwise be brought to the notice of the jury.

In the presence of the jury, the trial judge had said: "It is a fact that the hospital has certified that this man is competent to stand trial and there is no mental disease."

There was no attempt on the part of the court to tackle the major issue raised by he *Horton* case: namely, is addiction a mental disease. The court noted that there was a conflict in psychiatric testimony and, therefore, the issue was properly submitted to the jury. *Horton vs. United States*, Nos. 17,261 and 17,540, United States Court of Appeals for the District of Columbia (1963).

After the reversal of the *Horton* case by the Court of Appeals, the government allowed the defendant to plead guilty to a misdemeanor, for which he received a one-year sentence: three months in jail and nine months on probation. Horton is now back on the streets, without treatment or cure. Certainly, releasing him was not to his benefit, and confinement to a mental hospital might be of little or no help.

The implications of the *Horton* case are great for criminology and criminal law, and they will be discussed later in some detail.

In *United States vs. Bell*, Criminal No. 969-61, United States District Court for the District of Columbia, the defendant was charged with the illegal possession of narcotics. Bell was diagnosed as a sociopathic personality with drug addiction. The psychiatrist stated that drug addiction was a diagnosis and a symptom. She also testified that a direct relationship existed between mental illness and the use of heroin. When asked how this relationship was established, the psychiatrist replied:

> . . . a matter of definition. A man who has received a diagnosis
> of sociopathic personality with drug addiction, and his crime
> is the possession of the drug, then it seems such an obvious
> conclusion that I don't know how I can explain it otherwise.

Again, as in the case of alcoholism, the addict is a sociopath by definition. The symptom is the diagnosis: the defendant is a sociopath because he is an addict; he is an addict because he is a sociopath.

Another psychiatrist testified that the basis of the disorder is anxiety, which goes back to early childhood experiences. Drugs reduce the anxiety.

Bell was found not guilty by reason of insanity.

Another narcotics case was that of *United States vs. Purcell*, Criminal No. 487-62, United States District Court for the District of Columbia. The defendant testified that she started using narcotics after her mother, father, and baby had died. Her marriage had ended in divorce. "Only through the use of narcotics could I get over feeling alone and unhappy. . . Drugs could make me forget my troubles." The defendant had been in prison for a year, and had used no drugs for eight years. She began taking drugs again when a relative got into legal and family difficulties. "About two years ago I lost my job. It was then I started using narcotics very heavily again. It seems I have had troubles all my life."

The psychiatrist testified that the defendant's addiction was symptomatic of mental illness, characterized by anxiety and depression, and brought about by the loss of significant people in her life.

Mrs. Purcell was found not guilty by reason of insanity and was sent to Saint Elizabeths Hospital for treatment for drug addiction.

These cases illustrate the manner in which psychiatric categories are related to various types of criminal activities. In subsequent chapters, reference will be made to the cases as examples of the various issues that arise under the insanity defense.

The dissenting opinion in *Blocker vs. United States*, 274 F. 2d 572 (1959), perhaps summarizes one viewpoint concerning the *Durham* decision:

> I suggest that the new rule [*Durham*] is nothing more than a different and confusing way of saying that insanity does not relieve a defendant of criminal responsibility, unless it caused the unlawful act. It does not provide any new criterion for determining causation. The right-wrong and irresistible-impulse tests are criteria of causative insanity, that is, not only of insanity, but of causation as well. They are indeed the only true tests of causation. As I have heretofore suggested, it seems to me that one who knows right from wrong, but freely and deliberately chooses to do the wrong, cannot be heard to say that some mental disease or defect caused his criminal conduct. That is true even if the defendant's mentality actually deviates from the normal to the extent that psychiatrists say he has a mental disease or even insanity itself, so long as there is no causation. So, I say the right-wrong and irresistible-impulse tests remain the only criteria of causative insanity, and that the *Durham* case really adds no new standard for the determination of causation.

There has developed within the Court of Appeals for the District of Columbia a revolt against the *Durham* test. The reasons for this are well summarized by Judge Burger in his concurring opinion in *Blocker vs. United States*, 288 F. 2d 853

(1961). He was joined by Judges Miller and Bastian in his opinion.

Judge Burger reviewed the history of the *Durham* test in the District, in which he found the terms "disease" and "product" to be inadequate, and he also found the expert testimony of psychiatrists as presented under the *Durham* test to be an usurpation of the power of the jury to decide the issue of criminal responsibility. He then examined the basic assumptions of the criminal law, which is man's capacity to exercise free will and to make choices. He noted that the *Durham* test breaks with this assumption, although in the case of *State vs. Jones,* 50 N. H. 369 (1871), Judge Ladd wrote:

> If he could have controlled his act, then his will must have assented to the act, and it was not caused by the disease but by the concurrence of his will, and was therefore crime.

Judge Burger concluded that the *Durham* rule rejects the historical basis of criminal responsibility by ignoring the capacity of the defendant to exercise free will and choice. He proposed the following rule to guide jurors:

> The defendant is not to be found guilty as charged unless it is established beyond a reasonable doubt that when he committed the act, *first,* that he understood and appreciated that the act was a violation of law, and *second,* that he had the capacity to exercise his will and to choose not to do it. If, because of some abnormal mental condition, either of these elements is lacking, he cannot be found guilty.

Chapter 5

UNITED STATES vs. KENT

THE CASE of *United States vs. Morris A. Kent, Jr.,* Criminal No. 798-61, District Court for the District of Columbia, is presented here in detail because it provides examples of most of the problems involved in the insanity defense. The case is rich in psychiatric testimony: eleven psychiatrists and psychologists testified for the defense; two testified for the government.

Kent was sixteen years old when he was picked up and charged with three counts of housebreaking, three counts of robbery, and two counts of rape. After a long session in the Juvenile Court, he was bound over and tried in the District Court as an adult. The Kent trial of March, 1963 has the advantage of being the most recent one of its kind in the District of Columbia.

The government established the presence of the accused at the scene of the crime by eyewitnesses (the victims) and by many fingerprints taken from the three apartments where the crimes were committed. In his opening statement, the defense attorney said that he would not challenge the facts presented by the government, but rather he would base his defense on the issue of insanity at the time the crimes were committed. The defense called lay witnesses as well as experts in establishing the fact that Morris Kent was insane. An outline of the testimony is herein presented in order that the reader might become familiar with the type of evidence used to establish an insanity defense. To avoid distracting the reader with a discussion of the meaning or adequacy of the testimony, the record will be presented, without comment, as it occurred in the courtroom. Detailed comment on this testimony will appear in the second half of this book. This report of the testimony is taken from the official trial transcript, and is as accurate as such a record can be. The phraseology has been altered and collapsed, so that what is presented here is not a verbatim report but a condensed version of the trial record. Certain materials were selected because they illustrate major issues in the insanity defense. The writer was present in person throughout the trial, and has attempted to retain the flavor of the proceedings whenever possible.

LAY WITNESSES

The defense called several lay witnesses: the defendant's mother, his uncle, and two aunts. These relatives testified as to the behavior of Kent from birth to age sixteen. This testimony indicated that the defendant was reared in a home environment where the parents fought physically and verbally, and where there was a high degree of personal hostility between father and son. Kent feared his father and would hide whenever the man was around. The divorce of his parents took place during this period.

The defendant was described as nervous, agitated, easily upset, and prone to tears. He lacked control over his bladder and bowel functions. Once, it was reported, around the age of eight, he smeared feces over his body. He was distant, very shy, and a daydreamer. At night, he would wander about the streets, alone or with a friend. He did not like girls and never did establish a good relationship with females. Describing an incident at a summer camp, his uncle said Kent would, when asked to rake leaves or scrub floors, be observed laughing or talking to himself or daydreaming. He would say silly things, or would claim he had completed a task when actually he had not.

From the time he was twelve, Kent was in trouble with the juvenile authorities. Several times he was picked up for entering houses or stealing. When he roamed the streets, he claimed he heard voices—voices that told him to enter apartments where there were women. Apparently, he had killed several animals, including a puppy, although relatives testified that he was very fond of animals and would use his money to buy food for them.

He would pretend not to hear people talking to him, or he would ignore the ringing of a telephone or the doorbell. He had a poor academic record; his formal education ended at the eighth grade. He was a good athlete and liked especially to play basketball. He also liked to fish.

PSYCHOLOGICAL TESTIMONY

Psychologist A, Defense

Psychologist A testified that she had administered the following tests to Kent: the Wechsler Memory Scale, the Bender-Gestalt, the Rorschach, the Thematic Apperception test, the House-Tree-Person test, and the Szondi test. From this evidence, she diagnosed the defendant as schizophrenic, chronic undifferentiated type, characterized by abnormal thoughts, difficulty with emotional control, deficient in common sense judgment, and lacking in close relationships with other people. She testified that this is a psychosis, which is a mental disease, and that the crimes of housebreaking, robbery, and rape were a product of the mental disease.

Cross-examination by Government

Q[uestion]: What did the House-Tree-Person test reveal?

A[nswer]: The major finding was a feeling of withdrawal, running away from reality, feelings of rejection by women.

Q. And the results of the Szondi?

A. This showed a passive, depressed person who withdrew from the world of reality, with an inability to relate to others.

Q. Wasn't the Szondi test made up around 1900, or the early 1900 period? And wasn't it made up of a number of pictures of Europeans who were acutely psychotic?

A. Yes, that is true.

Q.   And this tells you something about his personality?

A.   Yes, you can tell something about the person from his responses to the photos.

Q.   And the House-Tree-Person test—you handed the defendant Kent a pencil and a blank piece of paper, is that right, Doctor?

A.   That is correct.

Q.   And you asked him to draw a house?

A.   Yes.

Q.   And what did this tell you about Kent?

A.   The absence of a door, and the bars on the windows, indicated he saw the house as a jail, not a home. Also, you will notice it is a side view of the house; he was making it inaccessible.

Q.   Isn't it normal to draw a side view of a house? You didn't ask him to draw a front view, did you?

A.   No.

Q.   And those bars on the window—could they have been Venetian blinds and not bars? Who called them bars, you or Kent?

A.   I did.

Q.   Did you ask him what they were?

A.   No.

Q.   What else did the drawing reveal about Kent?

A.   The line in front of the house runs from left to right. This indicates a need for security.

Q.   This line indicates insecurity! Could it also indicate the contour of the landscape, like a lawn or something?

A.   This is not the interpretation I gave it.

Q.   And the chimney—what does it indicate?

A.   You will notice the chimney is dark. This indicates disturbed sexual feelings. The smoke indicates inner daydreaming.

Q.   Did I understand you correctly? Did you say dark chimneys indicate disturbed sex feelings?

A.   Yes.

Q.   You then asked Kent to draw a tree. Why?

A.   We have discovered that a person often expresses feelings about himself that are on a subconscious level when he draws a tree.

Q.   And what does this drawing indicate about Kent's personality?

A.   The defendant said it was a sequoia, 1,500 years old, and that it was diseased. This indicates a feeling of self-depreciation. Also, the tree has no leaves and it leans to the left. This indicates a lack of contact with the outside world—the absence of leaves.

Q.   Don't trees lose their leaves in winter, Doctor? If you look out the window now, in Washington, do you see leaves on the trees? Perhaps the defendant was drawing a picture of a tree without leaves, as they appear in the winter.

A.   The important thing is, however, why did the defendant select this particular tree. He was stripped of leaves, of emotions.

Q.   You then asked him to draw a person?

A.   Yes.

Q.   And he drew this picture of a male?

A.   Yes.

Q.   And what does this drawing indicate about Kent?

A.   The man appears to be running. This indicates anxiety, agitation. He is running, you will notice, to the left. This indicates running away from the environment. If he had been running to the right this would indicate entering the environment.

Q.   How about the hands?

A.   The sharp fingers may indicate hostility.

Q.   Anything else?

A.   The head and the body appear to be separated by a dark collar, and the neck is long. This indicates a split between intellect and emotion. The dark hair, dark tie, dark shoes, and dark buckle indicate anxiety about sexual problems.

Q.   You then asked Kent to draw a person of the opposite sex. What did this picture indicate?

A.   The dark piercing eyes indicated a feeling of rejection by women, hostility toward women.

Q.   Are you familiar with the occasion upon which a Veterans Administration psychologist gave this House-Tree-Person test to fifty psychotics, and then gave fifty normal subjects the same test, and then had a group of psychologists rate them?

A.   No, I am not familiar with that research.

[At this point the prosecution asked the psychologist a hypothetical question. It was one of three that were long and repeated several times during the course of the trial. The three hypothetical questions will be outlined here and referred to thereafter by letter.]

Hypothetical A involved the first crime, in which the defendant allegedly entered the apartment of Miss X, asked, "Where is your money?" and dragged her over to the dresser. He took her money and then, when he saw her body bare from the waist up, said, "Well, I might as well get a little." Thereupon he dragged her to the bed, during which time a fight ensued and the victim was struck several blows and raped, after which the defendant fled from the apartment.

Hypothetical B involved the second crime, in which the

defendant entered an apartment occupied by two women. He placed his hand over the mouth of one of the victims, Miss Y, and told her not to scream. She did scream, however, whereupon the defendant fled. Afterward, the victims discovered that a purse containing some money was missing from a dresser drawer.

Hypothetical C involved the third crime, in which the defendant entered the apartment of victim Z, took some money, hit her with a flat-iron, raped her, and fled.

After presenting the facts in *Hypothetical A*, the government asked:

Q.   When the defendant entered the apartment, did he know right from wrong?

A.   I cannot answer that.

Q.   Did he know what he was doing?

A.   I cannot answer that either.

Q.   Did he know what he was doing when he raped that woman?

A.   I have no opinion.

Psychiatrist A, Defense: Direct Examination

Q.   Doctor, will you tell His Honor and the ladies and gentlemen of the jury what your examination of Kent revealed to you.

A.   I took a psychiatric record from Mr. Kent; I had several, three or four interviews with him at Saint Elizabeth's. I also had other records and test results available. I found that Kent had a very poor and disorganized childhood, with his parents separated and so forth. I am told that he smeared himself with feces at one time. He was withdrawn, did not associate with other children. He was advised by school authorities to seek psychiatic help.

Q.   And, based on your interviews, Doctor, did you

arrive at a diagnosis of the defendant's mental condition?

A.   I diagnosed Kent as a schizophrenic, chronic undifferentiated type. This is a mental disease, a psychosis, characterized by feelings and thinking that are not integrated, along with erratic behavior and distorted thinking.

Q.   Did this mental disease affect Kent's ability to control his behavior?

A.   Yes. In some cases, schizophrenics have volitional controls; in Kent's case the disease did affect the controls. There was a preoccupation with sex, with ideas of entering houses, with a compulsion to satisfy needs that built up in him. He had a need to feel important, a sense of power.

Cross-examination by Government

Q.   Is it true, Doctor, that the nature of the staff conferences at Saint Elizabeths are subject matter among the inmates of the John Howard Pavilion?

A.   Probably, yes.

Q.   Then Kent may have been told by other inmates how to act and what to say at a staff conference?

A.   Yes, this is possible.

Q.   The hospital report states Kent was friendly, playful, co-operative with other patients on the ward. Is this true?

A.   Yes, so far as I know.

Q.   At the time Kent was admitted to Saint Elizabeths, the admitting officer noted that he was oriented as to time, place, and person. Were you aware of that?

A.   Yes.

Q.   And that there were no unusual mannerisms,

speech was coherent, no depression, no ideas of suicide, no hallucinations, no ideas of reference?

A.   Yes.

Q.   What does a remission of symptoms mean?

A.   At times a schizophrenic can act as a responsible, normal person. Schizophrenics are often in contact with reality.

Q.   [*Hypothetical A* presented] Why did the defendant Kent flee?

A.   Fear of apprehension, I suppose.

Q.   Then he knew that he had done wrong?

A.   Yes.

Q.   [*Hypothetical C* presented] Didn't the defendant go into the apartment of Mary _____ to get money, and in two instances, when he saw an opportunity, to get some sex?

A.   He went in there ostensibly to get money, but his desire to do this was a result of the fact he had a mental illness.

Psychiatrist B, Defense

Psychiatrist B related the general social-historical background of the defendant, after which he diagnosed him as a schizophrenic, undifferentiated type. This condition was marked by a disorder of thinking, an inability to test reality, and the anxiety within him built up to a point at which he could no longer control his behavior.

Cross-examination by Government

Q.   What are the symptoms of schizophrenia?

A.   Affect change, fantasy, ambivalence, looseness of association, hallucinations.

Q.   [*Hypothetical* A presented] Was the act of the defendant planned and designed?

A.   It might be; it certainly might not be.

Q.   Does it sound as if he entered the apartment to get money?

A.   It does.

Q.   Did he know what he was doing?

A.   Did he know what he was doing? He may have known; he may not have known.

Q.   Did he flee because he was afraid?

A.   That is certainly a logical reason. It may not be the one he had.

Q.   Was he free to go in or not go in the apartment?

A.   No. There was enough pressure there so he was unable to control his behavior. He was not free to make judgments.

Q.   Does it seem logical he went there for money?

A.   The most illogical thing in the world, schizophrenia.

Psychologist B, Defense

Psychologist B testified that he administered the Wechsler-Bellevue, the Graham Kendall, the Rorschach, and the Symonds Picture Story tests. He also testified that he had diagnosed the defendant as schizophrenic, undifferentiated type, and that mental illness had produced the alleged crimes.

Cross-examination by Government

Q.   Did you administer the Szondi test, Doctor?

A.   No. I don't happen to think much of it. The test assumes a schizophrenic looks a certain way, and we have evidence this isn't so.

Q.   What responses did you receive from Kent on the Rorschach, the ink-blot test?

A.   Wolf, butterfly, vagina, pelvis, bats, buttocks, etc. [These were in response to given cards and given portions of the cards.]

Q.   And from this you concluded the defendant was schizophrenic?

A.   Yes, that and other things.

Q.   You gave him the Wechsler Adult Scale?

A.   Yes.

Q.   On the word-information part of the test, the word temperature appears. What question did you ask the defendant?

A.   At what temperature does water boil.

Q.   You gave him a zero. Why?

A.   Because he answered 190° and that is the wrong answer. The right answer is 212° F.

Q.   What question did you ask about the Iliad?

A.   I am not sure; I believe I asked him to identify the Iliad or who wrote the Iliad.

Q.   And he answered "Aristotle?"

A.   Yes.

Q.   And you scored him zero?

A.   That's correct.

Q.   Now you asked the defendant to define blood vessels, did you not?

A.   Yes.

Q.   And his answer was capillaries and veins. You scored him zero. Why? Aren't capillaries and veins blood vessels?

A.   I don't know. The norms don't consider that answer acceptable.

Q.   What norms?

A.   You see, these tests are scored on the basis of norms secured by administering the test to thousands of people.

Q.   On the comprehension section you asked Kent, "If you found a sealed, addressed, stamped envelope on the street, what would you do with it?" and he answered, "Turn it in." Why did you give him a 1? Why not a 2?

A.   Because of the norms. A 2-answer would require more—something like, "Mail it" or "Take it to the post office."

Q.   You asked Kent, "What does the phrase 'Strike when the iron is hot' mean?" What was his answer?

A.   "Strike when it is best to strike." I gave him a zero.

Q.   Why? Doesn't "Strike when the iron is hot" mean to strike when the opportunity presents itself?

A.   In terms of the norms, it is not an acceptable answer.

Q.   You asked Kent, "What is similar about the eye and the ear?" and he said, "They are organs." You gave him a 1. Why?

A.   Because a 2-answer is more precise, such as "organs of perception."

Q.   You asked him, "What is winter?" and he stated, "A season of the year." You gave him a 1—why not a 2? Isn't winter a season of the year, Doctor?

A.   Well, again it is a matter of the norms. A 2-answer would include a "cold season of the year."

Q.   You asked him, "What is a slice?" and he said, "to cut." What is wrong with that? You gave him a 1.

A.   A 2-answer would include "to slice thin" or "cut into thin pieces."

Q.   You asked him to define "conceal" and he said "to get rid of." What score did you give him?

A.   A zero.

Q.   You asked him to define "sentence" and he said, "A group of words, as a noun and a verb." Why did you give him a 1?

A.   A 2-answer would include the notion that a sentence expresses an idea.

Q.   You asked him, "What is a sanctuary?" and he said, "Protection." Why did you give him a 1?

A.   According to the norms, a 2-answer includes the notion of a place or a building.

Q.   You asked Kent to define "calamity," and he said "bad thing." You gave him a zero. Isn't a calamity a bad thing, Doctor?

A.   Bad is not an acceptable answer in terms of the norms.

Psychologist C, Defense

The witness testified that he administered the Wechsler Intelligence Scale, the Rorschach, the Human Figure Drawing, the Kohn, the Porteus Maze, and the Thematic Apperception tests.

Cross-examination by Government

Q.   You asked the defendant to draw a human figure?

A.   Yes.

Q.   And this is the figure he drew for you? What does it indicate to you about his personality?

A.   You will note this is a rear view of a male. This

is very rare, statistically. It indicates hiding guilt feelings, or turning away from reality.

Q. And this drawing of a female figure, does it indicate anything to you; and, if so, what?

A. It indicates hostility towards women on the part of the subject. The pose, the hands on the hips, the hard-looking face, the stern expression.

Q. Anything else?

A. The size of the ears indicates a paranoid outlook, or hallucinations. Also, the absence of feet indicates feelings of insecurity.

Q. On the Wechsler, you asked him, "What would you do if you found a sealed, addressed, stamped envelope?" and he answered, "Open it and find out who it belongs to. I will show you I know right from wrong." [This answer is quite different from the one given above.]

Q. [*Hypothetical* A presented] Did the defendant know what he was doing when he entered that apartment?

A. I really don't know. Schizophrenics can carry out planned action very often.

Q. Do they know right from wrong?

A. Sometimes yes; sometimes no.

Psychiatrist C, Defense

The direct examination by the defense brought out that Psychiatrist C had interviewed Kent three or four times and had attended the staff conference. The diagnosis was schizophrenia, chronic undifferentiated type, which is a mental disease. She testified that Kent led a lonely, isolated life, had a rich fantasy life, was preoccupied with ideas of sex, and had feelings of rejection, especially by women. She claimed the crime was a product of mental illness.

Cross-examination by Government

Q. How do you know that what the defendant told you was not fantasy?

A. Clinical judgment is the main thing.

Q. You questioned him about his sex life?

A. Yes. There was a history of voyeurism, and also excessive masturbation.

Q. Are masturbation and voyeurism symptoms not of schizophrenia but of a sociopathic personality, sexual deviation?

A. Yes. A number of the categories overlap.

Q. Is rape indicative of mental illness?

A. No, not in and of itself.

Q. [*Hypothetical A* presented] Was Kent aware of what he was doing when he entered the apartment?

A. His over-all thinking was disturbed, and he was not completely aware of what he was doing in the same sense a normal adult would have been.

Q. Now since the robberies came first, and then the rapes occurred afterwards only when the woman was exposed and when an opportunity was presented, doesn't this suggest that the motive for entering the apartment was robbery, not rape?

A. I feel the robberies were incidental to the rapes.

Q. What does it mean to you when the defendant fled after the crimes?

A. He didn't want to get caught. There is nothing inconsistent with this and the presence of mental disease.

Q. [*Hypothetical B* presented] The defendant placed his hand over Miss ....'s mouth and then fled. Wasn't the motive robbery?

A.	Human motivations are rarely so simple as that. I do not feel he had the same appreciation of having done something wrong as the normal adult would have had.
Q.	If the defendant had intense sex cravings, why did he rob first and then rape?
A.	It has been found that stealing itself has sexual significance.
Q.	Is there causation in the case of the two robberies?
A.	Yes, though the causation is less clear than in the sex offenses themselves.

Prosecutor, at the Bench: I intend to ask the witness if she did not testify in the *Ricks* case, which is very similar to the *Kent* case, that there was no connection between sociopathic personality, sex deviation, and robbery.
[Objection to question sustained]

Re-cross-examination by Government

Q.	If sex is such a predominant thing in Kent's life, why did he not rape the women first and then rob them?
A.	It is not fair to assume that an act which occurs first is the predominant motivation. Also, as I stated earlier, robbery may have sexual symbolic value. I would say the motivation for rape was predominant.

[Did Kent know there were women present when he entered the apartments?]

Psychiatrist D, Defense

Psychiatrist D testified that he had interviewed Kent several times in jail, at D.C. General Hospital, and at Saint Elizabeths Hospital. He related the social history of the defendant. His diagnosis was schizophrenia, undifferentiated type.

This psychiatrist explained the psychodynamics of the schizophrenia in terms of self-esteem and personal power. Kent
wanted to be a great basketball star, and his self-esteem was
shattered when he was removed from the team for academic
reasons. He went into a depressive phase, started wandering
around the streets, breaking into houses, etc. The motivation of
the crimes was his desire for mastery and power over others,
not the desire for money or sex gratification. When Kent raped
or robbed, the motivating factor was the power it gave him over
others.

Cross-examination by Government

Q. Who asked you to visit the defendant Kent?

A. His mother and Mr. Arens.

Q. Were you affiliated with the Washington School
of Psychiatry?

A. No.

Q. What other sources of payment were there?

A. National Institutes of Health.

[Objection by defense]

Defense Attorney, at the Bench: This brings into issue a battle
between the United States Attorney's Office and the National
Institutes of Health concerning the payment of psychiatric
fees, and it is not relevant to the defendant's case, and it might
prejudice the defendant's rights.

Court to United States Attorney: You may limit your questions concerning the creditability of the witness to the present
case.

Q. Do you believe in free will?

A. Am I on trial here?

Court: You answer the question. You are here as a
witness, not to question the lawyers.

A. I would first have to know what you mean by

free will. It would mean a philosophical discussion. I am a psychiatrist, not a philosopher.

Q.   Isn't it normal for a young man like Kent to want to be a great fullback or, in basketball, another Bob Cousy or Elgin Baylor?

A.   That is not a question but an oration.

Court to Defense Attorney, at the Bench: If your witness is going to continue to be a smart-aleck, I am going to cite him for contempt of court.

Defense: I will speak to him at the break, Your Honor.

Q.   You are telling His Honor and the ladies and gentlemen of the jury that Kent entered those apartments to prove his physical strength?

A.   Yes.

Q.   [*Hypothetical A* presented] Did the defendant enter the apartment to rob and to steal?

A.   His reasons were more unconscious than conscious. His unconscious motivation was to restore lost self-esteem. People are motivated from events occurring in childhood, events of a repressed nature. They are not aware of the reasons themselves. They are not going to tell you why they do the things they do.

Q.   Once Kent was inside the apartment, did he know what he was doing when he said, "Where is your money?"

A.   Money is not the important thing. The important thing is the power over others. Sexual intercourse is also a way of gaining power over others.

Q.   [*Hypothetical B* presented] Why did Kent enter the apartment?

A.   To overpower another person, as by placing his hand over her mouth and saying, "Don't scream."

Clinical Psychologist D, Defense

Psychologist D testified he saw the subject once at jail or the receiving home for an hour and a half; that he administered the Rorschach and started the Human Figure Drawing test. The testing was interrupted when the defendant's father was announced, and Kent became very upset, highly emotional.

He diagnosed the defendant as schizophrenic, undifferentiated type. He thought productivity existed; that is, the schizophrenia produced the housebreaking, robberies, and rapes. The test showed severe thinking disturbance, an inability to control impulses, and disturbed sexual feelings.

Cross-examination by Government

Q. Why did you see the defendant Kent?

A. Because of a call from Mr. Arens.

Q. Are you a member of the Washington School of Psychiatry?

A. No.

Q. The defendant made one drawing for you, right, Doctor?

A. Yes, that is right.

Q. After the announced arrival of his father?

A. Yes.

Q. Do you use the House-Tree-Person test?

A. Never.

Q. Does it have validity?

A. Yes.

Q. Do you use the Szondi?

A. Five or six times.

Q. When did you stop using it?

A. At the fifth administration, about nine years ago.

Q.   What does this drawing that Kent made for another psychologist indicate to you?

A.   The transparency of the picture—that is, seeing through the figure to something beneath—suggests pathology.

Q.   Do you usually use an extensive battery of tests before reaching a diagnosis?

A.   Yes.

Q.   Do you usually arrive at the diagnosis on the basis of one Rorschach administered twice within an hour?

A.   Frequently.

Q.   What else in the drawing is significant psychologically?

A.   The irregularity or sketchiness of the lines may suggest tensions and anxiety. The attention paid to details—to the belt, bowtie, and pockets—indicate a little-boy-like quality about the defendant.

Q.   Is it significant that the figure is running to the left, and not to the right?

A.   To some people, yes. I don't place any significance on it.

Q.   What about this drawing, made by Kent for another psychologist? What is significant about it?

A.   The minimization of the breasts and the three lines across the genital area indicate tension in the sexual area. Breasts are symbolic of motherhood and early infant experiences. By minimizing the breasts, the defendant indicates he has not received the satisfaction from women he had hoped to.

Q.   Now, I will show you the picture Kent drew for

you on September 9, 1961. What is significant about it?

A. The overemphasis of the breasts indicates how upset the defendant was because his father had been announced.

Q. You showed the defendant a series of Rorschach cards, right? And what responses did you get to card 1, card 2, etc.?

A. Cat, flying bird, a house, people, crab, wolf, pinchers, wings, clouds, blood, "like a vagina," menstrual blood, buckets, hipbones, breast, apes, butterflies, jet airplane.

Q. On the basis of these responses, you concluded the defendant was a schizophrenic?

A. Yes.

At this point in the trial, a stipulation was read to the jury, stating that two psychiatrists, if they testified, would testify that the defendant was schizophrenic, undifferentiated type, and the crimes were a direct product of the mental illness. At this point, also, a social study report from the juvenile Court record was read to the jury. It contained a statement concerning Kent's family background, school problems, lack of adult male supervision, and lack of self-identification. A letter from the probation officer to the juvenile Court judge was also read, which stated in part:

His sexual disorientation, as reflected in the more recent offenses, seems to indicate as much an unconscious striving to prove masculine prowess as much as it does a need for sexual expression. The marked duality in his pattern of adjustment suggests the rapid deterioration of his personality structure, and the possibility of mental illness.

Psychiatrist E, Defense

The witness testified that he had interviewed the defendant four times. He classified the defendant as a schizophrenic, undifferentiated type. The crimes of housebreaking, robbery, and rape were, in his opinion, a product of schizophrenia.

Cross-examination by Government

Q.   Who asked you to examine the defendant?

A.   His mother and his attorney, Mr. Arens.

Q.   How long did you spend with the defendant on each occasion?

A.   About an hour.

Q.   [*Hypothetical* A presented] Did Kent know what he was doing when he entered the apartment?

A.   I can't answer that. I don't know what his motive was for going into the apartment.

Q.   Why did he flee, after raping Miss ....?

A.   His motives were irrational.

Q.   Why did you state, Doctor, that causation was present—that schizophrenia produced rape, housebreaking, and robbery?

A.   Because of his bizarre and irrational behavior.

Q.   What is irrational about breaking into the apartment, taking money, and having sex relations with a woman?

A.   Could you do it?

Court: Answer the question or say you can't answer it. Your purpose here is not to question the attorneys.

A.   We generally assume that what is normal is the way we are ourselves, and these acts are something that normal people don't do.

Q.   Is any crime irrational?

A.   Sexual crimes are irrational.

Q.   Did the defendant Kent know right from wrong?

A.   I am not familiar with these terms. These are clergymen's terms.

Q.   What about free will?

A.   It is a term used by the Catholic clergy. It has a meaning to them, but I don't know what it means.

Q.   Did the defendant have the capacity to refrain from going into the apartment, stealing, and raping?

A.   Everyone has the capacity not to do a thing.

REBUTTAL BY GOVERNMENT

Psychiatrist F, Government: Direct Examination

Q.   By whom were you subpoenaed in this case?

A.   By the defense.

Q.   Did you have occasion to talk with me in my office last Friday?

A.   Yes.

Q.   What was your diagnosis of the defendant Kent?

A.   Schizophrenic reaction, chronic undifferentiated type.

Q.   [*Hypothetical A* presented] Did the schizophrenia cause the defendant to rob?

A.   Schizophrenia did not cause the robbery.

Q.   The housebreaking?

A.   Probably not. I would have no opinion about the housebreaking.

Q.   Would schizophrenia cause the defendant to rape that woman?

A.   I would have no opinion on that.

Q.   [*Hypothetical B* presented] Did schizophrenia

cause the defendant to rape Miss ....?

A.   I cannot say.

Q.   Why did you find a lack of causation as to the robberies and the mental disease, and have no opinion as to the housebreakings and rapes?

A.   He had the usual, classical symptoms of schizophrenia. If the primary motivation were his sexual desires, which are involved in this illness, then this would be productivity. If the primary motivation were robbery, then this would not be connected with his sexual preoccupation.

Q.   If the defendant entered the apartments, as described, and robbed the women first, raping them only after robbery and after he saw a semi-nude body, would the motivation be robbery or sexual?

A.   The primary motivation was robbery.

Psychiatrist G, Government: Direct Examination

Q.   Did you examine the defendant, Morris Kent?

A.   Yes. I examined him four times at D.C. General, at the request of the United States Attorney's Office.

Q.   Did he have a mental disease?

A.   He did not have a mental disease.

Q.   Will you tell His Honor and the ladies and gentlemen of the jury why you arrived at that conclusion?

A.   Mr. Kent appeared to be withdrawn. His withdrawal would be precipitated by a question he didn't wish to answer. He would withdraw to avoid answering a question. When confronted with criticism, he would become quite animated.

The defendant stated he had never been accepted by either race because of his light skin and eyes. He told me he hoped to marry a white girl, and his mother had encouraged him in this. He said he did not like Negro girls, and that white girls made him feel funny, by which he meant they excited him sexually. He had difficulty in dating girls. He wanted women to love him, but he felt nobody really loved him.

Concerning religion, he said he adored the Virgin because She had once helped him pass an examination in school. He claimed to have talked to God, and God forgave him in advance for wrongdoing. I did not interpret this as an hallucination or a delusion, but as evidence of a faith in his religion. These religious beliefs were not evidence of a psychosis.

He also stated, upon direct questioning, that he heard voices. I interpreted this to mean he was hearing his own voice—the voice of his conscience, because the voice told him, ". . . you can't get along with people," and this is what Kent had told himself many times. It sounded like his own voice, except a deeper tone.

He said he had strong feelings of sexual excitement when he smelled women's underpants, and he even put them on over his own clothing.

At school, he was president of his class in 1960 —elected by twenty-three girls and eleven boys. Although he professes to be shy, and not to be liked by girls, he was popular in school.

Cross-examination by Defense

Q.   Is Kent a normal individual?

A.   No, but he is free of disease.

Q.   Does he have a sociopathic personality?

A.   No, he has a schizoid personality.

Q.   What is a schizoid personality?

A.   There are four large groups of mental disorders.

The fourth group is known as personality disorders. These are not a result of conflict, of disease, of organic disease of the brain, but they are a result of a way of believing, an attitude toward society. A personality disorder in which the schizoid personality would be included does not represent a disease. It represents a way of behavior, and not a disease.

Q.   Does his schizoid personality influence his behavior?

A.   No, because it is his behavior pattern.

Q.   Does the fact that the defendant was stimulated sexually by smelling female undergarments indicate a symptom of mental disorder?

A.   It is a sex perversion, classified as sociopathic personality, sex perversion type.

Q.   Doctor, does the *Diagnostic and Statistical Manual of the American Psychiatric Association* classify sociopathic personality as a mental disease?

A.   It is a personality disorder, and in no place in the book does it say that a sociopathic personality is a disease.

Q.   Was there any condition present that would affect his behavior?

A.   One does have the freedom to act or not to act. I might be influenced to throw this glass of water at the stenographer, but I wouldn't.

Q.   This is free will?

A.   Yes.

Q.   Is this the basis for determining a mental disease?

A.   No. I recognize that there are individuals who have lost free will because they have been influenced by disease or defect so that they have lost the ability to make decisions.

This was the end of the psychological testimony. The jury returned a split verdict: guilty on the counts of robbery and housebreaking; not guilty by reason of insanity on the counts of rape. The reason for the split verdict is the "product of" aspect of the *Durham* rule. The jury must find not only the presence of mental illness, but the mental illness must have produced the crime.

The testimony of the two psychiatrists called by the government weakened considerably the defense of insanity, because these two witnesses testified that the crimes were not a product of the schizophrenia, and one witness testified that Kent was not schizophrenic.

Kent now faces both institutionalization for a mental disease and imprisonment for two felony convictions. He was sentenced to a maximum of ninety years in prison: five to fifteen each on six counts of robbery and housebreaking.

This is the second time in recent months that a defendant in a criminal case in the District of Columbia has been found guilty of robbery and housebreaking but not guilty of rape on the grounds of insanity. In the other case, the defendant received a twenty-to-sixty-year prison term, which he must serve when he is released from a mental institution.

Whether such a split verdict by the jury was an accident or was maneuvered by the government cannot be known. It can be stated that the defendant received the worst of all alternatives, for now he has been pronounced both *insane and a criminal*. In the future, government attorneys will certainly attempt to show, in multiple-offense cases, that there is no causation for some crimes, at the same time allowing the causation issue to stand for other crimes. The threat of a split verdict is certainly a consequence to be avoided by any defendant. Thus, in the future, the insanity plea is less likely to occur, as a result of the *Kent* case.

The psychiatric and psychological testimony in this case will be discussed and anlyzed in the second part of this work.

Chapter 6

UNITED STATES vs. JENKINS

JENKINS was charged with one count of housebreaking, one count of assault with attempt to commit rape, and one count of assault with a deadly weapon. Criminal No. 614-59, United States District Court for the District of Columbia. The defense relied on the insanity issue, and did not deny the facts of the crimes as stated.

This case is important because (1) it involves the issue of mental deficiency as a mental disease or defect, and (2) it involves the issue of psychologists testifying on the question of mental disease or defect.

The defense put on the witness stand the mother and sister of the accused. These lay witnesses testified that Jenkins had been backward all his life; he had never appeared to be normal; never played with other children, and was subject to sudden rage. By the age of sixteen, he had completed only three years of formal education and was unable to read. He was having sex experiences with seven- and eight-year-old girls. He would complain about violent headaches. At times he would lock himself in his room for hours. He appeared nervous, quarrelsome, and quite frequently he would break forth in silly laughter.

Psychiatrist A, Defense

The first expert witness for the defense was the Chief Psychiatrist for the D.C. General Hospital. She testified that she had not examined the defendant, although she had reviewed the records and had talked to another psychiatrist about the case. The defendant was certified by D.C. General as mentally deficient, with an IQ below 70. Over the signature of the Chief

Psychiatrist, the hospital sent a letter to the District Court stating that Jenkins was "suffering from an organic brain defect resulting in mental deficiency, and he is therefore incompetent to stand trial." The Court thereupon sent him to Saint Elizabeths, after which he was certified, at a later date, as being competent to stand trial.

At the trial, the Chief Psychiatrist testified that mental deficiency was a mental defect, whereupon there was a long verbal exchange between her and the judge. The judge denied that mental deficiency was a defect, and chose to characterize the defendant as illiterate and ignorant. Psychiatrist A found a causal relationship between the crimes and the mental deficiency, although she admitted she did not know the nature of the crimes for which the defendant was being tried. She then testified that she had changed her diagnosis from mental deficiency to schizophrenia.

Cross-examination by Government

Q.   You changed your diagnosis. Would you please explain?

A.   At the time I wrote the letter, I stated there was no mental disease. Now he has a mental disease. The evidence from Saint Elizabeths retesting his IQ shows it is now within normal limits. By definition, his defect has improved, so it is now a disease and not a defect.

Q.   You mean a normal IQ is a disease?

A.   No . . . no.

Court: The reason for the defect was a low IQ, and only that?

A.   Yes, Your Honor, nothing else.

Court: So now he is suffering from a disease instead of a defect because his IQ is within normal range?

A.   No—because other testing has shown there is another condition present. The report from Saint

Elizabeths indicated a schizophrenic reaction.

Court: Have you examined him since?

A. No, I have not. Doctor Levy gave the defendant an IQ test which scored in the 80's. A psychologist at Saint Elizabeths, not a psychiatrist, made the diagnosis of schizophrenia.

Court: Do you allow psychologists to make the diagnosis of schizophrenia?

A. Yes, we rely heavily on our psychologists.

Court: If psychologists are going to make a determination of schizophrenia, what do we need psychiatrists for?

A. It is the M.D. who must make the final medical diagnosis.

Court: Your diagnosis is thus based on the report of a psychologist?

A. Yes, my original diagnosis was wrong.

Court: You haven't examined the defendant since?

A. No, I have not. I cannot honestly say this is a schizophrenic reaction.

Court: Do you have an opinion as to the defendant's mental condition at this time or at the time of the crime?

A. I have no official opinion, not from a direct examination.

Court: Do you have a medical opinion, based on information you received as to his mental condition at the time of the crime?

A. He was suffering from some condition.

Court: What condition are you talking about?

A. He was suffering from a mental condition.

Court: What mental condition?

A.   This I cannot answer specifically. Since I have not examined the person, and the original diagnosis was in error.

Court: Was the defendant suffering from a mental defect at the time of the crime?

A.   No, he was suffering from a mental disease on June 10, 1959.

Court: Earlier you testified he was not suffering from a mental disease.

A.   That was before I was in a position to point out that I had changed my diagnosis.

Court: In your opinion the defendant was suffering from a mental defect and mental disease at the time of the crime, and the disease was schizophrenia?

A.   Yes.

Court: And it was not based on an examination you made?

A.   No, it was not.

Court: Is it customary for you to give medical opinions if you don't examine the patients?

A.   I can have an opinion, yes.

Court: Would you express an opinion on the basis of a psychological report?

A.   Yes, I very frequently do, Your Honor.

Court: Without seeing the patient?

A.   I made the wrong diagnosis. The diagnosis from a psychologist explains my wrong diagnosis.

Court: Do you give a medical opinion as to a patient's mental condition without ever examining the patient?

A.   Yes, Your Honor. I get reports by phone from social workers.

Court: Social workers?

A.   Yes, I admit patients from histories furnished by any number of individuals.

Court: Do you mean to tell me everyone admitted to D.C. General is presumed to be of unsound mind?

A.   They are presumed to have a mental illness until proven otherwise.

Q.   Do you have an opinion as to whether Jenkins was suffering from a mental disease or defect at the time of the crime?

A.   Yes.

Q.   And what is your opinion?

A.   He was suffering from a mental disease.

Q.   And was there a causal connection between the disease and the alleged crime?

A.   In my opinion that is so.

Re-cross-examination by Government

Q.   What disease?

A.   Schizophrenia.

Q.   Your original diagnosis was mental defect, right?

A.   Right.

Q.   And because of recent information, furnished to you by psychologists at Saint Elizabeths, you now state your original diagnosis was wrong and you have an opinion now that the defendant was schizophrenic on June 10, 1959?

A.   Right.

Q.   Without an interview with the subject?

A.   Right.

Q.   Because his IQ goes up to the normal range, he is schizophrenic?

A.   No, not exactly. If he were in a severe psychotic state he would probably drop to below the normal range. When he is less psychotic, his IQ goes up to the normal range. The schizophrenia interferes with the intelligence testing.

Q.   What is schizophrenia?

A.   Distorted judgment, bizarre thinking processes. They may or may not have hallucinations.

Q.   Did you find hallucinations in November, 1959?

A.   No, I did not.

Q.   Delusions?

A.   No delusions.

Q.   What else?

A.   Autism, preoccupation with self.

Q.   How did the disease cause him to commit the crime?

A.   This individual had poor judgment, his disease interferes with his mental processes. He is no longer capable of utilizing his intellect to know right from wrong. He is merely being driven by his mental illness into a situation.

Court: I am going to have stricken from the record any testimony by this witness that the defendant is schizophrenic or was schizophrenic on June 10, 1959.

Psychiatrist B, Defense

Psychiatrist B testified that the defendant was mentally defective and had a chronic psychosis of an undifferentiated type.

Court: Do you mean you don't know what is wrong with him?

A.   I think so. Undifferentiated psychosis is his inability to understand the external world and to act according to the stimuli he receives from the outside. He hasn't developed a mature enough personality to formulate acts based on reality, and therefore regulating his behavior properly.

Court: Would you say he had a schizophrenic reaction?

A.   Yes, if the psychological exams bear this out.

Court: But you cannot be sure in this case?

A.   Not from a clinical examination.

Q.   A higher IQ score would indicate schizophrenia?

A.   Yes, an abrupt change in IQ scores might indicate a psychological disorder.

Q.   Was the crime a product of the mental disease and defect?

A.   Yes.

Cross-examination by Government

Q.   What is an undifferentiated psychosis, Doctor?

A.   He has impaired ego functions. The ego is that part of the personality involved in learning, walking, or motor activities.

Q.   He can walk, can't he?

A.   Yes.

Q.   And talk?

A.   Yes.

Q.   What are object relations?

A.   The ability to form meaningful contacts with other people—love, affection, hostility—being able to accept people.

Q.   What else?

A. Being able to communicate, to make his needs felt by others.

Q. When did you arrive at the diagnosis of psychosis, undifferentiated type?

A. In retrospect.

Q. This was not your original judgment?

A. We felt the mental deficiency or impairment was primary in our original diagnosis. The information furnished later on by psychologists changed this diagnosis.

Court: When a psychiatrist arrives at a diagnosis of undifferentiated psychosis, doesn't that mean that you doctors believe there is something wrong but you don't know what it is?

A. This man falls in that category. We don't know what is wrong. There is something wrong, and this is the point.

Court: Do you believe there is something wrong with every man who commits a crime?

A. No, I do not.

Q. Your diagnosis was based on Saint Elizabeths records furnished by psychologists?

A. Yes.

Q. When did this occur?

A. Within the last two weeks.

Q. They found his IQ was in the 80's?

A. Right.

Q. Did you re-examine the defendant after you received these reports?

A. I didn't examine him.

Q. Is your diagnosis based on these reports by psychologists?

A.   No, not entirely.

Q.   You arrived at a firm diagnosis after seeing the psychological reports?

A.   That is correct.

Q.   Your final diagnosis on the hospital records was "mental deficiency"?

A.   That is correct.

Q.   What made you change your diagnosis?

A.   The higher IQ rating.

Q.   You depended on the psychologists?

A.   Yes, definitely.

Court: Would you give a medical opinion as to a person's mental condition on a report of a psychologist?

A.   We certainly use it very much, definitely.

Court: I am excluding any testimony of this psychiatrist because it was not based on proper evidence.

Q.   Will you explain the causality, the productivity, between the mental retardation and the alleged crimes?

A.   This man has certain feelings and tensions, stress in his daily living. He lacks ability to deal with tension. He doesn't have the capacity to delay action. The opportunity for tensions to build up is great, and his ability to discharge the tension is limited because he doesn't relate well to other people.

[The defense requested a mistrial because of the Court's criticism and skepticism concerning psychiatric witnesses. The motion was denied.]

Psychologist A, Defense

This clinical psychologist testified that he had administered the following tests to the defendant: Wechsler Adult Intelligence Scale, Bender-Gestalt, Rorschach, and Szondi. The IQ rating was 74, a dull normal.

Direct Examination by Defense

Q.   Why do you give these tests?

A.   To get at personality functioning—to get a sample of behavior. It is assumed that the sample is representative of how a person deals with other life situations.

Court: Do you say you can conclude that a person is suffering from schizophrenia from answers to a Rorschach?

A.   Yes. For example, if somebody looked at this card and described it as a church with a steeple with three men standing there and the Virgin Mary descending, with the Devil hiding behind the house, I would feel confident in thinking that person is suffering from disordered thinking.

Q.   As a result of your tests, what is your diagnosis?

A.   Schizophrenia.

Q.   And productivity?

A.   I cannot fail to see how a man's mental condition is unrelated to his behavior. I would expect there is a relationship, yes. I can not say definitely that one thing is a product of another.

Cross-examination by Government

Q.   Doctor, do you agree with this statement: "It is well established that psychiatrists and psychologists freely concede there is no absolute accuracy and reliability of tests in the measurement of intelligence."

A.   I do not agree.

Q.   How about this statement: "Two persons of substantially the same mental capacity may test with materially different scores or rating depending on education, training, environment, etc."

A.   Well, environment includes so much that I would think this would affect the performance on intelligence tests.

Q.   You can tell from responses to Rorschach cards what personality is like?

A.   From a global picture.

Q.   What responses did he give to card 4?

A.   He saw a frog.

Q.   And what significance do you attach to this answer, Doctor?

A.   This is not the response normal people give. People often see two boots.

Q.   And card 5?

A.   He saw a butterfly. This is a perfectly acceptable response. Many normal people see butterflies in this card.

Q.   Card 6?

A.   He said: "Don't see nothing—don't look like nothing."

Q.   What things about the defendant's responses to the Rorschach led you to your diagnosis of schizophrenia?

A.   The poor quality of his responses, the lack of seeing other kinds of responses, more typical responses you would expect from an adult.

Q.   You also administered the Draw-a-Person test?

A.   Yes.

Q.   And what did it indicate?

A.   The defendant drew the figure on the upper left-hand corner of the page. This indicated explosive feelings, insecurity, in a sense, holding onto the edges of the paper. This indicates anxiety and insecurity.

Q. What if he had placed the drawing in the middle of the page—what would that indicate?

A. It would mean he is a little less insecure.

Q. Do you believe in free will?

A. I believe it means complete control over one's actions and thoughts. I believe one's environment and heredity affect one's ability to exercise choice. Man has ability to make choices, but this is affected by other factors.

Q. Do you come from the so-called behavioristic school?

A. No, I am an eclectic.

Q. Do you believe all crime is a product of mental illness?

A. No.

Q. Any category of crimes?

A. I would expect bizarre crimes are often a product of mental illness.

Q. On the Wechsler, you asked him, "What color is the flag?" What did the defendant answer?

A. He answered, "Red, white, blue."—a 1, or perfect score. The test is scored 1-0.

Q. The second questions?

A. "What shape is a ball?" He answered, "Round."— a 1 response.

Q. The fifth question?

A. "What does rubber come from?" His answer was "wood." I gave him a zero.

Q. Why a zero—aren't trees wood?

A.	Yes, but it doesn't follow that rubber comes from wood.
Court:	You know where we get wood other than trees?
A.	No.

[Other questions, similar to *Kent* material used, not recorded here because of repetition.]

Q.	Why do you use pictures of insane people on the Szondi? Why not normal subjects?
A.	We know penicillin works; we don't know why it works. It's the same thing here. We know that certain kinds of tests work; we don't understand why they work.
Q.	You stated he was a chronic, undifferentiated schizophrenic. Can he also be an undifferentiated psychotic?
A.	No. Undifferentiated psychosis is not a recognized classification.
Q.	Do you know whether or not these schizophrenia symptoms were in remission on June 10, 1959?
A.	No, I do not.
Q.	You cannot state an opinion as to whether or not the schizophrenia caused the crime?
A.	Yes, that is right.

Psychologist B, Defense

This psychologist testified that she gave one part of the Szondi test. She made a diagnosis of schizophrenia on the basis of the increase in the IQ scores.

Direct Examination by Defense

| Q. | What background factors confirmed your diagnosis of schizophrenia? |
| A. | He was a withdrawn person who had few |

friends. He didn't associate with other children. He couldn't control his behavior.

Cross-examination by Government

Q.   What do you mean by adequate controls?

A.   When the tensions build up in him to a state of anxiety, anger, frustration, his emotions explode into behavior over which he has no control.

Q.   Do you believe in free will?

A.   That is a philosophic, not a psychological, problem. Free will is an arbitrary, sudden explosion without cause. I don't believe that. If I am free to choose, why is it I choose one thing and you choose another? It is because of the structure of the nervous system, and the influence of the environment.

Q.   You believe in God?

A.   Yes, certainly.

Court: You believe in free will, don't you?

A.   I believe I can make a free choice, based on what I am.

Court: Any individual is free to make a choice, isn't he?

A.   Yes.

Q.   Why did you use photographs of mentally ill persons—why not normal persons?

A.   Because photographs of mentally ill persons are supposed to accentuate the needs or drives or deprivations or frustrations that human beings experience. Normal people have managed to resolve their frustrations. I don't know why it works. It is something underneath. It is difficult to explain and understand. Doctors use digitalis for heart disease without knowing why it acts as it does.

[On questioning concerning the Szondi test, the witness testified that a psychologist could diagnose illness by the pictures a subject selected as those he liked or disliked. At this point the judge threw the cards down. At a Bench conference, the defense attorney asked, "May the record reflect that after the last question the Court slammed the cards down?"]

Court: The record may reflect it but the record may show I am throwing it all out. That will take care of that session.

Psychologist C, Defense

Psychologist C testified he had administered the Wechsler Adult Intelligence Scale, the Bender-Gestalt, the Rorschach, and the Projective Figure-Drawing tests. The IQ score given the defendant was 63. A later test, given two weeks before the trial, showed that the defendant now had an IQ of 90. This psychologist stated that he was unable to arrive at a diagnosis after the first examination in October, 1959, but now, in January, 1961, he could state the defendant's condition was schizophrenic since his IQ was 90. He was able to form an opinion as to causation between schizophrenia and the alleged crimes.

Psychiatrist C, Government: Direct Examination

Q.   Did you arrive at a diagnosis?

A.   Yes, he was not mentally defective; he was borderline, dull normal. He had no mental disease or defect.

Cross-examination by Defense

Q.   You saw the defendant only once at a staff conference?

A.   Yes.

Q.   For how long?

A.   An hour and a half. The entire conference is an
                    hour and a half, with all participants taking up
                    time.

Psychiatrist D, Government

This psychiatrist examined the defendant on several occasions
for fifteen to twenty minutes each time. His diagnosis was
without mental disorder.

Cross-examination by Defense

Q.   How accurate is your diagnosis, in light of the
                    length of time between the crime and the
                    examination?

A.   I saw nothing to indicate he was suffering from
                    mental disease.

Q.   If this man were released into society, would he
                    be dangerous

A.   He probably would be dangerous.

[End of trial. Following is a summary of the *Jenkins* case in
the United States Court of Appeals.]

The Court of Appeals heard the case in *Jenkins vs. United
States,* No. 16,306, United States Court of Appeals for the District
of Columbia Circuit.

The trial court had held that "a psychologist is not competent
to give a medical opinion as to a mental disease or defect"
because he lacks medical training. The Court of Appeals held
that the general rule is that:

> . . . anyone who is shown to have special knowledge and
> skill in diagnosing and treating human ailments is qualified
> to testify as an expert, if his learning and training show that
> he is qualified to give an opinion on the particular question
> at issue. It is not essential that the witness be a medical
> practitioner. . . If experience or training enables a proffered
> expert witness to form an opinion which would aid the jury,

in the absence of some countervailing consideration, his testimony will be received.

The court went on to note that many psychologists may not qualify to testify concerning mental disease or defect. Some psychologists teach and engage in research in fields unrelated to the diagnosis and treatment of mental illness. The language of the court makes it clear that a Ph.D in clinical psychology would be required in order for a psychologist to testify as an expert witness concerning mental disease.

In a concurring opinion, a Circuit Court judge noted that the real issue in the *Jenkins* case is whether a psychologist can make a diagnosis of mental disease, which is a *medical* diagnosis. The judge quoted from an American Medical Association resolution of 1954, in which it was stated:

> Psychotherapy is a form of medical treatment and does not form the basis for a separate profession. . . The application of psychological method to the treatment of illness is a medical function. Where *diagnosis and treatment* of mental illness is involved, the participation of a psychologist must be coordinated under medical responsibility.

In a dissenting opinion two Circuit Court judges wrote:

> We think it must be concluded beyond doubt that the existence of a mental disease or defect is, first and foremost, a *medical* problem. . . Time and again, where insanity is raised as a defense at the trial of criminal cases in this jurisdiction, sincere and experienced psychiatrists have taken the stand and voiced diametrically opposite opinions as to whether or not the defendant has a mental disease or defect. . . This illustrates how nebulous and uncertain is the issue of mental illness even to those of the *medical* profession who are experienced and trained in its diagnosis and treatment. If the issue is so debatable among conceded professional medical experts, it is sheer folly to attribute to a lay psychologist, who admittedly is not a doctor of medicine, such presumptive medical knowledge and diagnostic acuity as to entitle him to wear in a criminal courtroom the badge of an expert witness with respect

to the existence of that elusive *medical* condition known as mental disease or defect.

The American Psychiatric Association filed an *amicus curiae* brief, in which it was stated that:

A clinical psychologist, lacking *medical* training and the specialization required of the qualified psychiatrist, is not qualified to make the total medical diagnosis or to testify as a *medical* expert thereon.

The Court of Appeals reversed and remanded for a new trial. Jenkins was convicted by a jury on the second trial.

Chapter 7

CASES OF PERSONALITY DISORDERS

UNITED STATES vs. WALLACE H. CARROLL

CARROLL was indicted on nine counts of violation of the narcotics laws. Criminal No. 383-62, United States District Court for the District of Columbia. On all counts he was found not guilty by reason of insanity by a jury and was committed to Saint Elizabeths under D.C. Code 301-24.

A general practitioner, who was the medical officer at the District of Columbia jail, testified that the defendant had been using heroin for about ten years. The testimony herein reproduced is condensed and in many instances rephrased.

Psychiatrist A, Defense

The defense placed on the witness stand as an expert witness a psychiatrist who had worked with drug addicts at Lexington for several years. Psychiatrist A had never interviewed the defendant; so, in order to introduce evidence as to the defendant's social and psychological history, the defense attorney asked the psychiatrist a long, hypothetical question. The person described in the question is, of course, Carroll.

Q.   Doctor, I am going to describe a patient to you and then ask you to evaluate this man's personality. The patient is a twenty-eight-year-old Negro whose parents separated when he was nine. He felt his parents did not love him and that the world was against him. He would become tense and excited in a crowd. This man left school at the tenth-grade level and joined the

Navy. He began using drugs in Japan, while serving in the Navy. The drugs reduced his tension and made him feel better. Several times after his discharge from the Navy he tried to kick the habit. He found work as a cook or as a laborer, but was frequently fired from jobs because he would come to work woozy, in a stupor, moody, and sullen. He was taking thirty-five to fifty capsules of heroin a day, and he had to resort to selling narcotics in order to support the habit.

Did the defendant have a mental disease or disorder?

A. Yes, the fact of being addicted to the narcotic drugs is always a sign of serious mental disorder, the exception being probably only in the case of those people who are addicted because they have some incurable, painful disease.

Q. What disease is and was Carroll suffering from?

A. It is not possible for a psychiatrist to diagnose a patient without having examined him. Such a person is suffering from a psychosis, a psycho-neurosis, or a character disorder.

Q. Is a character disorder a mental disease?

A. No doubt about it.

Q. A drug addict has an overwhelming desire or compulsion to take drugs, and to obtain them by any means—is that right, Doctor?

A. It is our experience that they do. For instance, it is impossible to be addicted to drugs without possessing narcotic drugs. That is rather obvious. It is our experience that addicts do conceal and sell drugs.

Q. Would the possession and concealment and sale of drugs be a result of a mental disease?

A. Yes.

Cross-examination by Government

Q.   Doctor, do you hold that all addicts, with the exception mentioned in your direct testimony, are mentally ill?

A.   Yes.

Q.   You agree then with Lawrence Kolb?

A.   Yes.

Q.   Will you define mental illness for us, Doctor?

A.   To define a mental disease is to list all those characteristics which make up those things that we, as physicians, have decided to treat and to consider as mental illness. This includes psychoses, neuroses, and character disorders.

Q.   Given the hypothetical question asked you by the defense, would you say the defendant knew right from wrong?

A.   Yes.

Q.   Would he have sold the capsules to Garrett if he had known he was an officer of the law? Did he know what he was doing?

A.   Yes.

Q.   You have never interviewed the defendant?

A.   That is correct.

Q.   Nor administered any tests or exams?

A.   That's right.

Q.   You therefore have no definite diagnosis?

A.   No definite diagnosis.

Redirect Examination by Defense

Q.   Although you cannot make a definite diagnosis without interviewing a patient, can you state whether or not he has a mental disease?

A.   Yes.

Re-cross-examination by Government

Q.   Doctor, from what mental disease did the defendant suffer on January 17?

A.   I cannot answer that.

Q.   You have no opinion as to the disease because you did not interview the defendant?

A.   No, that is not correct. In my considerable experience in seeing hundreds of addicts, and on the basis of the history given by the defense counsel, I have not seen and do not believe that there are people who are addicted to drugs who do not suffer from a severe type of mental disorder.

Q.   The major basis for your opinion is that the defendant was seriously addicted to heroin?

A.   That is a major consideration.

Q.   And the reason it is a major basis is that you subscribe to the theory that all seriously addicted persons have a mental illness because they are addicts?

A.   No, because it is my professional opinion that all such people do suffer from mental disease.

Psychiatrist B, Defense

Q.   On the basis of these facts, do you have an opinion whether the defendant was suffering from a mental disease?

A.   Yes, he was suffering from a mental disease. On the basis of his background—his unstable background—he started taking drugs and found himself trapped. He was unable to quit using them even though he attempted to quit. On the basis of the fact that he continued fighting against this compulsion to take drugs but was unable to do so, I think he was suffering from a mental disease.

Q. Was the possession, concealment, and sale of narcotics related to his mental disease?

A. Yes, they were. A cycle is created. A person becomes addicted, his tolerance goes up, and he resorts to selling in order to obtain money to get drugs for himself.

Q. Do you have an opinion as to what mental disease the defendant is suffering from?

A. It is hard to state without an interview. It is probably a psychoneurosis or a personality disorder.

Q. Are these mental diseases?

A. Some psychiatrists would say no. I would say they are mental illnesses.

Court: Can you give a diagnosis of personality disorder for this defendant, assuming there is no addiction?

A. Without an examination, no.

Court: You are of the opinion that any serious narcotic addiction represents mental disease?

A. It is symptomatic of mental disease, yes. I cannot say what the disease is without an examination.

Q. Do you agree, Doctor, that the addict has a compulsion or overpowering need for drugs, that he will sell drugs in order to obtain drugs, and that the sale and possession are a direct result of the mental disorder?

A. Yes.

Cross-examination by Government

Q. How many times have you made a diagnosis without personally examining the patient?

A.   Never.

Q.   You usually have a battery of examination results available?

A.   That is correct.

Q.   Do you subscribe to the theory that all addicts are mentally ill?

A.   I would say if a person is severely addicted to narcotics, I would presume he is mentally ill unless something came up to prove to me otherwise. The medical addict is an exception.

Q.   What mental disease was the defendant suffering from one January 17?

A.   I don't know.

Redirect Examination by Defense

Q.   Did the defendant have a craving for drugs?

A.   If he didn't have drugs he would be in acute physical agony.

Q.   Like a starving man, from lack of food?

A.   Yes, it is a valid analogy to the extent that a person who is starving is going to steal food.

Q.   Will a normal person who is addicted medically continue to use drugs after leaving the hospital?

A.   No, he is able to resist the temptation to do it.

Psychiatrist C Defense

[Psychiatrist C has been an expert on drug addiction since 1923; he has treated 3,000 to 4,000 addicts, and is the author of *Narcotic Addiction, a Public Health Problem.*]

Q.   [Hypothetical question] Assuming these facts to be true, Doctor, do you have an opinion whether this man had an emotional disorder or mental disease on January 17, 1962?

A.   I would say he had. He was a badly neglected child. He felt inferior as people of this kind do. He was rejected by his parents. He had a life characteristic of persons who are mentally disturbed. He could not hold a job because of his narcotic problem. His general life is the life that addicts or sociopaths or neurotic, unstable people live.

Q.   Would the sale, possession, and concealment of narcotics be a direct result of the mental disease?

A.   They are a result of the mental disease, together with the fact he acquired the need for narcotics through use

Q.   What percentage of narcotics addicts that you have examined are abnormal?

A.   I should say about 90 per cent.

Court: What do you mean—"abnormal"?

A.   I mean disease or emotional disorder.

Q.   Do you have an opinion as to what mental disease?

A.   I would have to guess; I haven't examined him. I can't say positively unless I have examined him. I believe he has a sociopathic personality.

Q.   Would this man receive effective treatment at a prison?

A.   I think he would not receive as effective treatment in prison as in a hospital. Lexington isn't exactly a prison; it is a Public Health hospital where they have intensive treatment and do individual therapy.

Cross-examination by Government

Q.   Did you make a personal examination of this defendant, Doctor?

A.   I did not.

Q.   Can you make a diagnosis without an examination?

A.   You cannot.

Redirect Exmination by Defense

Q.   Is it necessary to have personal observation, personal examination, to reach the conclusion that a man has a mental disease?

A.   Some cases you can look at for two minutes and decide he has a mental disease, without doing anything else.

Q.   Then it is not necessary for you to examine the patient to come to the conclusion that this man was suffering from a mental disease?

A.   If all the facts in the hypothetical question are true, he is suffering from a mental disease.

Q.   And a personal examination is necessary if you're going to reach a definite diagnosis—definite as to a specific mental disease?

A.   A personal examination is necessary if you want to find out whether this fellow really has a mental disease.

Re-cross-examination by Government

Q.   Did you say if he really has?

A.   That he really has.

Redirect Examination by Defense

Q.   On page 566 of Noyes and Kolb, *Modern Clinical Psychiatry,* under "Drug Addiction," it is stated: "Drug addiction is usually symptomatic of a personality disorder. It might have been included in the chapter on Sociopathic Personalities." Do you agree with that statement?

A.   Yes.

Q.   In your opinion, these people who have come upon the addiction through medical means have emotional problems.

A.   At the present time, all of them have emotional problems.

Q.   Quoting again, from page 568: "It should be remembered that narcotics addiction nearly always results from emotional problems. In general, these emotional problems are the same anxieties, conflicts, and neuroses as those with which other emotionally unstable persons are confronted." Do you agree?

A.   That is true.

Q.   What effect does heroin have on the personality?

A.   It calms the patient down, makes him contented with himself, gets rid of anxieties. The great objection to opiates is that you form a physical dependence on them, a terrific craving, which must be satisfied. When the supply of drugs is cut off by Congress, the addict steals things to get drugs. No form of opium causes anybody to commit crimes. The idea heroin causes people to murder is nonsense.

Re-cross-examination by Government

Q.   Was the fact the defendant was an addict a major basis for your saying he is a sociopath?

A.   No, it was not a major part, but it was part of it.

Q.   Doctor, do you subscribe to the theory that all addicts are mentally ill?

A.   Not all, but practically all have emotional instability.

Q.   What percentage?

A.   I agree with the statement read, that drug

addiction does not occur in the absence of psychiatric pathology.

Q. You are saying addicts are mentally ill?

A. Are emotionally disturbed.

Q. Are all emotional disturbances mental diseases?

A. No. Some neurotics never commit crimes.

Q. Are sociopathic individuals mentally diseased?

A. I would consider it a mental disease.

Q. All of them?

A. Any person so diagnosed.

Q. Have you testified that you knew a physician who was taking forty grains of heroin a day?

A. Yes.

Q. And he was able to perform his duties as a physician?

A. They perform their duties just as well as if they were not addicts.

Court: Are all psychiatrists in agreement about sociopaths?

A. Most of them—not all of them.

Psychiatrist D, Government: Direct Examination

Q. Have you ever interviewed the defendant, Carroll?

A. No.

Q. [Hypothetical question read to witness] Can you tell His Honor and the ladies and gentlemen of the jury if the defendant suffered from a mental disease?

A. I am unable to give an opinion since I did not examine the patient.

Cross-examination by Defense

Q.   Doctor, I would like to draw your attention to a chapter on drug addiction in a basic textbook, and ask you to agree or disagree with the statement: "Drug addiction is usually symptomatic of a personality disorder." Do you agree?

A.   Yes, in most cases it is.

Q.   "Most members of the drug addict family are emotionally immature, hostile, aggressive persons who take drugs in order to secure relief from inner tension. . . Another group consists of frankly neurotic persons with anxiety, obsessive, compulsive, or psycho-physiologic symptoms which are relieved by drugs. A third group consists of persons who in the course of physical illness have received drugs over an extended period. . . In practically all addicts their previous adjustment to life was marginal or unsatisfactory." Do you agree?

A.   Yes.

Q.   According to the *Diagnostic Manual*, drug addiction is characterized as a mental disorder. Is that correct?

A.   No, I don't think so. I think it can be. I think the clarification there is that the big heading is the "Sociopathic Personality Disturbance," and under that is the subheading. There are a number of different subheadings, and one of them happens to be "Drug Addiction," which is one of the subclasses of the sociopath. Now it doesn't mean that all drug addicts are sociopaths because it takes more to be a sociopath than just taking drugs.

Psychiatrist B, Defense: Surrebuttal

Q.   Since you testified the other day, have you had

an opportunity to conduct an examination of Carroll?

A. Yes, I have.

Q. What is your opinion as to whether he was suffering from a mental disease?

A. He has a severe character neurosis, of a schizoid individual, with paranoid tendencies.

Q. Is this a mental disease?

A. A personality disorder is a mental disease.

Q. Would you say, Doctor, that but for this mental disease these crimes would not have been committed?

A. Yes.

Cross-examination by Government

Q. How long did you examine the defendant in a cell block?

A. Fifty-five minutes.

Q. You had already testified in this court that the defendant was mentally ill before you examined him, right?

A. Yes.

Q. Did you go down there with a preconceived conviction the defendant was going to have a mental disease?

A. I assumed that he would, yes.

Q. Do you believe all criminals are mentally ill?

A. No.

Q. Is drug addiction a separate mental disease, in and of itself?

A. The APA Manual lists it as a separate category, but I don't believe that it is a disease in and of itself unless there is a mental disease in addition to it, and I think that when a person is addicted there is some other disease behind this.

Q.   Are there people walking around Washington with character disturbances?

A.   Yes, a great majority of people.

Q.   A great majority?

A.   A great majority of people with mental illness do not commit crimes.

Psychiatrist A Defense: Surrebuttal

Q.   Since the last time you testified here, Doctor, have you had an opportunity to examine the defendant?

A.   Yes, I saw him on two occasions, about forty-five minutes each.

Q.   And what is your opinion as to his mental condition?

A.   He has a schizoid personality. He also shows traces of anxiety and neurosis.

Q.   Was the sale, possession, and concealment of narcotics a result or product of this mental disease?

A.   Yes.

Cross-examination by Government

Q.   You don't equate drug addiction with mental disease, do you?

A.   Yes, I do.

Q.   You do? You say that every addict is mentally ill?

A.   With the exception of people suffering from a painful medical disorder.

Q.   Well, when you went downstairs to examine the defendant, you knew you were going to find something wrong with him, did you not?

A.   I would have been very surprised not to.

Q.   So you had a preconceived notion before you examined this man.

A.   My theory wasn't changed by examining him.

Psychiatrist D, Government: Rebuttal

Q.   Did you, at my request, examine the patient over the noon hour?

A.   I did. Carroll said he had been advised by his attorney not to discuss the case with me.

UNITED STATES vs. EUGENE CAMPBELL

Campbell was indicted on two charges of robbery, and was found guilty by a jury. Criminal No. 339-60, United States District Court for the District of Columbia. The defense relied on the issue of insanity. This case is important because in it a diagnosis of emotionally unstable personality was regarded as mental illness. An emotionally unstable personality is classified in the APA Manual as a "personality disorder, sub-type personality trait disturbance." It is the same category as the old "psychopathic personality with emotional instability."

The following testimony is abstracted from the trial transcript in order to give the reader some basis for evaluating the meaning of the category "emotionally unstable personality" in its relation to mental disease and to criminality.

Psychiatrist A, Defense

Q.   When did you examine the defendant?

A.   On May 20, 1960, he was admitted to Saint Elizabeths. I arrived at an opinion at a staff conference on August 8, 1960.

Q.   And in your opinion, Doctor, what was the mental condition of the defendant on those dates?

A.   He was suffering from an emotionally unstable personality, which is a mental disease.

Q.   Could you describe more fully this mental disease?

A.   This individual was extremely emotional. He reacted to minor stress with a major emotional reaction. He reacted to the staff conference with great emotional pressure.

Q.   Does the APA *Diagnostic and Statistical Manual* classify emotional instability as a mental disease?

A.   Yes.

Q.   Could the mental disease cause the offenses?

A.   Yes.

Cross-examination by Government

Q.   What are the major symptoms of emotional instability?

A.   He does not react to major or minor stresses of life in a mature emotional manner.

Q.   I take it there are lots of emotionally unstable people walking around the streets.

A.   That's right.

Q.   How long has this diagnosis of emotionally unstable persons been considered a mental disease at Saint Elizabeths?

A.   Administratively, the hospital has considered this a disease since November, 1957 [*Leach* case].

Q.   Before November, 1957, it was not a mental disease?

A.   That is correct.

Q.   Why was this change in policy made?

A.   It was a decision of sudden change in hospital policy to classify sociopaths or any type of personality disorder as suffering from mental disease in November, 1957. That was begun by the *APA Diagnostic Manual* in 1952.

Q.   Does everyone who has an emotionally unstable personality suffer from a mental disease?

A.   Yes, if it is severe enough to be classified as an emotionally unstable personality.

Q.   When you examined the defendant at the staff conference, there were eight psychiatrists, three psychologists, and some chaplains present, correct?

A.   Correct.

Q.   What made you say the defendant was tense?

A.   He was not relaxed; he was sitting in a rigid position.

Q.   What kind of a chair was he sitting in?

A.   A straight-back chair.

Q.   People sitting in straight-back chairs usually sit up straight, don't they?

A.   Yes, they usually do.

Q.   What else was he doing?

A.   He was not relaxed, you could see discomfort in his facial expression, body position, the way he walked, they way he answered questions. He was wringing his hands, he was perspiring. That is tension.

Q.   And now in arriving at your diagnosis, you relied for the most part on what Campbell told you at the staff conference?

A.   Yes.

Q.   Could he have been putting on an act?

A.   The wringing of his hands could have been.

Q.   Were the alleged crimes a product of the emotionally unstable personality?

A.   I have no opinion on that.

Q.   Now, assuming the truth of the facts of the case, that the defendant told a police officer he robbed the airlines office because he was out of work and had a wife to support, would you say this man's desire to get money and to support his family was the cause of the crime, rather than this emotional instability?

A.   I would say yes.

Psychiatrist B, Defense

Q.   [Deposition read] When did you interview the defendant Campbell?

A.   At Saint Elizabeths, when I was a resident there.

Q.   And what was your diagnosis?

A.   Emotionally unstable personality. We have no opinion on whether the alleged offenses were a product of this mental disease.

Psychiatrist C, Government

Q.   Is emotionally unstable personality a mental disease?

A.   No. It may be part of a normal personality, or a part of a character deviation, or a mental disease.

Cross-examination by Defense

Q.   Doctor, can there be more than one kind of emotionally unstable personality?

A.   In the past, an emotionally disturbed personality has been considered a mild case of sociopathic personality, because no one wanted to commit

himself to the diagnosis of sociopathic personality.
It has been a wastebasket diagnosis.

Q.   There is a great amount of disagreement among
          psychiatrists on whether sociopathic personalities
          are mentally ill?

A.   Yes, that is right.

The *Campbell* case was appealed in *Campbell vs. United
States*, No. 16,414, United States Court of Appeals for the District
of Columbia. The appellant alleged that the trial judge was in
error when he did not order a directed verdict of not guilty by
reason of insanity. The Court of Appeals found that the testimony by defense psychiatrists was far from conclusive; they
could not state definitely that the emotional instability caused
the alleged offenses. The motion for a directed verdict was
properly denied by the trial court.

The Court of Appeals did reverse and remand for a new trial
because of the instructions given on the test of responsibility to
be applied in this case. In a dissenting opinion, a judge stated:

The second phase of this case relates to the expansion of the
meaning of mental disease to include yet another concept
which was not considered a mental disease when the product
test was adopted in 1954. As in the prior instances when
"psychopathic personality" was added to the list of insanities,
we are left totally uninformed as to any scientific basis for
the change. It is not suggested that any medical discovery or
recent scientific revelation accepted generally by psychiatrists
warrants this change in the administrative policy which has
such a far-reaching impact on the administration of criminal
law. . . No one has ever advanced a suggestion that psychiatric
treatment of psychopaths was any different after they achieved
a new status in 1957 as persons with mental disease. The only
change we are aware of is that after November, 1957 they
became *prima facia ex culpable* for their unlawful acts. This
would suggest the possibility that the change in labels had no
medical significance, but only legal significance.

How would a prosecutor prove beyond a reasonable doubt
that a crime of violence, such as a rape, is unrelated to emo-

tional instability? Does the majority seek a standard of criminal responsibility under which the prosecution cannot meet its burden in any case? This holding is a long step in the direction of substituting the deterministic philosophy for the belief expressed by Justice Cardozo that all law in Western civilization is guided by a robust common sense which assumes the freedom of the will as a working hypothesis in the solution of legal problems. This is the meaning of Professor Berman's statement: "The lawyer in all countries will answer if there is no reason, no choice, no will, then there can be no law; we will not sacrifice the legal order to the vagaries of your science." [Law as an instrument of mental health. *U. of Penn. Law Review, 109*:361 (1961)]

Campbell was found not guilty by reason of insanity by a jury on a second trial. He was then committed to Saint Elizabeths Hospital.

UNITED STATES VS. GILLEO, CRIMINAL NO. 583-59

DISTRICT COURT FOR THE DISTRICT OF COLUMBIA

Psychiatrist A, Defense

Q.   What is your opinion as to the mental disease suffered by the defendant?

A.   A passive aggressive reaction.

Q.   What else?

A.   Chronic alcoholism.

Government. If Your Honor please, I would like to object to chronic alcoholism. I don't think it is a mental disease.

Court: Do you consider chronic alcoholism to be a mental disease?

A.   Yes, I do.

Q.   Doctor, what was the manner in which the alcoholism manifested itself on May 4, 1959?

Court: How can the witness state how it manifested itself on May 4, 1959, if he did not see the patient until January 25, 1960?

Q. Do you have an opinion as to the nature of the alcoholic episode?

A. Part of the patient's mental disorder involves a considerable amount of dependency, and in each case when his wife was pregnant, this defendant suffered from an increase in his mental disorder. The increased dependency precipitated an acute bout with alcoholism and he seemed to go into rather a psychotic state showing marked poor judgment. This individual, at a time of stress, seems to show little judgment. This involves his excessive drinking and his recurrent need to be punished or to get into trouble.

Court: What is a passive agressive reaction? Is it a form of a disease?

A. Yes, it can be of psychotic proportions and other times it might be more neurotic.

Court: What does that mean?

A. A dependent person is the type of individual who cannot assert himself when he is asked to rise to the occasion to support his family. He has two of his children in an orphanage and cannot take care of them.

Court: Does this make a person insane?

A. Under stress, these people seem to become insane.

Court: How does the insanity manifest itself?

A. In the form of poor judgment and drinking.

Court: Is every drunkard insane?

A. No.

Q. Doctor, would you explain to the Court how the defendant's diseased mental state occurred and led to the crime?

Court: Ask specific questions, and don't give the witness a carte blanche to deliver a lecture.

Q. May I offer proof on this?

Court: No, you may not.

Cross Examination by Government

Q. Where did you examine the defendant?

A. At the D. C. jail.

Q. Now, did you have much chance to observe him other than when you were talking to him?

A. I had an opportunity to review military and hospital records.

Q. Do you consider chronic alcoholism a mental illness?

A. Yes, I do.

Q. Would you say that most alcoholics are mentally ill?

A. No, I wouldn't. I said chronic alcoholism.

Q. Was the defendant psychotic on April 3?

A. For three weeks prior to the crime, he had been drinking heavily, and had been reported to be hearing voices and having hallucinations.

Q. Who gave you this information?

A. His wife.

Q. About his hearing voices?

A. Yes.

Q. Did she hear them along with him?

A. He reported them to her. This is the only source of information I had.

Redirect Examination by Defense

Q. What diagnostic procedures did you employ?

A.   One determines the stream of speech that a person is presenting, one determines whether or not they are oriented for time and place and person, one determines his content of thought.

Q.   Did your diagnostic procedures conform to customary procedures?

A.   Yes.

Court: Isn't the term "psychosis" synonymous with mental illness?

A.   No, that is not correct.

Q.   What is the difference between them if they are not synonymous?

A.   Insanity is a legal term; psychosis is a medical term.

Court: Can there be a mental disease without psychosis?

A.   Yes.

Court: Some people are sane but mentally diseased?

A.   Yes.

Cross-examination by Government

Q.   If it were not for the acute alcoholism would you still say he is mentally ill?

A.   Yes.

Q.   We have eliminated stress from pregnancy, psychosis, and alcoholism. On what do you base your opinion?

A.   He has a passive aggressive reaction. The other things are aggrevating factors that we assume affected him. I wasn't there.

Psychiatrist B, Defense

Q.   What is your diagnosis?

A.	Passive aggressive personality. This person is dependent on other people. He has to lean on others. He shows some tendency toward helplessness.
Court:	You wouldn't say that a clinging vine is suffering from mental disease, would you?
A.	Not this one thing, but in combination with his entire personality makeup he suffers from a mild mental disease.
Court:	In your opinion, this disease was not severe enough to constitute insanity?
A.	That is correct.
Q.	Would the crime have been committed if this personality defect had not been present?
A.	No. He would not have gotten into these situations, he would not have been in Washington.

Cross-examination by Government

Q.	Are there mild forms of passive aggressive reaction?
A.	Yes.
Court:	I would say it was a mild degree.
Q.	Was the crime of May 4 the product of a mild mental illness?
A.	No, I don't feel there was any direct causative connection between the crime and the disease.

Psychiatrist C, Government

Q.	What was your diagnosis?
A.	Personality disorder common to a great many people who are not mentally ill. He is not mentally ill in the sense he has a psychosis. There are no delusions or hallucinations.

Cross-examination by Defense

Q. Barring a hallucinatory experience, you would have difficulty in concluding the act was a product of mental illness.

A. Those would be the major considerations.

Q. Would the defendant benefit from psychiatric treatment?

A. Yes.

Q. Would the defendant have committed the crime if he had been in psychotherapy?

A. At this time we are not, in our present state of knowledge, able to say that we can cure people who have personality disorders.

Q. What treatment did the defendant receive at your hospital?

A. He received chloral hydrate for sleeping, tranquilizers, and some psychotherapy in the sense that our staff talked to him about his present situation.

Psychiatrist D, Government

Q. Was the crime a product of mental disease?

A. No.

Cross-examination by Defense

Q. How often did you see the defendant?

A. Two, three, or four times.

Q. Alone?

A. I don't think so. I may have seen him around one place or another. I don't think I have ever had a pesonal interview with him alone.

UNITED STATES VS. WATSON, CRIMINAL NO. 907-60
DISTRICT COURT FOR THE DISTRICT OF COLUMBIA

The defendant was charged with manslaughter. He killed four persons while attempting to escape from the police in a stolen car.

Psychiatrist A, Defense

Q.   What is your diagnosis, Doctor?

A.   Paranoid schizophrenia with delusions of persecution. He felt that people in the police department were out to get him. He told me he was out to get a certain person.

Q.   Is the defendant exhibiting other symtoms?

A.   Yes, he often rocks back and forth, and he has a history of head banging. He also has a flattening of mood when he talks. His mother had trouble with an alcoholic husband, and there was violence and hatred in his home. The defendant hated his father and threatened him with a knife.

Cross-examination by Government

Q.   You testified as to auditory hallucinations. If I told you that Doctor .... did not testify as to hallucinations, would you change your opinion?

A.   No.

Psychiatrist B, Defense

Q.   Did you meet the defendant?

A.   Yes, at a staff conference at the hospital.

Q.   What is your opinion concerning the nature of the mental illness?

A.	There were no flagrantly psychotic symptoms.
Court:	Did you see him at any other time?
A.	No, only during thirty-five minutes of interviewing.
Court:	And you have a medical opinion he is psychotic?
A.	No, he is mentally ill.
Court:	What label would you put on it?
A.	Emotionally unstable personality.
Court:	Was this the diagnosis of the staff conference?
A.	No, they felt he was without mental disorder.
Q.	Is it possible for the defendant to improve in the hospital so as not to have psychotic symptoms at the time of the conference?
A.	Yes.
Court:	Is there a distinction between mental disorder and psychosis?
A.	Yes, mental illness can refer to difficulty in dealing with stress situations, easily panicked, a life of irrational behavior, and short frustration tolerance.
Q.	What symptoms did the defendant have?
A.	He showed hatred and swore at police officers.

Cross-examination by Government

Q.	What is psychosis?
A.	He may have hallucinations, ideas of reference, or he may have a flattened mood affect.
Q.	Did you notice a flattened affect in the defendant?
A.	No, but he was influenced by his preoccupation with hate.

Q.   You did not observe auditory hallucinations?

A.   No.

Q.   What is a character neurosis?

A.   The person does not deal with conflict or adapt to situations well.

Q.   How does a character disorder differ from a sociopathic personality?

A.   A sociopath is a person with short frustration tolerance who cannot postpone gratification and who uses people.

Court: It means he cannot get along with other people?

A.   That is correct.

Q.   Could you explain to the Court why the staff conference found the defendant was sick, but not sick enough?

A.   Many psychiatrists feel that people who act out against society are sick.

Court: Everybody that commits a crime is mentally sick?

A.   Yes.

Court: Do you believe that?

A.   Yes.

Q.   Would the diagnosis be different if it were made in another ward of the hospital?

A.   Yes. Many of my colleagues feel that psychiatrists are used in court to kill the *Durham* rule. The diagnosis is different if there are criminal proceedings pending.

Psychologist A, Defense

Q.   What tests did you administer?

A.   I administered the Wechsler, the Bender-Gestalt,

the Rorschach, projective drawings, and the Szondi.

Court: Don't give the Szondi results because that test is out in this court.

Cross-examination by Government

Q.   On the Wechsler, what did he score?

A.   77, borderline.

Q.   The Memory Test?

A.   79.

Q.   Benton Visual Retention Test.

A.   Average.

Q.   Bender-Gestalt?

A.   Average.

Q.   Rorschach?

A.   The Rorschach showed a disturbed, panic-stricken person.

Q.   I thought the Rorschach showed a lack of imagination.

A.   It can, but it can also indicate panic.

Psychologist B, Defense

Q.   What did your examination consist of?

A.   Clinical interview and tests. The clinical interview was designed to make friends with the defendant and to understand his problems. I also administered the Rorschach and the Human Figure Drawing Test. The defendant said he did not deserve a good lawyer or good treatment. He said he was never safe because the police were after him.

Q.   What are the results of the Rorschach?

A.   Some people see a teddy bear or bunny. The test results indicated the defendant is severely disturbed.

Cross-examination by Government

Q.   How long did you test the defendant?

A.   One hour of interviewing and one hour of testing.

Q.   Is the Rorschach old and obsolete?

A.   No. It is used to get at the personality of the defendant.

Q.   Wasn't there some way of arriving at this before the Rorschach?

A.   Yes. One man used cloud formations.

Court: Do you use clouds?

A.   No, only ink blots.

Court: What if the defendant answered "bat" to Card 1?

A.   That answer would indicate that he is thinking the way many people think.

Q.   And if he saw nothing?

A.   It would indicate he was frightened or resistant or some patients have heard from others that it is not a good thing to answer.

Q.   What were the results on the Human Figure Drawing Test?

A.   He drew pictures that were accurate and consistent with the diagnosis I had in mind.

Court: Did you say you can look at a figure and come to a conclusion as to his mental condition?

A.   No. I'm doing research on this issue now, and in another five years this may be a possibility.

Redirect Examination by Defense

Q.   What did he answer to Rorschach Card 1?

A.   It looks like two bears. Two men got ahold of the bear. It looks like the bears are bleeding because they are torn up. French poodles are working on the bears, biting them.

Q.   Card 2?

A.   It looks like two rabbits. They are trying to mash a butterfly. Two ducks are arguing who is going to win. Two needles are trying to stick one another.

Chapter 8

RELEASE PROCEDURES

A FTER the *Durham* decision, there was great concern lest dangerous criminals be let loose upon the community. As a result, in 1955, Congress enacted legislation making hospitalization automatic and mandatory in any case in which the defendant was found not guilty by reason of insanity. The statute does not require a separate, posttrial hearing to determine the mental condition of the accused at the time of the verdict.

D.C. Code 24-301 provides in part:

> (d) If any person tried upon an indictment of information for an offense . . . is acquitted solely on the ground that he was insane at the time of its commission, the court shall order such a person to be confined in a hospital for the mentally ill.
>
> (e) Where any person has been confined in a hospital for the mentally ill pursuant to subsection (d) of this section, and the superintendent of such hospital certifies (1) that such person has recovered his sanity, (2) that, in the opinion of the superintendent, such person will not in the reasonable future be dangerous to himself or others, and (3) in the opinion of the superintendent, the person is entitled to his unconditional release from the hospital, and such certificate is filed. . .

The statute came before the Court of Appeals for the first time in 1957, in the now-famous *Leach* case. Leach was charged with robbery, and his defense was insanity. *United States vs. Leach*, Criminal No. 450-57, United States District Court for the District of Columbia. Seven psychiatrists testified that Leach was a sociopathic personality. Prior to November, 1957, the staff at Saint Elizabeths had certified the sociopath as "free from mental disease." At a staff conference at Saint Elizabeths on

November 18, 1957, the assistant superintendent and the superintendent agreed that "people suffering from sociopathic personality disturbances should be labeled as diseased, as mentally
ill, mentally sick, suffering from mental disease." Leach was
found not guilty by reason of insanity. In April, 1958, a petition
for a writ of habeas corpus was filed for Leach's release. The
District Court ordered his discharge and the Court of Appeals
reversed the release order. *Overholser vs. Leach*, 257 F. 2d 667
(1958). [See also *In Re Rosenfield*, 157 F. Supp. 18 (1957).]
The Circuit Court noted that two psychiatrists had testified that,
although Leach was a sociopath, he was not mentally ill. This
opinion of the two staff psychiatrists was contrary to the official
policy of the hospital. In refusing to release Leach, the Court
of Appeals used the following language:

> The phrase "establishing his eligibility for release," as applied
> to the special class of which Leach is a member, means
> something different from having one or more psychiatrists say
> simply that the individual is sane. There must be freedom from
> such mental disease or defect as would make the individual
> dangerous to himself or the community in the reasonably fore-
> seeable future.

Later the Court of Appeals revised its opinion to read:

> There must be freedom from *abnormal mental condition* as
> would make the individual dangerous to himself or the com-
> munity in the reasonably foreseeable future. [Order, *Over-
> holser vs. Leach*, No. 14,480, United States Court of Appeals
> for the District of Columbia.]

The *Leach* case placed the court in an awkward position. If
the meaning of mental disease was to be extended to include
the sociopath, as it did in this case, it would then be necessary
to commit such individuals to a mental hospital upon acquittal.
Here, however, we have a sociopath petitioning the court that
he is illegally held because he is a sociopath. If the court had
not used the language "abnormal mental condition," it would be
possible for sociopathic individuals to roam the streets with
immunity after committing crimes. Here we may see how

judicial behavior is governed by its consequences: the court had to decide the *Leach* case as it did in light of the Saint Elizabeths decision concerning sociopaths. This also illustrates how the behavior of judges is dependent on the behavior of attorneys and psychiatrists.

On the basis of the *Leach* decision, a new trial was ordered for Blocker. *United States vs. Blocker*, 274 F. 2d 572 (1959), United States District Court for the District of Columbia. In this case, Judge Miller, in a dissenting opinion, argued that the 1952 *APA Diagnostic and Statistical Manual* stated that "individuals to be placed in the category of sociopathic personality are ill primarily in terms of society and of conformity with the prevailing cultural milieu." The psychiatrist testifying in the *Leach* case also had stated:

> . . . as of today we, the superintendent and I, have agreed that hereafter we will eliminate from our records the words "without mental disorder" where the diagnosis of this particular group of personality disorders is made; and we will hereafter let the diagnosis stand on its own feet.

Judge Miller argued that this should be interpreted to mean that sociopaths may or may not be mentally ill. It seems that, in the light of court opinions in other cases, whether a behavioral disorder is or is not a mental illness is a matter of fact for the jury to decide. It should be pointed out further in this regard that, following the logic of the *Leach* decision, in the eyes of some psychiatrists all criminals are mentally ill and belong in hospitals. Since sociopathy is characterized by antisocial behavior, and criminality is antisocial behavior, by definition criminals are sociopaths. Since sociopaths are mentally ill, criminals are mentally ill. If criminals are mentally ill, they belong in hospitals, not prisons. As has been noted by Krash, any congressional action to provide for release, upon proof that the party has recovered his sanity, would result in the discharge of all individuals acquitted by reason of insanity who were not psychotic. Sociopaths and psychoneurotics could not be detained even if dangerous to themselves or others. This could result in seriously discrediting the insanity defense in the public mind.

> Any test must necessarily reconcile the right of the public to
> protection from persons who by definition have not been
> deterred by the usual criminal sanctions, and the right of the
> individual to be free from confinement because of alleged evil
> propensities, a notion fundamental to Anglo-Saxon criminal
> justice.[1]

In *United States vs. Starr*, 264 F. 2d 382 (1958), United States
District Court for the District of Columbia, Judge Miller stated:

> A sane person, one free of mental disease or defect, cannot
> be confined in a mental hospital under 24-301(d), D.C. Code,
> simply because he is thought to be potentially dangerous if
> he is released.

Likewise, in *Hough vs. United States*, 271 F. 2d 458 (1959),
the Court of Appeals held that a person with an abnormal mental
condition cannot be held if he is not dangerous. In this case,
the court stated that the standard to be used in case of a *condi-
tional release* is that "such person will not in the reasonable future
be dangerous to himself or others."

Very similar to the *Leach* case is that of *Pettit vs. Overholser*,
Criminal No. 590-57, United States District Court for the District
of Columbia. Pettit had a long record of prior offenses, including
several commitments to reformatories. He came from a broken
home where alcoholism and sex perversion were present.

At the trial, a psychiatrist testified that the defendant was a
sociopath. Sociopathy is classified as a mental disease. The
Pettit case occurred in the spring of 1957, before the *Leach*
decision and before Saint Elizabeths began certifying sociopathic
personalities as mentally ill. The psychiatrist could not state that
the mental disease had produced the criminal act. Upon cross-
examination, he stated that the type of crime committed would

---

[1]Krash, Abe: The Durham rule and judicial administration of the insanity defense
in the district of columbia. *Yale Law Journal, Vol. 70*, No. 6, May, 1961, p. 946;
see also Goldstein and Katz: Dangerousness and mental illness: some observations on the decision to release persons acquitted by reason of insanity. *Yale
Law Journal, Vol. 70*, p. 225 ff.

be of no importance in terms of the diagnosis made: ". . . a person who is suffering from a mental illness, all of his daily actions, whether they be criminal or noncriminal, are influenced by his mental condition." When the judge asked this witness if, lacking the element of causation, a sociopath could ever commit a crime, the psychiatrist answered that causation is always present if mental illness is present.

A psychiatrist called by the government testified that the defendant was not a sociopath, adding that sociopathy is sometimes a mental illness and sometimes it is not. A jury found Pettit guilty. On a motion for a new trial, the judge stated that the government had not rebutted the defense of insanity. He set aside the verdict of guilty, and entered a verdict of not guilty by reason of insanity.

Pettit then petitioned for an unconditional release from Saint Elizabeths. The same psychiatrist from Saint Elizabeths who had previously testified for the government was now used as a witness for the defense to testify that the defendant was without mental disease.

The judge refused the petition for unconditional release, using the following language in his decision:

> It will be observed that the certificate of the superintendent does not state that the defendant has recovered his saniy. . . The absence of a statement that the defendant has recovered his sanity is substantial. It is not an inadvertence. The testimony shows that Saint Elizabeths Hospital is not willing to certify that he has recovered his sanity because it had previously certified that he was free from mental disease at the time he committed the offense. In other words, a person cannot recover his sanity unless he has been insane.
>
> Now we find this result: If this defendant is to be released on the basis of this certificate, it is obvious that he will have perpetrated a fraud on the administration of justice. He secures an acquittal on the ground that he was insane . . . and now he seeks to be released from the institution to which he was committed on the ground that he is sane and actually he has never been insane.
>
> If I may use the vernacular, he cannot have his cake and

eat it too, and it would be a travesty of Justice for this Court to permit such a result, especially in the case of such a dangerous offense as armed robbery. The purpose of the safeguards against the release of a person who has been acquitted of a serious crime on the ground of insanity is to protect the public. . .

In a petition for a writ of habeas corpus, No. 269-61, the defendant again alleged he was not now suffering from a mental disease. In his brief, the defense attorney argued that the appellant was not receiving therapy or treatment at Saint Elizabeths, and that this was an illegality since confinement of a citizen to a mental hospital is justifiable only on the assumption that he would receive treatment. The language of Judge Fahy, in *Ragsdale vs. Overholser*, 281 F. 2d 943 (1960), is cited:

> The confinement of a citizen within a mental hospital without adequate psychiatric treatment would transform the hospital into a penitentiary where one could be held indefinitely for no convicted offense, and these even though the offense . . . might not have been a serious felony.

The same judge who denied the petition for unconditional release also denied the writ of habeas corpus, using the same language as quoted above.

The crucial point again, however, is that the defendant who had been declared insane on the basis of a sociopathic personality diagnosis later appeared before the court to argue he was being illegally detained because he was a sociopath, and sociopaths do not belong in mental hospitals. According to the *Leach* case, a sociopath is mentally ill, and here is a defendant arguing that the court cannot hold a sociopath in a mental hospital. Such tactics have embittered judges and government attorneys, as well as the general public. Much of the adverse criticism surrounding the *Durham* rule is a result of such legal maneuvering.

In respect to D.C. Code 24-301(d), the section on automatic commitment, the issue has been raised whether the defendant has a right to a posttrial insanity hearing before he is sent to a mental hospital. In *Ragsdale vs. Overholser*, 281 F. 2d 943

(1960), the court stated:

> Under statute providing for the commitment to a mental institution of a person acquitted of criminal charges by reason of insanity, it is contemplated that a person acquitted on a charge calling for a maximum sentence of eighteen months may be confined to a mental hospital for two, five, or ten years or beyond that, and nothing less will fulfill the protective and rehabilitative purposes of the statute.

> The purpose of the mandatory confinement provision is to protect the public, and to rehabilitate the subject. The defendant alleges a separate hearing to determine his present mental state is needed before he can legally be confined to Saint Elizabeths. Congress did not provide for a hearing immediately upon the verdict to determine the defendant's then mental condition. It can be assumed that time would be needed to determine the present mental state of the defendant, and the automatic commitment would provide such an examination. To allow the defendant to go free after the trial, however, would not be providing protection to the public or the subject.

The use of the insanity defense reached one climax in the *Horton* case, discussed above; it reached another in *Overholser vs. Lynch*, 288 F. 2d 388 (1961). Lynch was an army officer with no previous criminal or antisocial record. He was charged with a misdemeanor, cashing checks without sufficient funds. The checks amounted to about $50 each. Ordinarily, the Municipal Court would accept a plea of guilty to a misdemeanor and place the defendant on probation. In this case, the government requested a mental examination, and the judge ordered Lynch committed to the D.C. General Hospital, where he was certified incompetent to stand trial. A month later, he was certified competent to stand trial, but suffering from a psychosis, manic depression, and the crimes alleged were regarded as a product of the psychosis.

When Lynch appeared before the Municipal Court, he attempted to withdraw an earlier plea of not guilty and to plead guilty to a misdemeanor. The judge refused to accept the change of plea, and Lynch was declared not guilty by reason of insanity. This judicial action was based on a psychiatric report that Lynch was psychotic. The unusual feature of this case is that the insanity defense was imposed by the government, not by the defense. We have here a reversal of roles: the government defending the accused because he is insane, and the defense attorney arguing that his client is guilty.

The case was appealed in the District Court, which held that the Municipal Court was without power to commit the defendant under D.C. Code 24-301(d); and the District Court Judge ordered the release of Lynch within ten days unless civil commitment proceedings were instituted.

The Court of Appeals reversed the District Court, finding that the defendant had been legally committeed under 24-301(d), and noting that Municipal Court rules grant the judge a discretionary power to accept or reject a plea of guilty. This is also found in case law, e.g., in *Tomlinson vs. United States.* Citing the language used in *Holloway, Douglas, Blunt,* and *Williams,* the court stated that the purpose of the insanity plea was to rehabilitate a sick man and restore him to usefulness:

"Our collective conscience does not allow punishment where it cannot impose blame." "Only the guilty are to be punished." "Mentally responsible lawbreakers are sent to prison; those who are not mentally responsible are sent to hospitals. It is both wrong and foolish to punish where there is no blame. The community's security may be better protected by hospitalization than by imprisonment." The court then concluded, "The cases above cited establish almost a positive duty on the part of the trial judge not to impose a criminal sentence on a mentally ill person." It went on to say:

> By its very nature, a jail sentence is for a specified period of time, while, by its very nature, hospitalization, to be effective, must be initially for an indeterminate period. This difference is not fatal because of the overriding interest of the community in protecting itself and its interest in rehabilitating the defendant himself. Certainly a man is not truly free if he has a sickness which results in his continual criminal activity, which

in turn leads to a lifetime in jail, with only short breaks between sentences. In the case before us, had Lynch not been treated, he might have been in and out of jail for the rest of his life on bad check charges. Now that he has received treatment, he is well on his way to unconditional release, without the probability of repeated offenses.

Colonel Lynch committed suicide by throwing himself under a truck while he was confined at Saint Elizabeths.

A dissenting opinion by Judge Fahy, joined by Judges Edgerton and Bazelon, supported the language of the District Court that, unless civil proceedings for commitment are undertaken, the defendant must be released.

The Supreme Court reversed the Court of Appeals. *Overholser vs. Lynch,* 369 U. S. 705 (1962). The Supreme Court held that D.C. Code 24-301(d), to the effect that a person acquitted solely on the ground that he was insane at the time of the commission of an offense shall be confined in a hospital, is applicable only to a defendant who affirmatively relies upon the insanity defense in any way. The statute does not apply to one who has maintained that he was mentally responsible when the alleged offense was committed. The civil commitment must commence with the filing of a petition and supporting affidavits. Commitment can be effected under D.C. Code 24-301(d) or by recourse to civil commitment provisions in Title 21 of D.C. Code.

D.C. Code 24-301(a) provides for commitment of an accused to a mental hospital *unless* the accused or the government objects.

> If the accused denies he is mentally ill, he is entitled to a judicial determination of his present mental state despite the hospital board's certification that he is of unsound mind. And it should be noted that the burden rests with the party seeking commitment to prove that the accused is then of unsound mind.

The court did not rule on the constitutional issue concerning 24-301(d).

In a dissent, Justice Clark stated:

> The statute is not only designed to protect the public from

the criminally incompetent but at the same time has the humaniarian purpose of affording hospitalization for those in need of treatment . . . But insane offenders are no less a menace to society for being held irresponsible, and reluctance to impose blame on such individuals does not require their release. The community has an interest in protecting the public from anti-social acts whether committed by sane or insane persons. . . The insane who have committed acts otherwise criminal are a still greater concern, as they have demonstrated their risk to society.

In short, petitioner has no constitutional right to choose jail confinement instead of hospitalization. It is said that automatic hospitalization without a finding of present insanity renders the statute invalid, but Congress may reasonably prefer the safety of compulsory hospitalization subject to the release procedures offered by the statute and through habeas corpus.

The *Lynch* case posed an issue that has not been mentioned in any of the many court decisions. This issue is touched upon by Justice Clark when he said "the petitioner has no constitutional right to choose confinement instead of hospitalization." There are many who feel that Lynch should never have been in a mental hospital under a criminal action. However, a question to be considered is whether it is to the benefit of the public or to the defendant to allow the accused or his attorney to decide whether he is mentally diseased. Under the District Court decision, a defendant who pleads guilty is not considered mentally diseased, though in fact he may be very ill, as was the case with Lynch. The insanity plea negates responsibility, e.g. it establishes the fact that there was not the required *actus reus* and/or *mens rea*. The purpose of the insanity plea is to keep the defendant out of prison, not to afford him treatment. If the purpose of the insanity plea is to help the mentally ill, then lawyers and defendants should not be empowered to decide whether the defendant is mentally ill. This decision should be made by behavioral experts.

The point thus becomes obvious that one must not necessarily be a criminal to require psychological help for behavioral disturbances. Lynch needed help because he was psychotic—not because he had cashed two bad checks totalling $100. If psychological knowledge and facilities are inadequate—and this is the real tragedy of the case—allowing a defendant to plead guilty is of benefit neither to himself nor to the public. Nor does it help to allow the defendant (or the government) to use the insanity plea and find him not guilty by reason of insanity, as is illustrated by the *Lynch* case. Whether he was found guilty or not guilty, Lynch needed help. Releasing him to the community was not the answer; placing him in Saint Elizabeths was not the answer. Behavioral problems cannot be solved by court action unless legal procedures are based upon adequate scientific knowledge of human behavior.

In a discussion of the problem surrounding the *Lynch* case, Professor Sheldon Glueck has commented:

> In this connection, it seems that some lawyers in the District of Columbia have developed the practice of estimating the probable length of hospital stay against probable prison term, in deciding on their course of action. . . [In the *Lynch* case] The Court of Appeals of the District of Columbia, in a strong effort to limit the accused's power of choice of plea under the adversary system, upheld the trial court, saying that "society has a stake in seeing to it that a defendant who needs hospital care does not go to prison." The Supreme Court reversed.
>
> The absurdity as well as the danger to social order to which partisan shopping around for the procedure deemed most lenient to the accused can lead is illustrated by *Rex vs. Binns* [31 Cr. App. Rep. (1946) 55], a decision in the English Court of Criminal Appeal rendered a century after *M'Naghten*. This was an application for leave to appeal against a sentence of four years' penal servitude for the crime of wounding with intent to do grievous bodily harm. The judges denied the application; but the importance of the case derives from the illustration of the helplessness of some courts to prevent socially harmful manipulation of the processes of justice even where clear evidence of dangerous mental disease exists. I quote an extract from the opinion of one of the judges: ". . . I observe that this is yet another case similar to at least two which

have been before this Court recently, where a person who is in fact a lunatic and certifiable as such is brought up and charged on indictment with a crime. That person has acuteness enough to realize that, if she sets up the defense of insanity which would certainly be accepted by the jury, she would go to a criminal lunatic asylum, but that if she pleads guilty to the crime the Court has no power to make any such order, and she will go to prison for a comparatively short time—a time much shorter than the period which she could be kept in a criminal lunatic asylum. She therefore pleads guilty, and so the Court has no power to do what everyone must agree it ought to have the power to do, that is, to send her to a criminal lunatic asylum, which is the only place where she can properly be kept. That is what has happened in this case. It has happened twice before. This Court has drawn the attention of the authorities to the matter and has suggested that this is a case where the state of the law is in urgent need of alteration. This wretched woman is not responsible for her actions according to our law. The medical officer, an independent witness, says she is a dangerous homicidal lunatic, and yet the only thing the Court can do is to say that she must go to prison like any other person who has broken the law . . ."

This absurd situation has at long last been remedied by judicial decision holding that the prosecution may, and indeed has a duty to enter a defense of insanity where necessary to protect the public against a dangerous mentally ill defendant. I quoted the case as an illustration of the need of legislative or judicial control of an expectable tendency of defendants and lawyers to look at the problem of an accusation of crime in terms of what course of action will be most "lenient" to the accused rather than in terms of therapeutic opportunity and of protection of the public.[2]

The problem created by the insanity defense is that it frees the defendant from criminal responsibility, while at the same time it does not afford him treatment. The basic philosophy

---

[2]Glueck, Sheldon: *Law and Psychiatry.* Baltimore, Johns Hopkins Press, 1962, pp. 127-29.

of the criminal law is such that a man who is not punished must be rehabilitated and/or the punishment must aid in rehabilitation. If a defendant is acquitted on grounds of insanity, he is sent to a mental hospital for rehabilitation. If the facilities and procedures available are not adequate, then there is no justification for saying we send some criminals to mental hospitals in order to rehabilitate them. It is within this context that defense lawyers find themselves fighting both to get clients into and out of mental hospitals. The inadequacy of our knowledge of behavior is the basic tragedy in the *Lynch* case.

In order to grasp the full significance of the development of a legal doctrine, we must consider the proposition that behavior is governed by its consequences. The insanity plea is used by the defense so that the defendant may escape or avoid an undesirable consequence. Like the criminal law in general, however, the insanity defense is a two-edged sword. The law gives to individuals certain rights; it also creates certain rights for the State against the individual. Why should the government raise the insanity plea in a minor case such as *Lynch*? The insanity defense is a harassment to the government; if the government uses it, the weapon is turned against the defendant. The judges of the Court of Appeals who voted against Lynch's release were opposed to the expansion of the insanity defense. The men who dissented, including Judge Bazelon who had advocated the *Durham* rule, were those who favored a liberal construction of the insanity defense. It should be remembered, also, that although Lynch was charged with a minor offense, he was suffering from a very serious psychotic condition; this was not a case involving a neurosis or a personality disorder.

Recently, a clarification of the *Lynch* case was put forth in *Cameron vs. Fisher*, No. 17,364, United State Court of Appeals for the District of Columbia. Fisher wished to plead guilty to a charge of unlawful threat of personal violence. The Municipal Court refused the plea and the defendant was found not guilty by reason of insanity. He was committed to Saint Elizabeth's Hospital under 24-301(d) of the D.C. Code. The District Court ordered the defendant's release, whereupon the government filed a motion for a hearing under 24-301(a). Again the District Court ordered the release of the defendant, and this time the Court of Appeals upheld the District Court.

In the *Lynch* case, the Supreme Court had stated that 24-301(a) could be used "any time prior to the imposition of sentence." This section of the D.C. Code is available to determine whether the defendant is competent to stand trial. The District Court held that "since there was no pending criminal proceedings, the Municipal Court was lacking jurisdiction to commit the petitioner to Saint Elizabeth's Hospital pursuant to Section 24-301(a) of the D.C. Code." The Court recommended civil proceedings for such cases. *Lynch* does not extend such availability beyond the end of the criminal trial. The effect of *Lynch* and *Fisher* appears to be that criminal proceedings cannot be used for commitment to a mental hospital unless the defendant uses the insanity defense. Otherwise, civil proceedings must be used.

The Court of Appeals noted that, in the *Lynch* case, the Supreme Court has suggested that 24-302 of the D.C. Code was also available: ". . . if an accused who pleads guilty is found to be in need of psychiatric assistance, he may be transferred to a hospital following sentence." One Circuit Court judge recommended that this procedure be used for Fisher, who was recently convicted of arson and sentenced to prison for two to six years.

In the *Fisher* case, we have another example of the return of a defendant to the courtroom for a crime committed after his first release. Releasing Fisher did not help him or the community; nor did it meet the objections raised by defense attorneys who point out the unsavory conditions of Saint Elizabeth's.

In some respects, the case of *Tremblay vs. Overholser*, Habeas Corpus Petition No. 288-61, United States District Court for the District of Columbia, is similar to that of *Lynch*. Joan Tremblay had a long history of alcoholism. Two psychiatrists, however, testified that, although she was classified as a sociopath, she was not mentally ill. She was found not guilty by reason of insanity.

In the appellant's brief, the attorney for Miss Tremblay listed testimony that she was confined in shabby surroundings in an unhealthy and unsafe place, together with other patients who were in psychotic episodes, frothing at the mouth, smearing human excrement on themselves, and so forth. Saint Elizabeths was described as noisome, unnatural, and violent. The judge in the case asked the psychiatrist if the description of the hospital—the odors, the violence, the soiled linens—was true as stated in the petition. Although denying it was as bad as pictured, the psychiatrist admitted it must have been a horrible experience for the petitioner. The judge also described the petitioner as a "lady of refinement and education." The District Court ordered her release. The language of the judge was as follows:

> There was a time when insane people were placed in jails. We looked upon this as a barbaric custom that has been pretty well eliminated. But we have reverted to it in reverse; we are placing sane people in insane institutions, which I think is even more barbaric. This is due very largely to the very unfortunate classification with which a majority of psychiatrists disagree, on the part of Saint Elizabeths Hospital, of sociopaths as persons having a mental disease.

The Court of Appeals reversed the District Court, and ordered the case back to the District Court. The District Court judge then set Miss Tremblay free on a finding that she was sane. After her release, she was arrested several times for public intoxication. She followed Lynch in death. On October 8, 1963, Miss Tremblay committed suicide by jumping from the Calvert Street bridge in Washington, D. C. She had been in and out of Saint Elizabeths several times on a voluntary basis. She had also sought private psychiatric care. The legal maneuvers that had gained her freedom from Saint Elizabeths did not help her any more than did the psychiatric facilities available to her.

In the *Lynch* case, an effort was made to keep the defendant out of the hospital; yet, *Lynch* is cited in the trial of Sutherland as evidence that the court "had almost a positive duty not to impose a criminal sentence on a mentally ill person." In the *Sutherland* case, the defense stated that "alcoholism is a result of anxiety and the alleged criminal offense was the result of alcoholism." Sutherland was found guilty and sent to a reformatory, whereupon he refused to appeal his case because he felt he was receiving better care at Lorton than he would at Saint Elizabeths. In the *Horton* case, the defense lawyer argued that drug addicts ought to be hospitalized because they are all mentally ill.

The logic here is difficult to comprehend and to support. It states that it is all right to place some addicts and some alcoholics in mental institutions because they are sick and need treatment rather than punishment. Other addicts and alcoholics, however, do not belong in mental institutions because fellow patients froth at the mouth, smear feces on their bodies, and soil the linens. It is difficult to understand why Sutherland and Horton would enjoy or benefit from an environment which, in the cases of *Lynch* and *Tremblay*, is cited as evidence for their immediate release from a mental institution. The same arguments used in *Lynch* and *Tremblay* could be used against the insanity defense in general. The real problem is that psychiatric facilities may be no better than prison facilities. The same defense lawyers who use the insanity defense in one case oppose its use in another, or oppose the incarceration of criminals in Saint Elizabeths if the insanity defense is used.

The *Durham* rule has created very serious civil liberties issues, as illustrated by such cases as *Leach, Horton, Lynch,* and *Tremblay.* The late Robert Lindner wrote that when we classify homosexuality as a disease rather than a crime we are not helping the homosexual; rather we are creating new oppressive measures to use against him.[a] The same can be said for alcoholism, addiction, and other so-called personality disorders. The *Horton* defense, if successful, would make life-long incarceration for addicts a real possibility, a threat that few legislative bodies and few judges have seen fit to use in the past against drug

---

[a]Lindner, Robert: *Must You Conform.* New York, Rinehart, 1956, p. 204.

addicts. In the future, there may be such confinement of addicts in hospitals with psychotics who froth at the mouth and besmirch themselves with excrement, and all without the benefit of statutory enactment, or without judicial recourse for the defendant. The American Civil Liberties Union noted, in connection with the *Lynch* case, that it was not farfetched to envision the presentation of testimony that a parking violation is attributable to mental disorder. Commitment to a hospital would then follow. On the basis of the *Horton* case, one can argue that smoking is an addiction, rooted in a physiological need, and thus smoking becomes evidence of mental illness. This is the result of expanding the meaning of insanity to include all behavioral problems.

Summary

The insanity plea has created a serious problem for the defendant: How does he get out of the hospital once he is committed? This problem is compounded by legal maneuvers to secure the release of defendants once they are committed to mental hospitals, thus allowing them to escape both imprisonment and medical treatment.

The problem is further compounded by the lack of adequate facilities for the care and treatment of the mentally ill. If defense lawyers are going to argue that mentally ill criminals belong in hospitals, then they must accept the unsavory condition and the stigma attached to such hospitalization.

In the District of Columbia, the insanity defense has had three serious setbacks. In the *Lynch* case, the defense lost when the government raised the issue of insanity. Although the Supreme Court reversed the Court of Appeals in this case, Lynch is dead, and the issue of release from a mental institution is still a major concern for any defendant using the insanity plea. Even under the Supreme Court ruling, Lynch would have been committed to Saint Elizabeth's under 24-301(a) or under Title 21 of the D.C. Code. He could have committed suicide under other commitment procedures. The consequences of using this defense are often less desirable than a prison sentence.

The defense lost the *Horton* case when a jury decided that

drug addiction was not a mental disease or defect and Horton was released without treatment or cure. The *Kent* case was lost when the jury returned a split verdict, declaring Kent to be *both insane and a criminal*. This was possible because there can be insanity without productivity; that is, insanity does not necessarily cause robberies and housebreaking. The *Tremblay* case was lost when the defendant was released without cure, after which she committed suicide.

A comparison of psychiatric and legal labels before and after *Durham* would look something like this:

BEFORE DURHAM

Psychiatric Labels:	Psychotic	Neurotic	Personality Disorder	Normal
Legal Labels:	Insane	Sane Sane	Sane	Sane

AFTER DURHAM

Psychiatric Labels:	Psychotic	Neurotic	Personality Disorder	Normal
Legal Labels:	Insane	Insane*	Insane*	Sane

---

*In some cases, but not in every case.

PART II

BEHAVIORAL SCIENCE, MENTAL DISEASE, AND CRIME

Chapter 9

CLINICAL METHOD

INTRODUCTION

WE HAVE reviewed the insanity plea as it has developed in the District of Columbia; we have said nothing about the adequacy of the statemetns made in court concerning criminal behavior and mental disease. The purpose of Part II of this book is to evaluate the testimony given in court concerning human behavior in the light of modern psychology, psychiatry, and sociology.

Two assumptions underlie the *Durham* rule: (1) There is an entity called "mental illness' or "mental disease;" (2) Mental disease produces, causes, or is a factor in criminal behavior. An assessment of the insanity defense in terms of the manner in which it is established in court will be undertaken. As has already been indicated in the testimony and court opinions cited above, lawyers, judges, psychiatrists, and psychologists are not in agreement as to the meaning of "mental disease" or "productivity," either interprofessionally or intraprofessionally. The psychiatric profession itself is aware of this problem, as seen in the above quoted opinions, and lawyers often object to the validity of psychiatric testimony.

The following statement summarizes succinctly the present state of the behavioral sciences:

A behaviorist defines psychology as "the science of human behavior" (or of the behavior of organisms)—he is concerned with the description, prediction, and control of that behavior. But other reputable psychologists have defined their field as "the science of mind" or "the science of conscious processes." And still others—the psychoanalysts—are much more concerned with unconscious processes than conscious ones. If psychologists of different persuasions come to different conclusions about the nature of man, the reason may be that they start from different premises and ask different questions.

In 1957, Ernst Helgard said of his discipline, "The state of factual knowledge is not very satisfactory . . . the number of dependable facts in the various fields of psychology is not very impressive." When the Ford Foundation was reassessing its program in behavior sciences, a report made to the officers concluded "our storehouse of verified knowledge of human behavior has a relatively low inventory."[1]

Because of basic disagreements in psychiatry and psychology, which always exist in any scientific discipline that is undergoing growth and change (even chemistry or physics), the lawyer is able to select a psychiatrist who will present testimony favorable or unfavorable to the defendant. There are several conflicting theories of behavior today in the behavioral sciences. Lawyers and judges are caught in the uncomfortable position of trying to evaluate conflicting expert testimony in an area in which they (lawyers and judges) are not professionally trained.

Since behavioral scientists are in disagreement as to the explanation of human behavior, it might be helpful to review some of the sources of difficulty as they bear on the insanity issue. The conflicts herein are presented not as a way of making any given group of experts a whipping boy or as a way of selling any given school of thought, but rather as a plea for further research in the area of criminal behavior. Because of the contributions of psychiatrists, psychologists, and sociologists we know a great deal about behavior today, but we still do not have any final answers.

The writer is prejudiced in favor of an experimental sociological approach to the study of behavior. Many experts will disagree with this approach. The important thing is not that we agree or disagree, but that we utilize these differences of opinion as a basis for further investigation of a problem. One

---

[1] *Saturday Review,* March 21, 1964, p. 76.

of the difficulties with expert testimony in the courtroom is that psychologists and psychiatrists testify as to the behavior of the defendant *as if* these conclusions are beyond question or dispute, when other evidence and contrary testimony suggest that such conclusions are often more of a hypothetical than a verified nature.

The testimony presented above in the cases of *Kent, Jenkins, Carroll,* and *Campbell* affords us an opportunity to see how the presence of insanity or mental disease is determined. The evidence presented is based on either (1) test results, or (2) verbal behavior from an interview situation. At the present time, there is professional disagreement as to the reliability and validity of data gained from testing and clinical situations. Some of these issues are discussed below.

TESTS

Tests can be divided into the projective type (the Rorschach, TAT, House-Tree-Person) and the actuarial type (intelligence tests such as the Wechsler or the Stanford-Binet, or the MMPI).

The Rorschach and the House-Tree-Person tests are often used in diagnosing mental disease, as was witnessed in the testimony presented in the *Kent, Jenkins, Carroll,* and *Campbell* cases. The validity of projective tests has been seriously questioned in recent years. A British psychologist, H. J. Eysenck, has stated, concerning the Rorschach:

> On all usual criteria, therefore, it must be concluded that the Rorschach has failed to establish its scientific or practical value. This is becoming more recognized, largely as a consequence of the improved standards of Rorschach research in recent years, which has given rise to many well-controlled and well-analyzed studies, the results of which have been uniformly negative.[2]

At Maudsley Hospital in London, the Rorschach has been dropped as a clinical tool. However, it is still required of graduate students in clinical psychology at Columbia University

---

[2]Gross, Martin L.: *The Brain Watchers.* New York, Random House, 1962, p. 246.

in New York City. Super discusses the reasons for this in these words:

> We have agreed that they [projective techniques] have no validity, but we retain the requirement. We do this for three reasons: (1) the unsatisfactory but practical consideration that such psychologists are expected to have these skills and are likely to both feel and be handicapped if they do not, (2) the fact that they can learn something useful about clinical inter-action by studying these procedures, and (3) the hope that familiarity with these methods may yet provide psychologists with a basis for some major breakthrough in the field of per-sonality assessment.[3]

Gough asked a group to simulate psychoneurosis and then schizophrenia on the MMPI, and the results were similar to those of genuine patients. The F score minus the K score did provide a means for detecting fakers. Similar results were ob-tained by Goldstein and Pollaczek, using a standard intelligence test.[4]

Gross quotes a study in which it is stated:

> [T]here is no evidence that the Rorschach can be used to assess whether or not individuals are well or poorly adjusted . . . There is no evidence that the test is of any practical use at the moment, either for describing personality or for predicting behavior.[5]

Using the Draw-A-Figure test, a group of psychologists were unable to match the figure drawings of normal and disturbed children with other clinical diagnoses of the same children.[6]

A postwar study of the screening program of the Armed Services for recruits revealed that the screening devices were

---

[3]Bachrach, A. J. (ed.): *Experimental Foundations of Clinical Psychology.* New York, Basic Books, 1962, pp. 61-62.

[4]*Ibid.,* p. 78.

[5]Gross: *op. cit.,* p. 263.

[6]*Ibid.,* p. 262.

very ineffective and had little predictive value.[7] Paul Meehl has discussed in detail the problem of clinical versus statistical prediction, in his book by that title.[8] He has commented that it has often struck him as paradoxical:

> . . . to find a near-routine battery of complex, skill-demanding tests being administered in a clinical setting where the median number of therapeutic hours per case is not appreciably in excess of the total skilled time expended by the psychologist on the case in making often dubious dynamic and prognostic inferences from the test data.[9]

Doctor Little, in a review of some of the experimental work accomplished with the Rorschach test since 1950, has discussed one major assumption related to this—what he refers to as the assumption of *psychic determinism.* Of this he says:

> [T]his assumption in relation to projective technique is, specifically, the assumption that when an individual is presented with semistructured ambiguous stimuli his responses are determined by his enduring and dominant personality characteristics . . . People may have a response role labeled "use in case of semistructured ambiguous stimulus presented by a psychologist."[10]

Bachrach and Pattishall have experimented with "the fallacy of personal validation." They used a series of items that described personality in such general terms that most of the subjects stated the tests described them with great accuracy. These statements are similar to those found in fortune cookies or on penny weight machines, "You have a great need for people" or "At times you have serious doubts as to whether you made the right decision." Such a test had high personal valida-

[7]Ginzberg, Eli, *et al.*: *The Ineffective Soldier.* 3 vol., New York, Columbia University Press, 1959.

[8]Meehl, Paul E.: *Clinical versus Statistical Prediction.* Minneapolis, University of Minnesota Press, 1954.

[9]Bachrach, A. J.: The Psychodiagnostic Test Battery: Test Selection. *Progress in Clinical Psychology.* Vol. III, New York, Grune and Straton, 1958, p. 41.

[10]*Ibid.*, pp. 45-46.

tion because of the universality of the statements made about behavior.[11] Bachrach summarizes these problems in testing by noting that:

> . . . with the use operationally defined concepts, testable hypotheses, and approaches toward adequate theory building, the decision process of test selection and test interpretation can advance our knowledge, our effectiveness, and our service.[12]

The reader who is interested in a detailed discussion of the problem of test validity is referred to the *Annual Review of Psychology* and to the *Mental Measurements Yearbook*. There is also a chapter in *The Experimental Foundations of Clinical Psychology* on the problem of verifying clinical judgment.[13]

As Gross has noted,[14] there are real moral issues involved in testing. If a student is rejected from law school or medical school, or if an employee is fired or not promoted, or if a criminal is executed rather than sent to a mental hospital on the basis of test scores, then these scores should be meaningful and valid.

Test results are an *indirect observation* of behavior—not a direct observation. The response observed is the response to test materials. This is not the behavior for which the subject is in a mental hospital or in criminal court. The testing procedure involves the fallacy of inference; and inference is made concerning responses to one situation (a criminal act) from a response to another situation (testing). A test situation reveals how a given individual responds to testing; it does not explain why he responded to money by stealing. Test behavior is under

---

[11]Bachrach, A. J., and Pattishall, Evan G.: An experiment in universal and personal validation. *Psychiatry*, August, 1960, p. 267 ff.

[12]Bachrach: The Psychodiagnostic Test Battery, *op. cit.*, p. 48; see also Psychological Testing, by William Schofield and A. J. Bachrach, in *Lawyer's Medical Cyclopedia of Personal Injuries and Allied Specialties*. Vol. III, Indianapolis, Smith, 1959, p. 191 ff.

[13]*Experimental Foundations of Clinical Psychology. op. cit.*, p. 26 ff.

[14]Gross: *op. cit.*, p. 276 ff.

the control of its consequences. For example, the responses to a driver's examination are under the control of the contingencies attached to the answers: receiving or not receiving a driver's license. In the case of a defendant in a criminal trial, the responses to tests are under the control of the contingencies associated with being found guilty or not guilty.

Tests are validated by comparison with other tests, or by comparison with a criterion group already selected and classified. For example, the Rorschach cards are shown to patients *already* classified as schizophrenic or neurotic, and then a statistical analysis is made of the responses to the cards by this class of subjects. If, in the future, a subject responds in a manner similar to that of the schizophrenic group, he is classified as showing schizophrenic responses to Rorschach cards. There is no attempt here to relate a schizophrenic response, e.g., hallucinations, to the environment that produced it; rather the *test behavior* of the criterion group is related to the *test behavior* of the subject being examined. However, the classification of "schizophrenic" is made prior to and independent of the Rorschach test. The classification of "schizophrenic" is never verified by an independent procedure, but is in turn to validate a test designed to reveal schizophrenia.

The theory of testing apparently is based on the theory of *projection;* that is, the individual will project through the test his inner needs, drives, mental states, anxieties, and so forth. There is no reason to believe that one response, such as schizophrenic verbal behavior, is related to or causes another response, such as seeing butterflies on a Rorschach card. It may be that the environmental variables controlling the Rorschach response, or a painting of a house, tree, or person, are different from those controlling stealing, rape, or murder.

Test scores are validated not on the basis of the individual tested but according to group statistics. A test can reveal certain dimensions of group performance, within the limits herein discussed; a test will never reveal the dimensions of an individual's behavior.

Suppose, for example, you have a test designed to indicate

success in medical school. This test is then validated by checking on the actual performance of the student in medical school.
However, the data are grouped as follows, and a perfect correlation between test score and performance would look like this:

	Test Score	
	High	Low
High	50	0
Performance		
Low	0	50

All subjects with high scores would be successful in medical
school; all those with low scores would be unsuccessful. More
typical results, however, are these:

	Test Score	
	High	Low
High	34	18
Performance	true positive	false negative
Low	16	32
	false positive	true negative

Sixty-six per cent of the scores are accurate; that is, high scores
match performance; low scores match performance. However,
16 per cent of those with high scores failed medical school,
whereas 18 per cent failing the examination completed medical
school. Those for whom success was predicted but who failed
are "false positive;" those for whom failure was predicted but
who passed are "false negative." How does one tell from the
test results if Joe Jones is in Category 1, 2, 3, or 4? The only
way of course is to admit Jones to medical school and see how
he behaves in this environment. One cannot say a thing about
Jones' behavior from his test results; the prediction must be
confined to groups of students. A statement that 66 per cent
of the scores are accurate will not tell us to what class Jones
belongs.

This raises another issue with respect to tests. They do not tell us (1) why a person is successful or unsuccessful in medical school, or (2) what changes must be made in order to produce successful medical students. Let us assume that a response of "frog" to Card 9 of the Rorschach test always indicates a schizophrenic reaction. Assume also that we can identify a schizophrenic reaction. We still do not know (1) what produces schizophrenic behavior, or (2) what one does to alter schizophrenic behavior.

For this reason behaviorists have advocated paying less attention to "diagnostic testing" and more attention to discovering how to produce the behaviors desired. If we wish school children to read well, we should develop techniques for good reading. If we aim to develop good executives for IBM or Westinghouse, we should determine what behaviors are needed and what procedures are useful in developing executive behaviors. Saint Elizabeths spends a vast portion of its time in diagnostic testing and placing patients in APA categories; yet this testing does not alter the behavior of a single criminal, nor has it prevented a single crime from being committed. It would be of greater social value to develop techniques for altering behavior, rather than testing to discover some diagnostic category.

FREUDIAN PSYCHOLOGY

What is the intellectual pattern within which the personality-testing movement developed? Why are these tests used? The theoretical framework for clinical psychiatry and psychology is derived to a large extent from the writings of Sigmund Freud.

Freud used the scientific model of the day, a closed energy system in which the potential energy plus the kinetic energy equalled a constant value. In this system, if one knows the amount of energy available, and the amount being dissipated, then the output can be predicted. Today, the model of science is an open energy system, which includes both input and output characteristics, and in order to predict output (behavior) we must know the input (experiences, stimuli).

In the Freudian scheme, the energy system is called the libido or id, referred to as the pleasure principle, usually of a sexual nature. In discharging this sexual energy, the id is further divided by the development of the ego, or the reality principle. The further development of the personality system leads to the super ego, or the punishing principle, or conscience.

Human behavior is viewed as a result of internal mental or psychic states, depending upon the interaction of id, ego, and super ego. In the attempt to satisfy the id's impulses and the super ego's demands for conformity to the moral code of family and community, the ego develops many defense mechanisms. The frustration of the id by the super ego can be handled by compensatory rationalization, identification, projection, repression, regression, fantasy, withdrawal, or reaction formation.

The function of the ego is reality-testing: the selection of objects in the environment capable of satisfying the pleasure principle of the id. The ego mediates between the blind or instinctual demands of the id and the moral requirements of the environment represented by the super ego. Anxiety can arise out of a fear that the id will conquer the ego, or from feelings of guilt growing out of a strong super ego. Freud discussed the development of personality in terms of four stages, placing emphasis on the early years or childhood experiences of the individual. The stages of sexual development were termed the oral, anal, phallic, and genital. During the phallic stage there may be developments such as the Oedipus complex or the castration complex. The phallic stage is followed by a latency period, to be replaced—in a normal, healthy individual— by the genital stage.

One of the important contributions made by Freud was to bring into the province of medicine the treatment of behavioral problems. Freud was a neurologist, and it was natural that he would include "mental disease" in the treatment of nervous diseases. This alignment of psychiatry with medicine occurred despite Freud's own warning that psychiatry should develop outside the confines of medicine.

INTROSPECTION

The techniques for gathering data in clinical psychiatry is

introspection, a critical examination by the individual of his inner feelings, emotions, and experiences. From such subjective evaluation comes insight as to the causes of behavior. "Freud's explanation scheme followed a traditional pattern of looking for a cause of human behavior inside the organism."[15] "We typically attempt to account for behavior by assuming internal subjective states, which are never observed, to be the determining events."[16]

The issue of subjectivism and introspection has divided the behavioral sciences since the nineteenth century. August Comte advanced the naturalistic, or postivistic, position, arguing that the method of the physical sciences must be applied to the study of human behavior.

The introspectionist position was advanced by the German school of sociologists, especially Dilthey and Weber. Dilthey argued that the social sciences deal with understanding, meaning, and interpretation. He made psychology an introspective science concerned with internal feelings, attitudes, motives, and goals.

Rickert, on the other hand, treated psychology and sociology as natural sciences, dealing with observable phenomena. The distinction drawn by Rickert was one between history as an idiographic science—an analysis of unique events—and natural science, a nomothetic science—an analysis of general causal laws among natural events.[17]

Hilgard summarizes this methodological issue as follows:

> At the height of behaviorism, not many years ago, many psychologists developed a "you must not say" attitude toward subjective experiences of all kinds (pleasures, pains, percepts,

---

[15]Skinner, B. F.: *Cumulative Record*. New York, Appleton-Century-Croft, 1959, p. 187.

[16]Staats, Arthur W., and Carolyn K.: *Complex Human Behavior*. New York, Holt, Rinehart, and Winston, 1963, p. 46.

[17]Martindale, Don: *The Nature and Types of Sociological Theory*. Boston, Houghton Mifflin, 1960, p. 378; Barnes, Harry Elmer, and Becker, Howard P.: *Contemporary Social Theory*. New York, Appleton-Century-Croft, 1940; Becker, Howard P., and Boskoff, Alvin, (ed.): *Modern Sociological Theory*, New York, Dryden Press, 1957, p. 195 ff.

images, ideas). When it was essential that reference be made to these states or experiences, they had to be translated into discriminatory responses or verbal responses and thus be made behaviorally respectable . . . The more extreme form of rejection of behaviorism is found in various forms of phenomenology, existentialism, and humanistic psychology. For example, the experimental phenomenology of Fritz Heider is called by him a "naive" psychology; it takes things as one finds them and does not attempt to reduce them to another level of analysis. Existentialism and humanistic psychology tend to reject the biological approach that has been characteristic of American psychology, seeing the problems of psychology rather in terms of human values, human concerns, individual uniqueness, and the individual meaning of life and destiny.

The mainstream of psychology in the years ahead is more likely to be influenced by the moderate alteration of the behaviorist position than by the extreme forms of phenomenology. The less extreme position permits a freer interest in cognitive process of all kinds, in dreams, in hypnotic phenomena, in intention, in problems of self-preception, playfulness, and will, without thereby rejecting the search for lawfulness in behavior, for objectivity in experimentation, and for clarity in scientific communication.[18]

INTERNAL MENTAL STATES

Freud was also concerned with the environment. He began with an environmental event, or stimulus, which experience had an effect on an internal mental process, which in turn produced a response. Thus the Freudian analysis of behavior is: environment → inner mental state → behavior; or stimulus—organism—response; or stimulus—meaning—response. A model of an intervening variable is the example of a man who sees a bear and runs. Why does he run? Because he is afraid. From the response, the emotion "fear" is inferred. In the next stage, the

---

[18]Hilgard, Ernest R.: *Introduction to Psychology.* 3rd ed., New York, Harcourt, Brace, and World, 1962, pp. 608-09.

fear has been used as a mental state to explain the running:

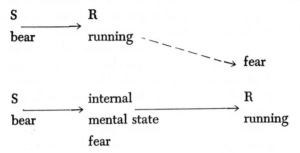

In the same way, we state a person eats because he is hungry:

How do we know he is hungry? Because he eats. Why does he eat? Because he is hungry. Such statements are not scientific because they are not subject to disproof. If a man eats, he is hungry; if he does not eat, he is not hungry. Such explanations of behavior use the internal mental state of the organisms as the independent variable, and the response is the dependent variable. The internal state is known only from the response; that is, the dependent variable is used as proof of the existence of an independent variable.

These inner determinants of behavior—such as anxiety, an Oedipus complex, ego, self, attitude, value, dynamic assessment— in turn require an explanation. However, these concepts are usually presented as explanations of behavior without further inquiry. What often happens in the course of an explanation is the elimination of the environmental event or stimulus, leaving only the internal mental state and the response. The reader may test his proposition by attempting to tell from a case study what specific behaviors occurred in relation to what environmental events. Thus the Freudian system perpetuated the dualistic system of nature: one part mental, one part physical. It also perpetuated the problem of the effect of the mental upon the physical, and vice versa.

Freud's theory of the mental apparatus had an equally damaging effect upon the study of behavior as a dependent variable. Inevitably it stole the show. Little attention was left to behavior per se. Behavior was relegated to the position of a mere mode of expression of the activities of the mental apparatus or the symptoms of an underlying disturbance.[19]

Many current publications use the internal mental state—introspection model of analysis.[20]

VERBAL BEHAVIOR

Besides testing, the psychiatrist or psychologist depends on the psychiatric interview to obtain information. The patient or subject is asked to talk about "his feelings, his emotions, his experiences." He engages in introspection and then communicates his subjective experiences to the psychologist.[21] On the basis of verbal reports, statements are made regarding why people behave as they do. The verbal reports are taken as evidence of other behaviors, i.e., thinking, feeling, seeing, hearing, etc. This again involves the *indirect observation* of behavior. One does not observe thinking, feeling, or seeing; rather one observes verbal behavior about thinking, feeling, or seeing.

In the courtroom, reliance is placed upon these verbal reports of defendants. A defendant may say he is having hallucinations or delusions: he is seeing little green men, or he hears voices telling him to enter apartments (as Kent did), or he talks with flowers (as Goforth did). Are these experiences reported by psychotics in the courtroom to be interpreted as perceptual experiences or as verbal statements? Do psychotics "see" or

---

[19]Skinner: *op. cit.*, p. 189.

[20]See, for example, Blum, Gerald S.: *A Model of the Mind.* New York, John Wiley and Sons, 1961; Scher, Jordan, (ed.): *Theories of the Mind.* New York, Free Press, 1962; Allport, Gordon: *Pattern and Growth in Personality.* New York, Holt, Rinehart, and Winston, 1961; Heider, Fritz: *The Psychology of Interpersonal Relations.* New York, John Wiley and Sons, 1958.

[21]Salzman, Leon: Psychiatric interviews as evidence: The role of the psychiatrist in court. *George Washington Law Review, Vol. 30*, June, 1962, pp. 853-74.

"hear" the things they report seeing or hearing?

This is the crux of the problem of introspectionism and experiences. Experiences are private events. There is no way in which an independent verification of a private experience can be made. However, as Boring has remarked, "Introspection is still with us, doing its business under various aliases, of which verbal report is one."[22]

Verbal behavior is often used as evidence of private events ("I have a headache" or "I am sick"). The verbal response may be under the control of painful internal stimuli, or it may be an operant response, i.e., under the control of its effect on the environment. A person who is sick is given special privileges, is excused from unpleasant tasks, etc. People will verbalize their private events so as to gain positive reinforcement or to escape punishment. In clinical psychology, this is known as rationalization, projection, and reaction formation. The problem lies in the inability to gain public access to these private events; there is no way in which they can be verified independently of the verbal report.[23]

People can also verbalize about past events, as they do during a therapeutic interview. Again, statements about past behaviors are usually not subject to independent verification.[24]

The field of perception is one in which verbal statements have been used as evidence of cognitive processes such as seeing or hearing. As Goldiamond has noted, ". . . the peculiar perceptual responses (hallucinations) of psychotics may refer to the same lack of stimulus control which is exhibited in their other behaviors rather than to a visual abnormality."[25] A person can be conditioned to respond "I am in Tucson" when a green

---

[22]Goldiamond, Israel: Perception, in *Experimental Foundations of Clinical Psychology, op. cit.*, p. 309.

[23]Nurenberger, John I., Ferster, C. B., and Brady, John Paul: *An Introduction to the Science of Human Behavior.* New York, Appleton-Century-Croft, 1963, p. 323 ff.

[24]*Ibid.*, p. 344.

[25]Goldiamond, Israel: Perception. *op. cit.*, pp. 299-300.

light is on, and "I am in Phoenix" when a red light is on. The verbal report is independent of the actual location of the subject. Schizophrenics discriminate between *up* and *down* staircases.[26] Vision must be defined as a response to a visual stimulus, and hearing must be defined as a response to an auditory stimulus. We cannot define perception by what a subject says he hears or feels. When we show a green card to a subject and ask him, "What do you see?" we do not know what he sees; there is no way to gain an independent verification of his private experience. We can, however, ask him to match the green color chip with color samples, and we can record his response. We do not know what he "sees," but we do know what behavior the subject exhibits in matching samples. The verbal report, however, is not evidence of seeing or hearing. "A verbal response is an operant, even when it has semantic reference to subjective experience . . ."[27]

The verbal behavior of a patient in therapy can be and is controlled by the therapist, who can—by his verbal responses, gestures, or by other means—encourage or discourage the subject from discussing a given topic. Thus the therapist who believes that sex is the crucial element in his patient's history can prompt him to talk at great length about his sexual experiences. Within a few weeks, verbal behavior can be shaped, as can any other behavior. Greenspoon has discussed this problem in some detail, and he has argued that therapists should regard verbal behavior as any other behavior rather than as interpretive or symbolic of other behaviors.[28]

Freud himself taught others to doubt the face value of verbal statements. It is recognized that a person will not always verbalize an experience, especially if in the past he has been punished for that response. This, then, in Freudian terms, becomes repression and the unconscious. A person may also say

---

[26]*Ibid.*, p. 303, 317.

[27]*Ibid.*, p. 300.

[28]Greenspoon, Joel: Verbal Conditioning and Clinical Psychology. *Experimental Foundations of Clinical Psychology. op. cit.*, p. 510 ff.

things he knows are not true because he is reinforced for so saying. This is called lying. A man can tell a woman he loves her in order to have sexual intercourse with her. The lawyer knows that verbal statements are not to be taken at face value, and he has constructed rules of evidence so that verbal testimony may be properly evaluated by the judge and jury. The "hearsay" rule is an example of this. The testimony that people give in court is in large measure dependent on the consequences attached to it: will it help convict the accused, or will it help to acquit him? The court attaches penalties for perjury, and the witness is sworn to the truth on a Bible. Yet it is well recognized that verbal statements in court are subject to other contingencies which control them. Lawyers and psychiatrists are most skeptical about verbal behavior, but in a psychiatric interview, verbal statements are often taken as evidence of other behaviors.

MANIPULATION OF BEHAVIOR

A related problem is that the therapist must manipulate the mental apparatus of the patient. How can this be done? The therapist treats not behavior but psychosis or neurosis or anxiety. He does this by manipulating the environment; but, in therapy, what is usually manipulated is verbal behavior. Not only is verbal behavior the evidence of a behavioral problem, but it is also the measure of changes in behavior. One of the major difficulties in such a situation is that, within the confines of the therapy setting, a patient's behavior is shaped in a given direction and he is under the control of that environment. Once he is removed from the therapy situation, however, other contingencies are attached so the behavior and other stimuli come to control it. A man may discuss his marital problems with his therapist. Upon returning home, the subject's behavior is under the control of another environment—his wife, the children, etc.— and not of the therapy setting.

The ability of verbal behavior to control other behaviors is a very complex issue. In some circumstances, a verbal command or statement will control another response. It is well recognized, however, that a therapist or an experimenter can gain control over his subject's verbal responses without having thereby gained control over his eating, smoking, voting, or sexual activities. Evidence of this is the fact that people say one thing and do another.

Staats and Staats have recently applied modern learning theory to clinical problems. They observe that motor behavior and verbal behavior may be in some way related according to the principles of R-R laws (response-response). "Paper and pencil tests may be considered to be measures of verbal behavior that have been found to be related to other behaviors of the individual. For example, obtaining a high score on a test of personality maladjustment might be found to be related to other aggressive behaviors." They point out that from R-R laws we can predict behavior, but we cannot control it. "If we are interested not only in predicting but also in controlling human behavior, we must search for stimulus-response laws."[20] This statement means that behavior is a dependent variable, and in order to control behavior, we must control the independent variable (stimuli). We cannot control one response with another response. We cannot control criminal behavior by predicting it on the basis of a pencil and paper test.

Staats and Staats discuss the therapeutic session in these terms:

> Furthermore, to the extent that the therapist relies upon the verbal statements of the patient to supply observations of the antecedent conditions which account for the patient's behavior, the therapist's principles may be built upon observations which are neither public nor repeatable. Many of the early experiences of the child are not accessible to anyone else, nor of course, could they be staged again to determine their effects upon behavior, or duplicated with someone else with other determining variables controlled as would be necessary to establish the relationship reliably . . . As Krasner points out, the therapist does not knowingly condition verbal behavior in his patients to support his theories. However, he

---

[20]Staats, Arthur W., and Carolyn K.: *Complex Human Behavior*. New York, Holt, Rinehart, and Winston, 1963, pp. 23-24.

may be conditioning verbal behavior without being aware himself of the principles involved. It might be added that because of the therapist's own training, certain of the patient's statements, such as those on the topic of familial relations, may be stimuli for the therapist's attention and approval. In common-sense terms, there may be the events which the latter considers "significant" and about which he encourages the patient to talk. In our terms, it may be said that the therapist responds to these statements of the patient in such a way that he operantly conditions the patient to speak on certain topics.[30]

They observe that even picture drawing tests, such as used in the cases of *Kent* and others cited above, are subject to such influence. "For example, Bach has observed that the human figures his patients draw in the process of psychotherapy are different from those drawn by patients under the aegis of psychotherapists of different theoretical orientations. . . Heine has also reported that patients who successfully completed therapy cite reasons for their improvement which correspond to the theoretical convictions of their therapist."[31]

Staats and Staats recommend an interaction of clinical and experimental methods:

At that point it may prove productive to return to the laboratory for the experimental principles and methods that may answer the questions raised . . . In these cases it can be seen that the growth of knowledge began with naturalistic observations, including those of the clinic, and returned to naturalistic observations, albeit ones which have been improved by stemming from experimentally established principles.[32]

EXPERIMENTAL CONTROLS

There are no experimental controls over the behavior in a clinical situation. The subject receives many stimuli, both in

---

[30] *Ibid.*, pp. 276-78.

[31] *Ibid.*, p. 279.

[32] *Ibid.*, p. 282.

and out of the therapeutic situation, and changes that occur in the behavior cannot be related to any one variable. By necessity, therapy is a multiple-variable situation, whereas the experimental environment is one designed to hold constant all variables except the independent one, which is manipulated by the experimenter. The clinician has no way of knowing what variable or variables produced the change: it could be the verbal exchange, the drug used, a change in the family situation or in the job, and so forth. It is nearly impossible to establish cause-and-effect relationships from such clinical interaction.

Cronbrach describes the two mainstreams of psychological thought as *experimental psychology* and *correlational psychology.*

> The experimentalist is concerned with controlling variables in experiments; the correlationist wallows in variables. The experimental psychologist has a goal to control behavior, and variation within treatments is proof that he has not succeeded; while the correlational psychologist (including the clinician) is interested in the already-existing variation between individuals, social groups, and species. . . While the experimentalist seeks to narrow dimensionality to controllable factors, the correlational psychologist is in love with just those variables the experimenter left home to forget.[33]

TIME SEQUENCE

The clinician operates in a *post hoc ergo propter hoc* (after this; therefore on account of it) type of situation. He observes behavior in the present, and then goes back into the past to find causes. For example, Abrahamsen states that Peter steals cars because he was orphaned as a child and cars represent symbolically his lost mother whom he is trying desperately to find.[34] Stealing cars is a response—a dependent variable. Now we wish to find out what independent variable or variables

---

[33]Cronbach, L. J.: The two disciplines of scientific psychology. *American Psychologist,* November, 1957, pp. 671-84.

[34]Abrahamsen, David: *Who are the Guilty?,* New York, Grove Press, 1952, p. 21 ff.

produced this behavior. The clinical method looks into the subject's history for this. In Peter's case, the analyst selected loss of mother; in another case it might be the father figure, or anxiety about homosexual feelings, or delinquent companions, or inadequate education, or slum area conditions that produced the response. Any past experience may be selected as the crucial variable, and there is no way of proving that it is not important. If Paul steals cars, but does have a mother, then he steals because his mother was overprotective or lax in discipline, or because of poverty, or some other such variable. Starting with a response, one can never accurately assign a stimulus to that response. Paul's case is not regarded by the clinician as a refutation of the explanation of Peter's stealing since, in Paul's case, stealing has different symbolic meaning for him.

When one searches the past for causes of behavior, it is easy to select experiences and call them causal factors, *post hoc, ergo propter hoc*. A time sequence of events does not demonstrate a cause-and-effect relationship. It must be shown that if X does not occur, then Y does not occur. This procedure is followed in the laboratory but not in the clinic. If Peter steals because he lacks a mother, it follows that, if he had a mother, he would not steal. This situation is impossible to duplicate in real life, so there is no way to test such a proposition.

> Let us turn to the argument that broken homes cause neurosis,
> and let us assume that it has been established beyond doubt
> that broken homes were more frequent in the histories of
> neurotics than in the histories of nonneurotics. To argue from
> this that the broken homes were in any way responsible for
> the subsquent neurosis would be a clear example of an an-
> cient logical fallacy, namely, that of the *post hoc, ergo propter
> hoc* argument. To the statisticians, this fallacy is known as
> arguing from correlations to causes. All that could be regarded
> as established would be that neuroses and broken homes are
> correlated; this correlation tells us nothing whatsoever about
> the cause sequence involved.[35]

[35]Eysenck, H. J.: *Uses and Abuses of Psychology*. Baltimore, Penguin Books, 1953, p. 239.

Schofield and Balian make a comparison of the background factors of schizophrenic and normal subjects[36] and concluded that, of the thirty-five variables they examined, 37 per cent failed to reveal any difference between the two groups. On five variables, the normals were more abnormal than the schizophrenics in terms of the frequency of pathological factors. These variables were poverty, invalidism, heterosexual adjustment, and ritualized orientation toward religion. In addition, there was a greater frequency of divorce in the homes of normal subjects. They concluded that "the notion that any single circumstance, deprivation, or trauma contributes uniformly and inevitably to the etiology of schizophrenia is called into serious question. . . The finding of traumatic histories in nearly a fourth of the normal subjects suggests the operation of 'suppressor' experiences or psychological processes of immunization."

One can seriously question the need for explaining these results through the concept of a "suppressor," since the only evidence of a suppressor is the absence of schizophrenic responses. Rather, it is possible and proper to state that schizophrenia may be under the control of stimuli in ways other than hypothesized in this study, and the reason the schizophrenic response appears to be "suppressed" is the assumption that these variables studied must produce schizophrenia. If one assumes, on the other hand, that these variables do not produce schizophrenia, there is no need to talk about the suppression of schizophrenic behavior.

This study does indicate quite clearly how questionable are the results based on a personal life history from which an investigator has selected events and assigned them a causal role for behavior seen in the present. Since such a procedure cannot be tested, it cannot produce *negative cases;* that is, cases disproving the proposition. There is no way in which the statement "Peter steals because he lacks a mother" can be proven false. A scientific statement is one so constructed that it can be shown

---

[36]Sarbin, Theodore (ed.): *Studies in Behavior Pathology.* New York, Holt, Rinehart, and Winston, 1961, pp. 130-41.

to be false. Statements about religion and the nature of God are not scientific; there is no way to prove the nonexistence of God or Heaven. This is a crucial difference between scientific and philosophical statements.

Since the clinician begins with the effect (the dependent variable) and then retraces to find the cause, he has no negative cases. The dependent variable (the behavior), which can be a negative case in an experimental setting, is not a negative case in a clinical setting.

One possible source of difficulty is that the scientific method has not yet been developed to the point where it can be applied to the clinical setting with any degree of sophistication. As a science of human behavior is developed, the difficulties encountered in the clinic will be more amendable to scientific analysis. Further research is needed in order to determine the variables controlling human behavior in or out of the clinic or therapy session.

LABELS FOR BEHAVIOR

Clinical nomenclature is a system for classifying and labeling behavior. Thus the term "schizophrenia" is a classification of a number of behaviors—hallucinations, delusions, catatonic depression, apathy. "Paranoia" refers to another class of behaviors —suspiciousness, envy, stubbornness, feelings of grandeur, feelings of persecution. It is a mistake, however, to regard the classification as an explanation of behavior. In the courtroom, statements are made that John Jones is a schizophrenic because he talks to God, and the reason he talks to God is because he is schizophrenic. Staats and Staats discuss this methodological error in these terms:

> It is easy, however, to fall into the trap of treating a descriptive term as a pseudo cause. In the field of abnormal psychology, investigators have been concerned with classifying and categorizing different classes of deviant behavior. These classification systems have proved useful for reasons already discussed. One such class includes the behaviors of suspicious-

ness, envy, extreme jealousy, and stubbornness, as well as delusions of persecution and/or grandeur, and so on. These types of behavior seem to appear together in many cases, and a term has been defined by these observations: paranoia. On observing this set of behaviors, the psychologist is in a position to state that the individual concerned is "paranoic," or may be labeled "paranoid." The danger enters when either he or his audience think that the undesirable behavior has been explained, *when indeed it has only been named.* The explanatory step of specifying why the individual acts as he does has not yet been taken. There is only a single set of facts: the observations of the behavior of the individual . . .

The circularity of this type of thinking is apparent when we ask the investigator, "How do you know that this person is paranoid?" and the answer is, "See how he behaves." The behavior is fallaciously *explained* in terms of the concept, and the concept is verified by the behavior.[37]

SERVICE VERSUS RESEARCH

The major disciplines concerned with behavior problems—psychiatry, clinical psychology, education, and social work—are not research oriented; they are service oriented. The conflict between service and research is apparent at every level. This does not mean a total absence of research, but it is true that research efforts are usually divorced from service activities. For example, the experimental program of a psychology department is usually operated as anentity separate from the clinic and the clinical training of therapists. Students who are in a clinical program do not take the experimental courses, and are not trained in research methodology. Often the two programs operate in antagonism to one another.

Skinner has noted that social scientists have fled from the laboratory under the guise of several types of activity: teaching statistics instead of scientific method; studying people in real-life situations; constructing mathematical models that analyze how man ought to behave; studying the inner man—his traits, per-

---

[37]Staats and Staats: *op. cit.,* pp. 14-15.

ceptions, experiences and ideas—or studying the everyday man.[38]

Skinner is here pleading for more basic research on human behavior, a goal most clinicians will share as long as clinical problems are not ignored in favor of research. Interaction of experimental and clinical psychology and psychiatry is now occurring.

SOCIAL PSYCHOLOGICAL THEORIES

The testimony given in the criminal trials cited above is based to a great extent on a Freudian interpretation of behavior, and the remarks in this chapter are in relation to the testimony given. It cannot be ignored that many psychologists and psychiatrists do not adhere to the assumptions made by those whose testimony is under discussion. It is not feasible to discuss within the limits of this report the many variations in psychiatric practice, but it might suffice to discuss briefly the social psychological theories of Erich Fromm, Karen Horney, and Harry Stack Sullivan.

Fromm's basic thesis is that man is suffering from loneliness and isolation, and in his pursuit of love and security, he attempts to escape from the freedom he has won for himself. This approach emphasized the need for love, identification, and orientation.[39]

Horney rejected the biological, instinctive aspects of Freud in favor of a sociological approach to neurotic anxiety. Interpersonal relations can result in feelings of rejection, overprotection, and a lack of confidence. Neurotic anxiety is a feeling of being helpless in a hostile world. The neurotic handles this anxiety conflict by moving toward, moving away from, or moving against people.[40]

---

[38]Skinner: *op. cit.*, p. 242 ff.

[39]Fromm, Erich: *Escape from Freedom.* New York, Rinehart, 1941; *Man for Himself.* New York, Rinehart, 1947; *The Sane Society.* New York, Rinehart, 1955.

[40]Horney, Karen: *Neurotic Personality of our Times.* New York, Norton, 1937; *New Ways in Psychoanalysis.* New York, Norton, 1939; *Our Inner Conflicts.* New York, Norton, 1945.

Harry Stack Sullivan viewed personality as a result of inter-personal relations, the ways in which a person relates to others in his psychological field. Thus Sullivan's interpersonal theory allied psychiatry very strongly with social psychology.

Neurotic anxiety is a consequence of a threat to one's security in his interpersonal relations. A person's reaction to others is governed by the need to gain love and to avoid pain. Behavior is learned in interaction with others. This approach is also a break with the more biological aspects of Freud's libido theory.

Sullivan made a major contribution to research method in his analysis of the therapeutic interview. He regarded the interview as an interpersonal process between therapist and patient. Com-munication, the verbal interaction of the parties to the thera-peutic process, is central to this view of the therapy session. The therapist becomes a participant observer.[41]

It is obvious that a social psychological approach states that behavior is learned as part of a group process, and as such has much in common with behavioral psychology which emphasizes that other people are the agents for many reinforcing (love) or aversive (punishment) consequences that attach to an indi-vidual's behavior. The close relationship between Sullivan psy-chiatry and experimental psychology can be seen in an example taken by Sullivan from Kafka of a cognitive process. A dog was urinating when it was given a bone, and from that time on the dog would lift its leg whenever he wanted food.[42] This type of conditioning of superstitious behavior has been studied by B. F. Skinner. Such behavior is created by presenting food to the organism on a schedule that bears no relationship to the organism's specific responses. In this way, any response which accidentally occurs when food is presented will now be connected with the presentation of food.

Another close relationship is to the study of verbal behavior in

---

[41]Sullivan, Harry Stack: *The Interpersonal Theory of Psychiatry*. New York, Norton, 1953; *The Psychiatric Interview*. New York, Norton, 1954.

[42]Hall, Calvin S., and Lindzey, Gardiner: *Theories of Personality*. New York, Wiley, 1957, p. 141.

the interview situation, as was discussed in this chapter. This interest in verbal behavior is in no small part due to Sullivan's analysis of the interview situation.

It should be noted that the social psychological approach to psychiatric issues has not found its way into the courtroom, since none of the testimony presented herein is based to any recognizable extent on the theories of Fromm, Horney, and Sullivan.

SUMMARY

The clinical method makes use of test results and interview data. Such data are based on indirect observation of the behavior which the therapist wishes to investigate. The clinical interaction involves the manipulation of verbal behavior, and it is not always possible to control other behavior (stealing, sex maladjustment, feelings of anxiety or rejection) through verbal behavior.

Within the therapy situation, experimental control and manipulation of variables influencing behavior is not always feasible. Behavior that is produced by one environment (the subject's past and present life history) is analyzed in terms of another environment (the therapy setting). It is difficult to analyze behavior separate from the environment that produced it.

Courtroom testimony is often subject to criticism for these reasons. The test results and interview data are now undergoing extensive research and revision, and psychologists are in disagreement as to the usefulness of some of these data. The structure of the psychiatric interview itself differs for different psychiatrists. The Fromm-Horney-Sullivan school of interpersonal relations places emphasis on social interaction in the present setting. This school of psychiatrists has not yet found its way into the courtroom, however.

Chapter 10

KENT AND JENKINS REVISITED

IN AN EARLIER chapter, the *Kent* case was presented in detail without comment. Now that the method used to diagnose Kent's schizophrenia has been discussed, it might be of value to analyze some specific features of the testimony.

The testimony given by the lay witnesses—the relatives of the accused—was verbal behavior. Like all verbal behavior, it was controlled by the stimuli and the contingencies in the situation. The testimony was presented so as to aid Kent in his insanity defense. Certain events were recalled and highlighted (hearing voices, smearing feces on himself, lack of bladder control, etc.) because they would establish a history of behavioral difficulties and would influence the jury to return a verdict of not guilty by reason of insanity. (This statement does not imply that the testimony was false, improper, or in any way unlike that presented in every criminal trial.) Here is an example of the use of present verbal behavior to reconstruct the behavioral history of a subject in the past.

The further implication is made here that certain behaviors such as hearing voices, poor bowel control, and witnessing family quarrels are somehow related to other behaviors such as housebreaking, robbery, and rape. Supposedly, by examining the history of Kent's behavior at the age of six or eight we can explain his actions at the age of sixteen.

On the basis of examinations given in the present, and responses recorded in the present, the psychologist testified as to Kent's early background and his personality structure. Thus Psychologist A testified that, from the Szondi test (responses to pictures of European psychotics), one can tell what kind of

185

person the subject is. From his drawing of a house it can be seen that the subject is withdrawing from reality, is insecure, and has disturbed sexual feelings, said the psychologist.

It is not possible to say here what early conditioning determined Kent's responses to these stimuli; but it can be stated that, in such a situation, a person's behavior can be shaped in any way desired. He could be so conditioned that, every time he was asked to draw a tree, he would draw a man or a house, or a tree with leaves, without leaves, etc.

In a drawing, dark hair, dark ties, dark shoes, and dark buckle are interpreted to indicate anxiety and sex problems. This is circular reasoning: the man draws dark ties because he is anxious; he is anxious because he draws dark ties. Thus the government could well ask why, when the House-Tree-Person test was given to fifty psychotics, the psychologists were unable to classify the pictures psychiatrically.

Psychiatrist A testified that Kent was schizophrenic. His diagnosis was based on interviews—that is, verbal behavior. Kent was never observed by this psychiatrist except in a structured clinical situation. It is generally known that one is supposed to behave a certain way in the presence of a psychiatrist. So the government could justifiably ask if it was not common knowledge among Saint Elizabeths inmates what one is supposed to say at a staff meeting. If one wishes to be diagnosed as mentally ill, one behaves accordingly. The reinforcement of such behavior is incarceration in a mental hospital instead of a prison. The legal process shapes behavior in the direction regarded by society as illness. Wartime experience indicates that some servicemen sought neuropsychiatric discharge by engaging in behavior which they understood would bring about the result.

During the testimony of Psychiatrist A, it was brought out that Kent was oriented, rational, and coherent at the time he was admitted to Saint Elizabeths, and that on the wards he acted quite normal most of the time. In psychiatric terminology, this is often referred to as "remission of symptoms;" behaviorally, it means that each response is reinforced independently of other responses. A psychotic response, such as sitting in a trance or talking to flowers, does not exclude playing basketball or talking coherently about his family or eating a meal. During the trial, Kent sat staring at the floor, apparently in a trance. Yet on the hospital wards, he was described as cooperative, friendly, and interested in sports. Certain behaviors were reinforced in the courtroom, but not on the wards. A man described by a defense psychiatrist as schizophrenic, characterized by withdrawal from reality, is likely to go into a trance and stare at the floor while in court. He will "play the role of a schizophrenic."

The observation that schizophrenics do not display schizophrenic behavior at all times and in all circumstances indicates that certain responses are reinforced at specific times. The term "schizophrenic" applies to a given class of responses labeled as schizophrenic; it does not describe the total behavioral repertoire of the individual. A good question for research is, "Why was Kent normal in some circumstances and not in others?" If the "remission of symptoms" (normal) period could be extended to all places and times, Kent would be cured of his schizophrenia. The point to be remembered is that behavior is under environmental control. A person may behave irrationally in one environment and appear quite normal in another.

The hypothetical questions presented by the government to the expert witnesses were designed to get at the issue of volition or free will. The questions asked dealt with the ability of the defendant to control his behavior. Did he know right from wrong? Did he have an irresistible impulse when he entered the apartment? Did he have a plan or a purpose? Was he acting rationally when he fled after the commission of a crime? These questions point out the fact that the right-and-wrong test (M'Naghten) is still used by the government, even in the District; they also show that free will is still a basic issue in the court. If a psychiatrist states he does not believe in free will, then he is saying all behavior is determined and no one is responsible for his behavior. This is not acceptable to the lawyer and the general public.

The quality of the examinations is always subject to attack.

The single psychiatric interview usually lasts no more than an hour, and often it is conducted in a jail or a detention home. It is difficult to arrive at any conclusions concerning behavior except after long and intensive research, lasting sometimes three or four years.

The testimony of Psychologist B indicated that he did not use the Szondi test because he did not regard it as valid. Because of the nature of the tests used, it is possible to criticize each of them in terms of validity and reliability. When Kent was asked at what temperature water boils, he answered, "190 degrees." Such a response is dependent upon one's knowledge of the physical world; it could easily be altered by telling the subject the correct answer. A correct response would be given if the right contingencies were attached. The same can be said for the answer to the question, "What is the Iliad?" It is difficult to understand why Kent scored a zero for answering "capillaries and veins" to the question, "What are blood vessels?" Certainly the answer is correct as far as general biological knowledge is concerned. The "norms" to which the psychologist referred are the responses made by a control group—in the case of the Wechsler Adult Intelligence Scale, 1,700 subjects—to each item on the test. A statistical analysis is then made of all the answers and a "correct answer" thereby determined. Such a procedure tells us how a group of subjects, selected with certain background factors, will answer a given question. It does not tell us why they respond as they do, nor why Kent responded as he did. Neither does it tell us how the answer to a test item is related to other behaviors such as schizophrenia, rape, or robbery.

The testimony of Psychologist C is—again—based on a drawing from which clinical inferences are made: for example, a rear-view picture indicates guilt feelings or withdrawal; a drawing of a female indicates hostility; the size of the ears indicates a paranoid outlook, etc. Since the testing procedure is *post hoc,* there is no way to determine whether the diagnosis is correct. If the subject so draws a picture of a female as to indicate hostility, then in the future he should act hostile. There is never an attempt, however, to find out whether such people actually do act hostile in the future, or why or under what conditions they may so behave. The hostility is observed in past behaviors; then the picture-drawing response is related *post hoc*.

It is of interest to note that Kent changed his answer to the question, "What would you do if you found a sealed, addressed, and stamped envelope?" At first he gave a correct answer. The second time, however, he answered, "Open it and find out who it belongs to. I will show you I know right from wrong." This answer is obviously incorrect, and is designed to indicate his ignorance (the right response would be not to open the letter). Kent's promise to show the psychologist he knew right from wrong, at the same time making the wrong response, could be interpreted to mean Kent had learned somehow that, in order to plead insanity, he must show he did not know right from wrong. This is what was referred to previously as "playing the role of the schizophrenic."

Psychiatrist C stated that she knew, from clinical judgment, that what Kent told her was not fantasy. This problem was explored earlier when the question was raised: Do psychotics really experience the things they talk about; or must this material be analyzed as verbal behavior and not the product of visual or auditory stimuli?

The cross-examination of Psychiatrist D by the government focused on the idea that a wish to become a basketball star is a perfectly normal response. A person may claim, verbally, that he is God or that he sees little green men, at the same time he plays basketball or writes poetry. The verbal behavior is under the control of another set of environmental conditions.

The exchange between the government attorney and Psychiatrist D brought a verbal rebuke from the judge. This witness was not responsive and was contemptuous, as were several of the psychiatrists. Judges and prosecuting attorneys are allowed to be contemptuous concerning psychiatrists. Psychiatrists and psychologists are openly ridiculed and harassed in court, and it comes as no surprise to find that many of them wish to remain as far as possible from the courtroom. For them it is an unpleasant, nonprofessional experience. There is no excuse for this since lawyers and judges could treat these witnesses with professional courtesy and still elicit certain facts for jury consideration. In his summary to the jury, the government lawyer spent most of his time belittling the expert witnesses who had testified, referring to them as people "with more degrees than a thermometer."

Psychologist D made a diagnosis after a one-hour interview with the defendant—this in the face of repeated claims that it requires a battery of examinations to make a proper diagnosis. Kent drew two pictures of the female figure: one in which the breasts were minimized; the other in which they were overemphasized. Psychologist D interpreted the minimization of the breasts as indicating poor relationships with women. The overemphasis was explained as anxiety produced when the defendant's father was announced. Could not the large breasts have indicated satisfaction with mother love, or a need for female tenderness and the milk of human kindness? We do not know why Kent drew the picture as he did; but it is obvious that he could have been conditioned to draw these figures in any way conceivable, including an abstract, symbolic representation. What history of conditioning is responsible for Kent's responses will probably never be known.

Psychiatrist G testified that Kent would avoid answering a question he did not want to answer, which is another way of saying that withdrawal is an avoidance response. In other situations, Kent would appear quite normal. This illustrates that verbal behavior can be shaped by the interview situation.

Psychiatrist G also testified that he regarded the voices Kent claimed to have heard as the voice of his conscience—a reflection of his religious training. If this psychiatrist is saying in effect that hallucinations are not to be taken as evidence of sensory processes, it would seem that he is in agreement with behavioral psychology. Also, Kent stated he talked to God, and Psychiatrist G interpreted this as evidence of religious faith. The social norms governing what is regarded as mental illness are illustrated by this reference to religious belief. Communication with

God is highly respected and revered within a church setting. Belief in supernatural powers is a routine part of Christian theology. Just this year the Catholic Church canonized a person for a miraculous cure of cancer.

JENKINS REVISITED

The *Jenkins* case involves many of the same basic methodological issues as were found in *Kent*. The indirect observation of behavior via interviews and tests, the use of intervening mental states, clinical inferences concerning behavior from verbal statements, and the searching for causes in the subject's past—all these are involved in both cases.

The important development in *Jenkins* was the change in diagnosis from mental deficiency to schizophrenia. This change was based on psychological tests, and did not involve further psychiatric interviewing by either psychiatrist. No direct observation of schizophrenic behavior was ever made or attempted. Also, this diagnosis of schizophrenia was based on an examination given in 1960 for a condition that existed in 1959.

Psychiatrist B testified that the defendant was a psychotic of an undifferentiated type. This classification does not appear in the APA Manual. The expert witness explained the undifferentiated psychosis to be the result of an impaired ego function. Here "ego function" is inserted as an intervening mental state between the environment and the behavior. The impaired ego function is recognized by the manner in which the subject interacts with others—that is, the ego function is inferred from the behavior. In turn, the behavior is explained by the concept of "ego function."

The category "undifferentiated psychosis" was described by Psychiatrist B as one for cases in which the psychiatrist does not know what is wrong. At that point he stated, ". . . but there is something wrong, and that is the point." Here, in effect, we have a diagnosis of a mental illness that is unknown and unspecified.

Psychiatrist B and Psychologist B testified that the defendant behaved as he did because he lacked adequate inner controls for coping with tensions, emotions, and frustrations. Again, "inner control" is derived from behavior: if the subject is not angry it is because he is controlling his anger, and the behavior is explained on the basis of "inner controls."

It was during the questioning of Psychologist B that the judge threw the Szondi cards on the table, thus expressing to the jury his complete lack of faith in the psychological testimony given.

Chapter 11

MENTAL DISEASE: WHAT IS IT?

SINCE the insanity plea depends upon the existence of a condition called mental disease, it is important to verify and examine the existence of such an entity. The simplest definition of mental disease is what psychiatrists decide to treat and call mental illness. This was the definition used in the *Carroll* case.

Mental disease refers to a group of behaviors that have been labeled "mental disease." As has been argued earlier in this book, the label does not explain the origin of these behaviors; the classification system is arbitrary and descriptive. The meaning of mental disease in our society has been so well captured and summarized by Thomas Szasz in his book, *The Myth of Mental Illness*, that a summary of his argument is herein presented.[1] Since Dr. Szasz is a psychiatrist, his views cannot be ignored on the ground that he does not understand psychiatry.

Szasz begins his analysis with Charcot's work on hysteria. Charcot was a neurologist and the teacher of Freud. Before Charcot's time, malingering was bad—socially unacceptable—and malingerers were punished. By calling malingering hysteria, and by labeling hysteria a disease, it was possible to make malingering respectable. Now the malingerer could be regarded as sick. He played the role of a sick person; and sick people are treated—not punished. This is *social reform, not science*. In the words of Szasz:

> Until now, under the old rules, we considered illness as a physiochemical disorder of the body which manifested itself in the form of disability. When disabled, the patient was to

---

[1]Szasz, Thomas: *The Myth of Mental Illness.* New York, Hoeber-Harper, 1961.

be rewarded in certain ways (he need not work, he could rest, and he could expect special kindnesses, etc.). When, however, he merely imitated being disabled, he was to be considered a malingerer and was to be punished. The new rules are: Persons disabled by phenomena which only look like illnesses of the body (hysteria) should also be classified as ill. We shall henceforth consider them mentally ill and treat them accordingly, i.e., by the rule applicable to persons who are bodily ill.[2]

This change in classification brought into the province of medicine the treatment of behavioral disorders (as mental disease); since physicians treat diseases, they should treat diseases of the mind. As Szasz points out, however, this classification is not without its detrimental effects to the subject-patient. This system ignores the differences between physical illness and behavioral problems, and it has led to a position whereby all behavioral problems are regarded as mental illness and subject to medical treatment.

We have thus come to regard troubles, delinquencies, divorce, homicide, addiction, and so on almost without limit as psychiatric illnesses. This is a colossal and costly mistake . . . Does it not benefit addicts, homosexuals, or so-called criminals that they are regarded as "sick"? . . . Socially deviant or obnoxious behavior may, in principle, be classified in many different ways. Placing some individuals or groups in a class of sick people may be justified by considerations of social expediency, but cannot be supported by scientific observations or logical arguments.[3]

Szasz notes that the expansion of psychiatry to include more and more behavior has been aided and abetted by lawyers, and certainly the *Durham* decision clearly exemplifies this trend, wherein we now include alcoholism, addiction, and personality disorders under the classification of mental illness. He uses the example of calling more and more colors green until finally

---

[2]*Ibid.*, p. 41.

[3]*Ibid.*, p. 43.

there is only one color—green.⁴ We are now calling more and more behavior "mental disease."

Szasz regards malingering and hysteria as nonverbal communication—an attempt on the part of the patient to tell the physician how helpless and unhappy he is. Mental illness is a way of avoiding or escaping from undesirable circumstances. In Russia, the relationship between physician and patient is public; malingering is regarded as cheating society and is therefore punished. In the United States, the relationship is private; malingering is regarded as an illness, and is treated.

The author of *The Myth of Mental Illness* regards psychiatry as more of a religion than a science. He notes that neuroses and psychoses are theories, not explanations of behavior. In mental science, a cause means volition, willing something to happen; whereas in physical science, a cause is a description of recurrent regularities. Thus, Cartesian dualism is retained—mind and body. The unsolved problem is, of course, how the mental operates on the physical. The meaning of pain (mental state) thus causes hysteria; or, as Sullivan stated, amnesia causes hysteria. This is like saying a fever causes pneumonia. A statement that "John Doe is psychotic" is not an informative sentence but a command. What it means is that Mrs. Doe wants her husband out of the way, and if he is declared psychotic, he will be placed in a hospital. If a man is declared insane, he is not held responsible for his crime. Szasz gives examples of helplessness: the schizophrenics who behave in a childlike manner (children are helpless and to be cared for); the wife who is sick and cannot work, or who develops a vaginal irritation so she is unable to have sexual intercourse with her husband. Also there is the case of Anna, who was faced with the unpleasant task of caring for her sick mother. She became hysterical and could now refuse to care for her mother without criticism from the group.

The Ganser syndrome, first observed in 1898, is a condition found among prisoners, where the individual appears stupid, is unable to answer questions intelligently, and gives absurd

⁴*Ibid.*, p. 44.

answers so that he will be found insane and not responsible. (This problem was discussed in detail in reference to the *Kent* case.)

The norms of helplessness and helping the sick are part of the Judo-Christian tradition. The psychiatrist is extending these norms when he classifies people as mentally ill. However, it is often very detrimental to the patient to be so classified. Such sick behaviors make the learning of new responses impossible and so prevent the learning of new behaviors.

The ethics of helplessness include the proposition that the helpless are inferior (women, slaves, children, mental patients). "When this role [sickness] is foisted on a person against his will, the maneuver serves the interest of those who define him as mentally ill."

Doctor Szasz concludes that psychiatrist are dealing not with illness but with social and ethical problems. As such these behavioral problems should be dealt with by behavioral experts, within the context of a science of man, and not by medicine. He recommends that the insanity plea be dropped, and that people be treated not for sickness but because they need training and re-education. He believes this would restore responsibility to the individual, where it rightfully belongs. He also recommends the use of behavioral experts in court—not only psychiatrists but psychologists and sociologists as well.

Most of the points discussed by Doctor Szasz have been mentioned in some connection in this book: the nonscientific aspect of psychiatry; the use of intervening variables as causes; the harm often done to patients, etc. We have created a situation wherein all social deviancy is viewed as mental illness and a medical problem. Mental disease is behavior that has been reinforced by society. As Doctor Szasz notes, by labeling crime as illness we can now treat rather than punish criminals. By attaching reinforcing consequences to the behavior we strengthen and encourage it. Psychiatrists can encourage "sick talk" from their patients by reinforcing such behavior. Nurses on hospital wards likewise encourage "sick" behavior; the patients are reinforced only when they behave normally. In this way normal behavior is encouraged.

There are many ways in which society encourages behavior known as mental illness. When a person claims he is God or Napoleon, he gets attention. When a child becomes hysterical, he controls the behavior of his parents. A mentally ill woman controls her husband. When a criminal is classified as mentally ill, he is treated and not punished. This shaping of behavior appeared to this writer to occur in the *Kent* case, as was noted at the time. Mental illness is a means of avoiding a painful consequence and, according to the principles of conditioning, this will increase and maintain a response. If it were not for the fact that (1) the courts have refused to accept the insanity plea in many cases, and (2) the consequences of the insanity plea are very aversive, there would be more shaping of behavior through the insanity defense.

Most obsessive-compulsive behavior can be explained by accidental conditioning. For example, a person may exclaim "Jesus!" and misfortune does not strike, so he uses the word repeatedly. Occasional misfortune will strike, as in the occurrence of shock in an unavoidable shock schedule, and such an event will reinforce the need to repeat the word. For that reason, such behavior lasts a lifetime: it is reinforced on an intermittent schedule often enough to be maintained.

A kleptomaniac is a person who has been conditioned to associate sex pleasure with stolen objects. A pyromaniac is a person who associates sex pleasure with fire. A masochist associates sex pleasure with pain. Such accidental conditioning can occur because sex pleasure can be paired with fire, pain, umbrellas, shoes, or other objects. Fetishists attach sexual significance to different stimulus objects because of their past history of conditioning.

Many of the behaviors classified as mental disease are produced by punishment and its related products—anxiety, behavior, avoidance behavior, and escape behavior. Withdrawal, characteristic of psychotic and neurotic behavior, is an avoidance or escape response. Anxiety, a basic ingredient in neurosis, is a product of punishment. Aggressive behavior under certain conditions is produced by punishment. Sociopathic behavior is maintained by an immediate reinforcement schedule, as is indicated by the inability of the sociopath to postpone gratification. The sociopath is a person who has been reinforced for manipulating other people in order to gain sex gratification, money, or power. A sociopath is under the control of such reinforcers rather than people. These illustrations exemplify the several ways in which behavioral disorders are created by a conditioning process. Such behavior is learned under given environmental circumstances.

EVALUATION OF PSYCHOTHERAPY

How effective is psychotherapy in the treatment of mental illness or criminality? A committee on the Evaluation of Psychoanalytic Therapy reported in 1950 that, since there had been no agreement on a definition of psychoanalysis, the committee was at a loss to evaluate it.[5] Raimy has defined psychotherapy as "an unidentified technique applied to unspecified problems with unpredictable outcomes. For this technique, we recommend rigorous training."[6]

Flowerman argues that if psychiatry is to become a science it must give up the nineteenth-century, Newtonian hydraulic model, and use instead those concepts which are scientifically testable. He notes that such concepts as "acting out," "castration complex," "anxiety," and "death wish" are not testable in an empirical, operational manner. He cites as an example Freud's hypothesis that if a child is seduced by an adult this experience will result in a neurosis in the child when she becomes an adult. Then Freud discovered that many of his female patients were concocting these theories about childhood seductions; they had never had these experiences.

Freud next announced that these fantasies were real, and that psychic reality causes behavior. It is not possible to test

---

[5]Flowerman, Samuel H.: Psychoanalytic theory and science. *American Journal of Psychotherapy, Vol. 8,* July, 1954, pp. 415-41.

[6]Eysenck, H. J. (ed.): *Handbook of Abnormal Psychology.* New York, Basic Books, 1961, p. 697.

this version of the hypothesis, as it would have been the earlier version. (A behaviorist would state that the therapist had shaped the verbal behavior of the subject so that eventually she would make reports of earlier childhood experiences, which he would reinforce. This is because the therapist would expect to find such experiences in adult females who are neurotic.)

Freud then resorted to a phylogenetic interpretation of *primal fantasies*, wherein the individual experiences the past events of a race—rapes and castrations that actually occurred three thousand years earlier and are being relived by a patient in the present. Seduction occurred three thousand years ago, so the hypothesis is now proven, according to Freud.[7] Such a statement is not verifiable by any standards of science.

Flowerman also uses the case of Dora to illustrate the problem of validity in psychiatry. Dora said "no" to the analyst's interpretation; therefore his interpretation was correct, because she was resisting the analyst and suppressing an experience into her unconscious.

The symbolism in Freudian psychology makes it difficult to verify the system. A woman's choking at the breakfast table was interpreted by Freud as the result of an Oedipal wish to kill her mother and have oral intercourse with her father.[8] Bachrach reported a case taken from the writings of Anna Freud about a girl "in the latency period, who had succeeded in so completely repressing her envy of her little brother's penis—an affect by which her life was entirely dominated—that even in analysis it was exceptionally difficult to detect any traces of it."[9] As Bachrach notes, the analyst expected to find penis envy in this young female because theory dictated that it be there. This is a remarkable example of the use of theory as an intervening variable to explain a response pattern.

In *Psychoanalysis as Science*, Hilgard *et al.* state:

---

[7]Flowerman: *op. cit.*, pp. 419-20.

[8]*Ibid.*, p. 430.

[9]Bachrach, A. J.: *Psychological Research*. New York, Random House, 1962, pp. 61-62.

> Anyone who tries to give an honest appraisal of psycho-
> analysis as a science must be ready to admit that, as it is
> stated, it is mostly very bad science, that the bulk of articles
> in its journals cannot be defended as research publications
> at all. If psychoanalysts are themselves to make a science
> of their knowledge they must be prepared to follow some of
> the standard rules of science.[10]

In evaluating psychotherapy, there are three problems: (1)
What baseline does one use for behavior before therapy, in order
to evaluate any changes that occur in behavior? (2) What is
therapy, or what are the variables that are manipulated during
therapy? (3) What criterion does one select for change, improvement, or cure of a behavioral problem?

Many studies of therapy have been made. As has been pointed
out, however, there is no definition of mental illness or therapy.
As Scott has written, the research definitions of mental illness
include all of the following: (a) hospitalization for a mental
illness, or in the care of a psychiatrist; (b) maladjustment or
violation of social norms; (c) psychiatric diagnostic labels;
(d) subjective feelings of happiness or unhappiness; (e) objective results of test scores; and (f) positive adaptation to
one's environment, or living up to one's potential.[11] Many such
definitions are circular, e.g., Jones is mentally ill because he
is in a hospital or in the care of a psychiatrist, and Jones is in
a hospital or in treatment because he is mentally ill.

Most studies lack real control groups, or controls over the
therapeutic process. If change does occur, it is often attributable
more to sociological variables (change in family or employment
situation) than to the therapy. Often these are *ex post facto*
studies; after the treatment is completed, an analysis is made
of a group of patients.[12] The Cambridge-Somerville study was a

---

[10]Hilgard, *et al.*: *Psychoanalysis as Science.* Stanford, Stanford University Press,
1952, p. 44; cited in Flowerman, *op. cit.*, p. 439.

[11]Scott, William: Research Definitions of Mental Health and Mental Illness,
reprinted in Sarbin, Theodore R. (ed.): *Studies in Behavior Pathology.* New
York, Holt, Rinehart, and Winston, 1961, p. 8 ff.

[12]Eysenck: *op. cit.*, p. 697 ff.

major attempt to study the effect of therapy on delinquency. The results were most discouraging: subjects from the treatment group committed 264 offenses, compared to 218 offenses for subjects not treated. Of the treatment group, 29.5 per cent had court appearances, whereas 28.3 per cent of the control group had to appear in court.[13] The conclusion drawn was that "the delinquency prevention program appears not only to be negative but paradoxical." The Gluecks discovered that, of 1,000 delinquents referred by the Juvenile Court to the Judge Baker Guidance Center, 88 per cent of them five years later had continued in their antisocial pattern. The directors of the child guidance clinic stated that the clinic approach to delinquency prevention was useless and the close of another chapter in criminology.[14]

Eysenck summarized the results of these studies as follows:

> In general, certain conclusions are possible from these data. They fail to prove that psychotherapy facilitates the recovery of neurotic patients. They show that roughly two thirds of a group of neurotic patients will recover or improve to a marked extent within about two years of the onset of their illness, whether they are treated by means of psychotherapy or not. This figure appears to be remarkably stable from one investigation to another, regardless of the type of patient treated, standard of recovery employed, or method of therapy used. These figures can hardly be called very favorable to the therapist's claims.[15]

Eysenck also quoted studies showing that soldiers who do not receive therapy return to duty at the same rate as those receiving therapy, after a neurotic breakdown. Similarly, soldiers discharged from the service for psychoneurotic reasons have the same chance for successful adjustment as the treated group.

[13]Powers, Edwin, and Witmer, Helen L.: *An Experiment in the Prevention of Delinquency.* New York, Columbia University Press, 1951.

[14]Witmer, Helen L., and Tufts, Edith: *The Effectiveness of Delinquency Prevention Programs.* Children's Bureau, Publication No. 350-1954, U. S. Department of Health, Education, and Welfare.

[15]Eysenck: *op. cit.,* pp. 712-13.

Neurotic patients treated by means of conditioning therapy based on modern learning theory improve more quickly than those in traditional therapy.[16]

> Psychoanalytic conclusions are based on unreliable data. Its data are introspection (of the analyst) and verbalized statements (of the patient) . . . In spite of repeated failures with alcoholics, neurotics, nail biters, drug addicts, and so forth, psychotherapists still claim that their procedures are the only ones applicable to the correction of this type of habit. Fortunately, there are signs that a more critical view is coming to the fore . . .[17]

Bandura summarizes the therapeutic approach to mental illness in these terms:

> The inner disturbing agents comprise a host of unconscious psychodynamic forces and psychic complexes — warded-off ego-alien impulses, oedipal, castration and inferiority complexes, ancestral unconscious and primordial images, latent instinctual tendencies, self dynamisms, counter-instinctual energies, wills and counter-wills, and ego instincts and apparatuses—somewhat akin to the hidden demonic spirits of ancient times. Thus, the prevailing theories of psychopathology essentially employ an amalgam of the medical and demonology models, which have in common the belief that the pathology and not the symptomatic manifestations must be treated. Consequently, therapeutic attention is generally focused not on the deviant behavior itself, but on the presumably influential internal processes. Indeed, direct modification of so-called symptomatic behavior is considered not only ineffective, but actually dangerous, since the removal of the symptom may lead to even more serious forms of symptom substitution.[18]

Paul Meehl has written that only 17 per cent of the clinicians interviewed by him believed that the techniques used in therapy

---

[16]*Ibid.*, pp. 719-20.

[17]Eysenck, H. J.: *Uses and Abuses of Psychology.* Baltimore, Penguin Books, 1953, p. 235, p. 219.

[18]Staats, Arthur W., and Carolyn K.: *Complex Human Behavior.* New York, Holt, Rinehart, and Winston, 1963, pp. 488-489.

were helpful or valid. He blamed this on the fact that clinicians do not do research, nor do they read the research literature.[19]

On the basis of a study of psychiatric examination of 100,000 inductees, Stouffer reported that rejections varied from 0.5 per cent at one station to 50.6 per cent at another. Those rejects classified as *psychoneurotic* varied from 2.7 per cent to 90.2 per cent, while the proportions classified as *psychopathic* varied from 0 to 81.3 per cent. "Such variations may seem almost fantastic, but of course one must remember that psychiatry is still far from an exact science. . ."[20]

In his dissent in the *Blocker* case, Judge Burger quoted several psychiatrists (Roche, Savage, Cavanagh) who have challenged the existence of mental disease, as follows:

> [Roche] I will say there is neither such a thing as "insanity" nor such a thing as "mental disease." . . . To the psychiatrist the "mental illness" can have a meaning only in the sense of what in the future will be done to or with the patient to relieve him and those around him.

> [Roche] Psychiatric nomenclature is undergoing revision and there is considered the possibility of discarding the terms "psychosis" and "neurosis" altogether in favor of a more flexible framework in keeping with our present knowledge and operational methods . . . It would be of interest to the legal profession that the term "psychopathic personality" is no longer regarded by psychiatry as meaningful, yet it will probably remain embalmed for some time to come in the statutes of several states.

> [Savage] Though widely heralded as bringing legal psychiatry more in line with modern psychology, the *Durham* rule actually does no such thing. It is a peculiar mixture of Aristotelian faculty psychology, metaphysics, mysticism, and medieval theology . . . It is indeed vague, particularly in the matter of the first test of responsibility: that of mental illness. There are very few people who could not qualify under this test.

---

[19]Meehl, Paul E.: The cognitive activity of the clinician. *The American Psychologist*, January, 1960, p. 19.

[20]Donnelly, Richard C., Goldstein, Joseph, and Schwartz, Richard D.: *Criminal Law.* New York, Free Press of Glencoe, 1962, p. 800.

[Cavanagh] It is not considered in keeping with the available facts to refer to psychosis as a disease . . . It view of this evidence, the term disease as applied to mental conditions should be dropped because it is misleading.

Judge Burger concluded, "Our 1954 opinion [*Durham*] purported to free the problem from labels, but we are now more prisoners of labels than before." [*Blocker vs. United States*, 288 F. 2d 853 (1961)]

Doctor Szasz has noted that:

> . . . disregarding even the most obvious doubt concerning exactly what the expression "mental illness" is supposed to denote, it denotes a *theory* and not a fact . . . To believe that one's own theories are facts is considered by many contemporary psychiatrists as a symptom of schizophrenia. Yet that is what the language of the *Durham* decision does. It reifies some of the shakiest and most controversial aspects of psychiatry, i.e., those pertaining to what is "mental disease" and the classification of such alleged disease, and by legal fiat seeks to transform inadequate theory into "judicial fact." . . . Is *Durham* an improvement if it merely changes the "criminal" to a "patient"?[21]

The investigators who surveyed the mental health problem in Midtown Manhattan concluded that 81.5 per cent of the sample of people were mentally diseased to some extent.[22] Using the concept of mental disease now present in the literature, it is possible to classify almost all people as mentally ill. The Joint Commission on Mental Illness and Health concluded that "there is no agreement among the experts on what constitutes mental health or mental illness; mental health means many things to many people. . ."[23]

Hollingshead and Redlich stated, "Mental illness is defined

[21]Szasz, Thomas S.: Psychiatry, ethics, and the criminal law. *Columbia Law Review, Vol. 58* (1958), pp. 182 ff.

[22]Srole, Leo, *et al.*: *Mental Health in the Metropolis: The Midtown Manhattan Study*. New York, McGraw-Hill, 1962.

[23]Gurin, Gerald, Veroff, Joseph, and Feld, Sheila: *Americans View Their Mental Health*. New York, Basic Books, 1960, p. x.

socially, that is, whatever a psychiatrist treats or is expected to treat."[24]

Hartung writes that:

> . . . one must conclude that when people use the term "mental disease," they literally do not know what they are talking about. Psychiatrists are even divided on the crucial issues as to whether there can be such an entity as mental disease.[25]

Berelson and Steiner, in their inventory of scientific findings on human behavior, concluded:

> . . . it cannot even be considered established that psychotherapy, on the average, improves a patient's chances of recovery beyond what they would be without any formal therapy whatsoever."[26]

THE FAILURE OF TALKING THERAPY

The failure of talking therapy is due to the fact that one cannot change a situation by talking about it. Altering verbal behavior does not alter other behavior such as depression, anxiety, homosexuality, alcoholism, or drug addiction. To alter behavior, we must alter the environment to which the individual responds. We cannot alter cancer by talking about it, nor can we alter behavior by talking about it.

SUMMARY

In recent years, more and more behavior has been classified as mental illness, although there is no agreement as to what is meant by mental illness. According to one recent survey, 81

---

[24]Hollingshead, A. B., and Redlich, F. C.: *Social Class and Mental Illness.* New York, Wiley, 1958, pp. 11-12.

[25]Hartung, Frank: Manhattan madness: the social movement of mental illness, *The Sociological Quarterly,* Autumn, 1963, pp. 264-65.

[26]Berelson, Bernard, and Steiner, Gary A.: *Human Behavior: An Inventory of Scientific Findings.* New York, Harcourt, Brace, and World, 1964, p. 287.

per cent of the population sampled had symptoms of mental illness.

By labeling behavior as mental illness, we have stated that behavioral problems are to be treated as a disease within a medical framework, utilizing a psychotherapeutic model. Evidence of success and validity for psychotherapy is lacking. Some investigators are now questioning basic concepts involved in the definition and treatment of mental illness.

Chapter 12

DOES MENTAL ILLNESS CAUSE CRIME?

STATISTICAL EVIDENCE

THE NEXT major problem to be tackled is whether mental illness causes criminal behavior. There are several ways to evaluate this relationship. One is by means of statistical analysis: How many criminals are mentally diseased?

The statistical picture is one of confusion because the meaning of mental disease, and of the standard diagnostic categories used, is subject to many interpretations. Healy and Bronner stated in a study that 91 per cent of the delinquents examined had deep emotional problems, compared to 13 per cent of the non-delinquents. The meaning of "emotional disturbance" is not made specific.[1] Since clinics will classify individuals in radically different ways, it is not possible to conclude that the 91 per cent is a figure maintaining any consistency from one study to another.

Guttmacher and Weihofen quote figures indicating that 1.5 per cent of the criminal population is psychotic; 2.4 per cent is mentally defective; 6.9 per cent is neurotic; and 11.2 per cent is psychopathic. East states that less than one per cent of the criminals he examined were insane, and 1.2 per cent were neurotic.[2] A study of 10,000 men in Sing Sing indicated that the prison population could be divided into the following five groups: psychotic, 1 per cent; mental defectives, 13 per cent; psycho-

---

[1] Sutherland, Edwin H.: *Principles of Criminology*. 4th ed., New York, Lippincott, 1947, p. 112.

[2] Guttmacher, M. S., and Weihofen, Henry: *Psychiatry and the Law*. New York, Norton, 1952, p. 382; East, Sir W. Norwood: *The Adolescent Criminal*. London, Churchill, 1952, pp. 233-34.

neurotic, 20 per cent; psychopathic type, 35 per cent; and dyssocial criminals, 31 per cent.[3]

Very few criminals are psychotic; and there are as many—if not more—neurotics in the general population as in the criminal group. The statistical evidence does not indicate that there is a higher rate of mental abnormality amongst criminals than in the general population. The one exception would be the category "personality disorders," and, since both criminality and personality disorders are defined as antisocial behavior, the two categories are related by definition, not by causation.

A high statistical relationship between crime and mental illness would not necessarily indicate a causal relationship. It is possible to have a large criminal population in the neurotic or psychopathic category without the specific conditions alleged to causing the criminality.

Guttmacher and Weihofen state:

> There are some radical theorists who go so far as to say that all criminals are mentally disordered, otherwise they would not engage in crimial behavior, with the attendant danger of incarceration and social stigmatization. Although an appealing brief can be written on behalf of this thesis, it is wholly impractical. It reduces the meaning of mental disorder to a point where it has no discriminating significance.[4]

After a survey of 4,000 British delinquents, W. Norwood East, a British psychiatrist, concluded:

> These figures disprove the assertion of those who declare that crime is a disease, for it is difficult to believe, and contrary to experience to find, that the number of boys who are mentally, temperamentally, or morally abnormal at the age of thirteen is nearly double the number at age nineteen, and there appear to be no facts to prove that eight men are abnormal in the above direction to one woman. No single place has yet been found for crime in any psychiatric scheme.[5]

---

[3]Coleman, James C.: *Abnormal Psychology and Modern Life*. 2nd ed., New York, Scott, Foresman, 1956, p. 349.

[4]Guttmacher and Weihofen: *op. cit.*, p. 24.

[5]East: *The Adolescent Criminal. op. cit.*, p. 300; East, Sir Norwood (ed.): *The Roots of Crime*. London, Butterworth, 1954, p. 116.

INDIVIDUAL CASE STUDIES

Another way to relate crime to mental illness is to find mental illness and criminality in the same individual. This can be done either psychodynamically (relating the criminal behavior to the subject's past), or by categorizing, in which case a label such as "schizophrenic" or "inadequate personality" is attached to the criminal. In psychiatry, the assumption is often made that man is born with criminal and antisocial instincts which, in most normal adults, are held in control by the ego. When these impulses break through the ego defense system, however, the result is criminal behavior. Inner controls are then inadequate to repress the aggressive impulses.[6]

Abrahamsen has written a great deal about psychiatry and crime. He begins by saying:

> Freud's contributions to general psychopathology were the greatest of all, particularly his idea that unconscious motivation is the drive for most of our actions. This has allowed the application of psychoanalysis to psychiatric criminology, which paved the way for a better understanding of the mind of the criminal and his act.[7]

Following are some examples of the psychodynamic interpretation of crime, found in cases discussed in psychoanalytic books:

Kleptomania (compulsive stealing) is interpreted as sex thrill, as is pyromania (compulsive setting of fires).[8]

In a case in which a man killed his pregnant girl friend, the murder is interpreted symbolically as the unconscious killing of the murderer's sister, whom he hated. In another murder case, a taxi driver killed a passenger who resembled his father, whom he hated; and in still another case, a man killed his wife who

---

[6]Watson, Andrew S.: A critique of the legal approach to crime and correction; Guttmacher, M. S.: The psychiatric approach to crime and correction, in *Law and Contemporary Problems*, Vol. 23, Autumn, 1958, pp. 611-49.

[7]Abrahamsen, David: *The Psychology of Crime*. New York, Columbia University Press, 1960, p. 12.

[8]*Ibid.*, p. 128.

symbolized the mother who had rejected him.[9]

Fred was described as a boy rejected by his mother and his teacher. He stole money as a form of revenge against both.[10] John was a middle-aged man who was convicted of embezzlement. He had bet large sums on the horses, and he borrowed company funds. John felt guilty about masturbating—a practice his parents had disapproved. To relieve his feelings of guilt, he had to find a way to be punished, which he did in his crimes.

> It may sound strange to the layman to be told that gambling unconsciously has a root in masturbation. But if we think of the fact that both are a kind of playing, it is more understandable.[11]

Another case involves a man who picked up a girl at a bar, took her to an automobile, and had sexual intercourse with her. The girl thereafter claimed rape. In an interview with Abrahamsen, the man confessed that he "liked to eat and drink." In discussing this case, Abrahamsen stated:

> The offender did not know how truly he stated his own situation when he said he liked to eat and drink. That was the crux of the whole matter. Of course drinking and eating are not manifestations that always lead to crime; only when they appear in exaggerated form and in a certain constellation with a particular personality makeup and a certain situation will a criminal act follow.[12]

In the case of Peter, an orphan who stole cars, Abrahamsen interprets this as a symbolic way of regaining the lost mother.[13] He concludes:

> I have never been able to find one single offender who did not show some mental pathology. If we had refined methods

---

[9]*Ibid.*, pp. 185-88.

[10]Abrahamsen, David: *Who Are the Guilty?* New York, Grove Press, 1952, pp. 14-15.

[11]*Ibid.*, pp. 83-85.

[12]*Ibid.*, pp. 89-90.

[13]*Ibid.*, p. 21.

of examining delinquents, we would find all of them suffer from some form of mental disorder.[14]

In another place Abrahamsen states:

It is a difficult task to predict when an emotional disturbance will give vent to itself in the form of a neurosis, a psychosis, or a psychosomatic disorder, and when it will lead to criminal behavior.[15]

In commenting on the *Durham* decision and the causation requirement of that rule, he notes that "to establish the connection between a criminal act and a person's mental condition is extremely difficult, if not impossible, in many cases."[16] In light of his previous discussions of crime and mental pathology, this is an interesting admission.

Alexander and Staub cite the case of a woman in her sixties who shot and killed her pregnant daughter-in-law. The analyst explained this in terms of penis envy and an unresolved Oedipus complex. The baby to be born was a symbolic substitute for a penis.[17] Alexander and Healy discussed the case of Richard, who was a thief because his mother loved his brother but not him. His crimes were a way of getting punished and thereby relieving guilty feelings.[18] Sigrid was a kleptomaniac who stole pocketbooks, symbolic of the vagina. She felt her genitals were inadequate; she had unconscious sex urges, and she was possessed by penis envy and an unresolved Oedipus complex.[19]

In discussing delinquency, Heilbrunn has stated:

It is accurate to decipher a car theft or burglary as the boy's hostility toward members of the family, and it is equally valid to link a girl's promiscuous behavior to a com-

---

[14]*Ibid.*, p. 125.

[15]Abrahamsen: *The Psychology of Crime. op. cit.*, p. 116.

[16]*Ibid.*, p. 250.

[17]Alexander, Franz, and Staub, Hugo: *The Criminal, the Judge, and the Public.* New York, Macmillan, 1931, pp. 190-93.

[18]Alexander, Franz, and Healy, William: *Roots of Crime.* New York, Knopf, 1935, p. 67.

[19]*Ibid.*, pp. 77-110.

bination of unresolved incestuous longings, identification with her older sister . . .[20]

CAUSATION

The term "product of" in the *Durham* decision can be interpreted to mean at least three possible relationships between mental disease and crime. (1) Products can mean that two conditions—mental disease and criminality—are observed in the same person, as, for example, are red hair and criminality, or age and criminality. (2) Product can mean that mental disease is a factor in criminality; that is, it contributed in some measure to the criminal behavior. (3) Product can mean that mental disease is the independent variable in a functional relationship in which criminal behavior is the dependent variable. This is causation in the scientific sense. The legal meaning of causation is usually of the first type. For example, a psychiatrist may testify that the defendant was schizophrenic, or obsessive-compulsive, and that the alleged crimes were a product of the mental pathology. In some instances, the second view of productivity is taken: a psychodynamic interpretation of behavior is presented in which a social case history is given, and these early life experiences are then related to criminality.

It has been pointed out several times in the course of this study that the psychiatrist who testifies as to productivity finds himself in an impossible situation, for he must testify as to an earlier mental pathology and, further, he must find a relationship between the mental pathology and an alleged criminal act. There is absolutely no way in which a scientific statement can be made concerning two variables, both of which exist in the past, and neither of which is manipulated by the investigator independently of the other.

Mental disease is a term referring to a class of behavior—hallucinations, delusion, anxieties, phobias, hysteria, antisocial acts. Crime is also behavior. Both crime and mental disease are

---

[20]Heilbrunn, G.: Psychoanalysis of yesterday, today and tomorrow. *Archives of General Psychiatry, Vol. 4*, April, 1961, p. 324.

dependent variables, and the statement "crime is a *product of mental disease*" contains no independent variable. Behavior is what we are attempting to explain, and we canont explain one class of behavior in terms of another class. Behavior cannot be used as an explanation of itself. When we relate crime to mental illness, we do not know whether the crime produced the mental illness, the mental illness produced the crime, or both were a product of a third factor.

Both mental disease and criminal behavior are produced by the past experiences of the individual in his environment. An individual can be in an environment that produces both mental disease and criminal behavior. Behavior labeled "mental illness" can coexist with behavior labeled "criminal," without the existence of a causal relationship between the two. A person can have symptoms of schizophrenia or sociopathic personality (having delusions, being aggressive, or being antisocial) while at the same time he is a criminal; just as one can eat, drink, drive a car, engage in sex relations, or engage in verbal behavior and at the same time behave criminally.

In the *Ray* case, the defendant was diagnosed as a schizophrenic because he made verbal reports about talking to God, ran out of the church during a Sunday morning service, claimed people were persecuting him, and so forth. There is no evidence that these behaviors are related to larceny and forgery. The psychiatrist at the trial testified that Ray committed these offenses to get back at society, and therefore the motive was revenge. It was also brought out that Ray spent the money for liquor. Did he steal money to buy liquor or to get revenge against society? It is possible to verify empirically that stolen money is used to buy liquor; it is not possible to verify empirically that stealing is a form of revenge.

In the *Gilleo* case, the defendant was classified as a passive-dependent personality. He had oral needs that led to his drinking, and to the crime of embezzlement. The last act of embezzlement came when Gilleo's wife became pregnant, and he could not accept the responsibility of this burden. Again it must be pointed out that money is reinforcing, in and of itself.

Normal people spend most of their adult lives working for money. Why should it be assumed that stealing represents insecurity or dependency or oral needs? Such an explanation of behavior ignores the obvious stimulus-response relationship involved. It can also be noted that embezzlement might be related to any number of personality disorders, and any given personality disorder can be related to a great number of crimes.

Watson was charged with manslaughter, for killing four people while fleeing from the police in a stolen car. He was diagnosed as a paranoiac, and his flight from the police was interpreted as a panic reaction resulting from feelings that the police were after him (which was the case). Paranoia is used as a label to explain why Watson fled from the police. Again, the consequence of fleeing from the police is avoiding arrest and punishment; it is an avoidance response. One need not be paranoid to flee from the police, nor to have an accident on the highway.

Sutherland was charged with grand larceny and embezzlement, which crimes were related to alcoholism. The psychiatrist testified that "alcoholism was a result of anxiety and the alleged criminal offenses were a result of alcoholism." If we regard anxiety as a behavioral phenomenon, and not as an intervening mental state, then it is quite possible that alcohol reduces anxiety. There is experimental evidence that such is the case: alcohol intake increases as anxiety increases. It is also possible to regard drinking as an avoidance response.

Jackson killed his employer while committing a robbery. He was diagnosed as a schizoid personality. Under the pressure of debts, Jackson committed his crimes. The solution to debt is money; the relationship of money to the behavior is obvious. The relationship of a schizoid personality to robbery and murder is not so obvious.

Sociopaths, including drug addicts and alcoholics, merit special attention in this respect. The symptom is also the diagnosis; or, to state it another way, the behavior for which the defendant is in court is also the behavior for which he is labeled "antisocial" or "sociopathic."

In the *Blocker* case, a psychiatrist said, "The two diagnoses are really one, the chronic alcoholism being the kind of socio-pathic personality disturbance that the man represented."

In the *Marocco* case, the psychiatrist stated, "His mental illness reflects itself in the profound incapacity to adjust to the moral obligations of his culture." (He is sociopathic because he is antisocial; he is antisocial because he is sociopathic.) In the *Bell* case, when asked how causation was established, the psychiatrist replied that it was

. . . a matter of definition. A man who has received a diagnosis of sociopathic personality with drug addiction, and his crime is the possession of drugs, then it seems such an obvious conclusion that I don't know how I can explain it otherwise.

In such cases, the man is regarded as mentally ill because he has committed a crime. Equating crime and mental illness is not a desirable way to consider a behavioral problem. The *Model Penal Code* of the American Law Institute states in part, "The terms 'mental disease or defect' do not include an abnormality manifested only by repeated criminal or otherwise antisocial conduct."[21]

In the *Kent* case, the issue of causation involved schizophrenia, housebreaking, robbery, and rape. The defense was never able to demonstrate that the crimes were related to his other behavorial problems—lack of bladder or bowel control, talking to God, hearing voices, preoccupation with sex, disliking females, etc. The government attorney pointed out repeatedly that the robberies and housebreaking were related to the desire for money, not to any sex drive. The fact that Kent robbed first and then raped was used as evidence that money was the motive for the crime. From a behavioral standpoint this is sound, since money is a very strong generalized reinforcer. Sex is also a powerful primary reinforcer, but a man can seek sex gratification without being mentally ill. Rape cannot be related causally to schizophrenia unless rape, in and of itself, is regarded as a symptom of mental disease (which is not the case). One

---

[21]Donnelly, Richard C., Goldstein, Joseph, and Schwartz, Richard D.: *Criminal Law.* New York, Free Press of Glencoe, 1962, p. 838, note 32.

defense psychiatrist attempted to show that robbery had a symbolic meaning—that it represented a sex need in itself. Several defense witnesses testified that Kent had a need for power, for a feeling of importance. He was also described as lacking inner controls. As has been repeatedly pointed out, these are not causal factors of behavior, but theories or intervening mental states used to label the behavior.

The first psychiatrist called by the government had been subpoenaed by the defense. This witness stated he could find no causal relationship between schizophrenia and robbery, a conclusion he made after learning that the robberies occurred before the rapes. He had no opinion on productivity as related to housebreaking and rape. The second government psychiatrist testified that Kent was not schizophrenic.

The *Kent* case has been hotly debated since its conclusion. Some psychiatrists and defense lawyers have stated that it is not logical for a jury to bring in a split verdict. In the light of the psychiatric testimony, however, the decision is quite logical. In order to establish the insanity defense under *Durham*, the jury must believe that the crime was a product of mental disease. Since causation was not present in the crimes of robbery and housebreaking (nor in the rapes, it could be added), it should not be difficult to understand the split verdict.

The diagnosis of schizophrenia in the *Jenkins* case was never related causally to the crimes. Psychiatrists testified that he had poor judgment, his disease interferred with his mental processes, he was unable to make decisions or to act on the basis of reality, he could not form meaningful relations with other people, and that he could not control his behavior. Were the housebreaking assaultive behaviors of Jenkins caused by poor judgment, lack of reality-testing, and lack of inner controls? There is no way to demonstrate that assault and rape are caused by other behaviors from which inferences concerning poor judgment or lack of inner controls can be made.

In the *Campbell* case, an emotionally unstable personality was called a mental disease which produced robbery. Such a disorder was defined as overreaction to minor stress. Campbell was described as under great emotional stress at a staff conference, where he was tense, showed anxiety in his face, and wrung his hands. It was pointed out by the government attorney that many, if not most, people exhibit these behaviors at one time or another. The vagueness and universality of the diagnostic category led a court of Appeals judge to say, in a dissenting opinion, "How would a prosecutor prove beyond a reasonable doubt that a crime of violence is unrelated to emotional instability?" If we accept the argument by the defense—that emotional instability is a mental disease—then every criminal defendant can be found "not guilty by reason of insanity."

The government pointed out that the defendant in this case was out of work and had robbed an airlines office to get money to support his family. A behavioral statement such as "Does money act as a reinforcer?" can be empirically tested. A statement such as "Does emotional instability cause robbery?" cannot be empirically tested.

The narcotics cases, especially *Horton* and *Carroll,* push the causation issue to an extreme. In the *Carroll* case, a defense psychiatrist testified that all addicts are mentally ill, with the possible exception of patients who are receiving morphine for cancer or some other painful disease. Often addiction itself is the disease. Another psychiatrist in this case stated that the presence of addiction is evidence of mental illness unless there is evidence to the contrary.

Drug addiction is usually regarded as symptomatic of a personality disorder. Anxieties, conflicts, and neuroses cause addiction, according to this theory of behavior. The APA diagnostic manual defined addiction as "symptomatic of personality disorder . . . the proper personality clasisfication is to be made as an additional diagnosis." This statement does not clarify whether addiction is the disease or a symptom of another disease. In the *Horton* case, a psychiatrist for the government stated that addiction by itself (without an additional illness) is not mental illness.

In the *Horton* case, statements were made to the effect that all addicts are mentally ill, although the four psychiatrists who testified for the defense could not agree on what kind of mental disease addiction represented. Each witness offered a different diagnosis. Horton's addiction was related to his early social and family history, and to the many difficulties he had experienced. These background factors, however, were never causally related to his addiction.

The claim that mental disease causes addiction is based on the argument that behavior causes behavior, or behavior causes itself: one dependent variable is used to explain another.

The most fascinating development throughout the trial of cases took place in the appeal of the *Horton* case, when an amicus brief for the defendant was filed by a group of prominent psychiatrists, including several nationally known figures in the field of psychiatry. At the original trial a psychiatrist for the government stated:

> The drug addict can postpone his immediate act, a temporary postponement, because drug addicts, if on drugs, have a craving, a tremendous urge, to obtain the medication that they are receiving, and I think they can postpone temporarily this desire, but they eventually have a tremendous urge and a desire to satisfy both the physiological and psychological need to obtain narcotics.

In the amicus brief the defense seized upon this point and made the following statement:

> The state of chronic narcotics addiction is characterized by an overpowering desire or need to continue taking the drug and to obtain it by any means. The testimony of the expert witnesses for the Government and the defense, in the court below, dwelt to a large degree on the *causes for addiction* and on the question of whether a *mentally normal person* may become an addict. Yet the main issue should have been *not what causes addiction,* but how the affliction itself, once established, affects its victims. The *physiological changes* which opiates create in the body produce an overpowering need for their continued use. Such *physical dependence* has been described as "the body's slavery to the continued use of opiates." Of the three phenomena which characterize addiction to opiates, the development of physical dependence is

considered of paramount importance, followed by the development of dosage tolerance and emotional dependence.

Once addiction is established the motive for using opiates is not pleasure but the avoidance of pain. . . When an addict seeks drugs he is acting under the compelling force of his physical needs. He is not a responsible agent. To hold him criminally responsible for possessing drugs under these circumstances is contrary to the traditional American precepts of justice. There is no rational basis for the differentiation of *pharmacological duress and compulsion* from other forms of duress and compulsion which have been recognized as bringing about an exemption from criminal responsibility. [*Horton vs. United States*, No. 17,261, United States Court of Appeals for the District of Columbia.] [emphasis added]

This brief stated that the trial testimony concerning addiction and mental illness was a mistake, and the issue was physiological dependency and pharmacological duress caused by the prolonged use of drugs. Addiction to opiates is characterized by extreme distress when the drugs are withdrawn. This is a most painful experience, which the addict will avoid through the continued use of drugs. Undoubtedly, a strong factor in the maintenance of addiction is withdrawal distress.

Addiction can be regarded as an avoidance response. This is good behavioral psychology. The remarkable point here, however, is that the *Horton* case was based on the insanity defense and the amicus brief clearly negates the insanity issue by claiming that behavior is based upon physiological needs. If Horton's behavior stemmed from physiological needs, then his drug addiction cannot be regarded as a personality disorder. It cannot be claimed that a physiological need for drugs produces a mental illness, and this claim was never made in the brief. Even if a biochemical condition produces a response pattern which can be classified as mental illness, the behavior can be explained as a biochemical function and not as a mental illness. Since mental illness is behavior, it cannot be used to explain behavior. If one takes the amicus brief seriously, then it must be concluded that all behavior is determined. The behavioral scientist regards all behavior as determined; but the legal system operates on the assumption that some behavior is determined and some is not. If the Court of Appeals had accepted the argument as presented in the *Horton* amicus brief, it would have negated *in toto* the assumptions of the criminal law, including the insanity plea, because it would have used *physical* in place of *mental* constructs to explain behavior, and it would have denied free will. If addiction is caused by physical dependency, then it can be argued also that eating is caused by physical dependency; and, since money can be used to buy food, stealing is caused indirectly by physical needs.

There are several aspects of the *Horton* case in particular, and of drug addiction in general, that should be noted in summary.

(1) The problem of addiction is causation, not mental disease. If taking drugs is an avoidance response, to avoid anxiety (defined behaviorally, not clinically) or to avoid withdrawal distress, then in order to decrease or eliminate addiction, one must manipulate relevant variables. This might mean placing the organism in an environment in which there is less anxiety, or by providing other responses that would avoid anxiety or withdrawal pain. However, by withdrawing drugs from the addict, we increase the deprivation level and thus increase the reinforcing value of drugs. The addict will work harder therefore to get drugs, as a hungry man will work harder to get food.

The ABA-AMA joint report used the following language:

> Even the most casual reading of psychiatric and psychological literature on drug addiction indicates that psychology and psychiatry are still far from satisfactory explanations as to why specific individuals take to drugs and why others who may be similarly exposed do not take to drugs to resolve their personal problems. Over and over again, one reads that drug addiction is an expression of personality disturbance or maladjustment. . . Not all drug addicts fit into a single psychiatric classification or diagnosis. The personality disorders of drug addicts run the gamut of the standard psychiatric nomenclature from the single anxiety states to a major psychosis. Thus all kinds of people, both normal and abnormal, become drug addicts. . .
>
> A consideration of the aforementioned classifications makes

it obvious that none of the classifications provide specific explanations for drug addiction. Large numbers of individuals fitting into the categories of psychopathic diathesis, psychopathic personality or psychoneurosis, never take drugs as a means of resolving their personality difficulties or emotional problems. One begins to see the wisdom of Doctor Wikler's observations, "The attractiveness of morphine for certain individuals seems to be related to some remarkable pharmacological properties, namely, its effectiveness in reducing anxiety as is associated with fear of pain, anger, and sex urges, without seriously impairing the sensorium or the effectiveness of internalized controls of behavior. The intensity of this attraction is enhanced greatly for such individuals as have been unable to gratify these needs by other means, be they normal, neurotic, or psychopathic. . ."[22]

(2) By calling addicts mentally ill, we are not curing their addiction; we are creating new aversive controls to be used against them. If the defense attorney had convinced the court that Horton was mentally ill, it would then follow that Horton could have been incarcerated in a mental institution for life. This is an aversive measure against addicts that few courts and legislative bodies have been willing to use. We can deal more punitively with the addict if we call him mentally ill and treat him than if we proclaim him a criminal and punish him. This problem was discussed earlier in Chapter 8 under Release Procedures.

(3) Chimpanzees have been addicted to morphine, and they will work to get it: morphine is a reinforcer for a response pattern that leads eventually to the drug.[23]

The manner in which chimpanzees are addicted is the same as any operant response. The crucial issue here, of course, is why is morphine reinforcing? Why is food reinforcing? We can assume that all behavior has a physiological basis, and that such

[22]*Drug Addiction: Crime or Disease?* Bloomington, Indiana University Press, 1961, pp. 51-58.

[23]Schuster, Charles R., and Thompson, Travis I.: Self-Administration of Morphine in Physically Dependent Rhesus Monkeys. Technical Report N. 62-29, Department of Psychology, University of Maryland, July, 1962.

behavior is maintained on a biochemical level. However, at this time we can only state that morphine is reinforcing. It alleviates anxiety, pain, and withdrawal distress; it is an avoidance response. To state that addicts are mentally diseased is neither accurate nor necessary.

(4) The major issue raised by the insanity plea is that of determinism. This is a way to sneak through the back door the deterministic argument that lawyers refuse to consider in its own right. The lawyer is caught in an unscientific view of behavior, and with it a punitive penal code; and he has dragged the insanity issues into the courtroom in order to mitigate the system.

Hall has noted many of the ways in which capital punishment has been avoided by lawyers, prosecutors, and jurors.[24] The insanity defense (which, up to the time of *Durham*, was used almost exclusively in capital cases) is another technique used by the judicial system to avoid punishing people. As Flannery has noted:

> The frequency of its use as a defense in criminal cases seems to rise almost in direct proportion to the severity of the punishment; it is seldom used in less serious felony or misdemeanor cases where there is no possibility of the death penalty or a long term of imprisonment.[25]

Instead of coming right out and tackling the problems of determinism and punishment, the law plays a game of myths: some men are insane and we are too humane to execute sick people; we must cure the sick and then execute them. This is the old ethics (discussed by Szasz) of helping the helpless—and by helpless we mean those who cannot help themselves. These people cannot control their behavior and therefore are not held responsible.

The important feature of the insanity plea is that it allows

---

[24]Hall, Jerome: *Theft, Law and Society.* 2nd ed., Indianapolis, Bobbs-Merrill, 1952, p. 141.

[25]Flannery, Thomas: Meeting the insanity defense. *Journal of Criminal Law, Criminology, and Police Science,* September-October, 1960, p. 309.

psychiatrists and psychologists to present evidence as to the determinants of behavior. Such clinical evaluation is made rather unscientifically, but it does bring to the trial materials that relate to behavior. This deterministic argument is seen in the amicus brief in the *Horton* case where physiological processes are cited as proof of causation.

Doctor Szasz has stated:

> . . . Today psychiatrists would testify (a) that the murderer suffers from schizophrenia, and (b) that schizophrenia was the "cause" of this act. . . I maintain that it is utter nonsense to ask, much less to answer, whether in the hypothetical case cited the murderer's "schizophrenia" was the cause of his criminal act. An explanation or theory can never be a cause.[26]

Doctor Roche has written:

> . . . This is the kind of alchemy that has no counterpart in the data of experience and which is responsible for much loss of communication. The idea that mental illness *causes* one to commit a crime or that it produces a crime has an unmistakable lineage from demonology. . . Can one supply an explanation for the observation that "mental illness" does not invariably produce crime; in fact it is the exception to the rule.[27]

The above quotations were cited by Judge Burger in his dissent in the *Blocker* case.

In a recent article David C. Acheson, United States Attorney for the District of Columbia, stated that under the *Durham* rule the prosecution labored under a decided handicap.[28] The blame was placed on the vagueness of the "product of" part of *Durham*. Because of it, psychiatrists refuse to testify on productivity—it is impossible to claim that a crime was *not* a product of a mental illness; and once mental disease is indicated there is a presump-

---

[26]Szasz, Thomas: Psychiatry, ethics, and criminal law. *Columbia Law Review,* Vol. 58, 1958, p. 191.

[27]Roche, Philip: Durham and the problem of communication. *Temple Law Quarterly, Vol. 29,* Spring, 1956, p. 269.

[28]Acheson, David C.: McDonald v. United States; the Durham rule redefined. *Georgetown Law Journal, Vol. 51,* Spring, 1963, p. 582 ff.

tion that the act was a product of the disease, without further evidence of a causal relationship. For these reasons, the government must prove the absence of mental disease in the defendant or face a directed verdict of not guilty by reason of insanity. [It could be noted at this time that, in the *Kent* case, for example, productivity was not inferred from the acts of robbery and housebreaking, although according to the jury mental disease did exist. It appears that Mr. Acheson has a good point, but he overstates it.]

Mr. Acheson writes that the decision in the *McDonald* case goes a long way in correcting the inequities of *Durham*. *McDonald vs. United States*, No. 16,304, United States Court of Appeals for the District of Columbia. Here the Court stated, "A mental disease or defect includes any abnormal condition of the mind which substantially affects mental or emotional processes and substantially impairs behavior controls." This definition of productivity comes close to the "capacity for control" test which the Circuit Court rejected in *Campbell vs. United States.*[29] Mr. Acheson writes:

> If the jury finds the defendant is suffering from a mental condition which impairs his control over his behavior, which is the *McDonald* standard, then it is easy to find that the *mental condition caused the behavior* involved in the criminal case.[30] [emphasis added]

The main issue is "finding a behavioral consequence of the mental condition."[31] One cannot be certain what is meant by "behavioral consequence." If it means that the mental disease must have had a behavioral manifestation, then this is repetitious since—as has been argued throughout this book—mental disease is behavior. If it means that the mental disease must affect behavioral controls, i.e., negate free will, then how does one test the proposition? Behavior is always under the control of environmental contingencies. If we talk about "inner controls,"

---

[29]*Ibid.*, p. 582.

[30]*Ibid.*, p. 587.

[31]*Ibid.*, p. 588.

how do we know whether a defendant had the capacity to control his behavior? If he responds, the behavior is controlled; if he does not respond, the behavior is also controlled. If the statement means that the mental disease must be related causally to the criminal act, then we are stating that mental disease causes crime, a problem that has already been reviewed herein.

Mr. Acheson makes two statements in his article that could be challenged. He says that the issue of productivity is not a scientific fact and is therefore not a question for the psychiatrist but for the lawyer and the jury. He further states that there must be a separation of medical and legal standards.[32] Productivity, if it means causation in a scientific sense, is a scientific fact that can be ascertained only by behavioral scientists, not by lawyers and laymen. The question "What is mental illness?" and the related question "Does mental illness cause crime?" are subject to scientific analysis. The statement "John Doe committed a crime because he was schizophrenic" is either scientifically valid or it is not. There can be only one standard at this level of anlysis. In the *McDonald* case, the court held that the medical standard and legal standard are not the same. The position is possible because the lawyer has one theory of behavior and the scientist has another. The lawyer is free to hold any view of nature he wishes (including views on cancer and space rockets); he must be willing, however, to accept the consequences of maintaining that a legal theory of behavior is superior to a scientific theory. The lawyer argues that the legal standard is an ethical not a scientific one.

SUMMARY

Neither statistical nor individual case studies support the claim that mental illness causes crime. There are several major methodological problems involved in any attempt to establish a causal relationship between crime and mental illness.

(1) The term "mental illness" has not been defined in such

---

[32]*Ibid.*, p. 583, p. 587.

a way as to be acceptable to scientists using standard scientific procedures. There is no agreement in the professional community as to the meaning of "mental illness." It is difficult therefore to relate the term "mental illness" to a criminal act.

(2) The term "mental disease" includes a great many different behaviors. The psychiatric nomenclature is a classifactory system for a group of socially undesirable behaviors. The criminal law also classifies a group of socially undesirable behaviors. The two systems—legal and medical—overlap at various places, but they are not causally related. Behavior is a dependant variable; it is caused by something else. The independent variable (cause) is located in the environment to which the organism responds. Behavior labeled criminal is caused; behavior labeled mental disease is caused, but not by each other. One dependent variable (effect) cannot cause another dependent variable (effect).

Chapter 13

ALTERNATE THEORIES OF BEHAVIOR

EXPERT testimony, as introduced into the criminal trial when the issue of insanity is raised, is medical in nature. Insanity is a mental disease, and physicians treat disease. The theory of behavior used in analyzing criminal behavior is to a great extent Freudian, as seen in the courtroom testimony herein presented. The law has relied upon psychiatry almost exclusively for testimony and evidence concerning human behavior.

The purpose of this chapter is to review two alternative theories regarding why people behave as they do, or why individuals become criminals. One theoretical framework is sociological; the other is from the laboratory work of experimental psychologists.

SOCIOLOGICAL THEORIES OF CRIMINALITY

The sociologist places more emphasis on the environment in which the individual responds than on the inner psychic processes. The individual interacting with his environment is the paradigm used. Sociological theories emphasize groups and group processes. Norms, status, roles, attitudes, self-images, and the like are concepts the sociologist stresses in his attempt to understand human behavior. Human behavior depends on the environment in which it occurs, including the societal and cultural forces present.

A statistical analysis will reveal that a large majority of criminals are young adult males who live in slum areas and who belong to minority ethnic groups. The fact that given age, sex, and minority groups who live in specified areas of the city contribute more than their share to the delinquent or criminal

population of the country is well documented by many sociological studies over the past fifty years.

The major attempt to explain this sociological phenomenon is
E. H. Sutherland's theory of differential association, which
states that criminal behavior is behavior learned in association
with criminal and anticriminal patterns.[1] This learning process
involves communication, and it includes techniques of committing the crime, motives, drives, and attitudes. Sutherland's
major contribution to American criminology, from 1920 to 1950,
was his vigorous opposition to the biological and psychoanalytic
schools of criminology. He objected to any attempt to reduce
criminological theory to a biological or Freudian model. Today,
due primarily to his work, criminality is regarded as a social
phenomenon. Sutherland also strongly opposed the notion that
criminals are mentally ill people, or that psychiatry could cure
or treat criminality.[2]

Michael Hakeem, a sociologist in the Sutherland tradition, has
written that psychiatric testimony in court is unscientific and
not founded on empirical data; that crime is now regarded as
a medical problem requiring psychiatric techniques; that crime
is often in itself regarded as the symptom of mental disease by
psychiatrists; that psychiatric categories are unreliable; that
psychiatrists disagree on diagnosis, observation, and theories;
that there is no agreement regarding the meaning of psychopathic
pesronality; that there is no evidence that mental disease causes
crime; and so forth. He concludes by saying:

> Psychiatric testimony should not be admissible in court.
> The courts have traditionally followed the principle that expert
> testimony and evidence that purport to be scientific will not
> be admissible unless their reliability and validity have been
> amply tested. . . Further, courts . . . should not consider
> psychiatrists to be experts on human behavior, motivation,
> personality, interpersonal relations, problems of social organi-
> zation, emotional reactions, crime and delinquency, and other

---

[1]Sutherland, E. H.: *Principles of Criminology.* 4th ed., New York, Lippincott,
1939, pp. 6-7.

[2]*Ibid.,* pp. 103 ff.

social problems, and similar nonmedical topics. It is astounding that judges and correctional officials continue to view psychiatrists as experts on human behavior. . .[3]

Though many readers may feel that Hakeem has been much too severe and extreme in his indictment of psychiatry, the issue raised by Hakeem remains, "Are psychiatrists experts on social problems, including sex offenses, delinquency, addiction, and sociopathic behavior, and what should the courts do in the face of sociological data and theories which are in disagreement with those put forth by psychiatrists concerning the causes of criminal behavior?"

Delinquent Subcultures

Recently several sociologists have attempted to explain the origin of delinquent norms and delinquent subcultures—a problem touched upon by Sutherland but left unexplained. Two of Sutherland's former students, Albert K. Cohen and Lloyd Ohlin, have pursued this approach to criminal behavior.[4] Cohen views delinquency in the lower class as a "reaction formation" to middle-class ideals. Because the lower-class male is unable to realize the middle-class values, he inverts the value system and devalues middle-class norms. The delinquent resorts to aggressiveness, laziness, negativism, and nonutilitarian thefts and vandalism. Alienation from the middle class, plus identification with middle-class values, leads to the development of a delinquent subculture.

Ohlin and Cloward have analyzed delinquent subcultures by

[3]Hakeem, Michael: A critique of the psychiatric approach to crime and correction. Law and Contemporary Problems, Autumn, 1958, pp. 650 ff.

[4]Cohen, Albert K.: Delinquent Boys. Free Press of Glencoe, 1915; Cloward, Richard, and Chlin, Lloyd: Delinquency and Opportunity. New York, Free Press of Glencoe, 1960; see also Bordua, David: Sociological Theories and Their Implications for Juvenile Delinquency, Children's Bureau, U. S. Department of Health, Education, and Welfare, 1960; Bloch, Herbert, and Geis, Gilbert: Man, Crime, and Society. New York, Random House, 1962, pp. 128 ff.

combining Sutherland's theory of differential association with Merton's theory of *anomie*. Merton has related Durkheim's concept of *anomie* (normlessness) to social structure by use of the means-and-ends scheme of Weber and Parsons. Merton hypothesizes that the goals or ends of society are not available to all members because the institutionalized means are not available to them. This conflict between means and ends creates deviant behavior.[5]

Ohlin and Cloward select innovation and retreatism as two patterns of adaptations found in delinquent subcultures. They emphasize the crucial role played by delinquent norms in *delinquent subcultures*. These norms support the performance of delinquent roles in a group in that these rules of conduct support antisocial behavior. Cloward and Ohlin admit that a great deal of delinquency is individualistic and is therefore not explained in terms of the concepts of delinquent norms and delinquent subcultures. Since the delinquent lacks legal means to social goals (ends), he must resort to illegal means (Merton's innovation pattern). However, differential access to illegitimate means exist within the society. The authors thereupon hypothesize the existence of three types of subculture:

(1) The criminal subculture, which develops in neighborhoods where there is an integration of illegal and conventional values. Organized crime exists in this environment, and "big shot" models exist for the young delinquents who then have access to a career in adult crimes. Such a subculture supports the learning and performance of criminal roles. Deviant behavior in such a group is utilitarian and businesslike; crimes are committed as part of a regular professional operation.

(2) The conflict subculture develops in lower-class areas without organization and unity. Such areas have a high rate of mobility and a transient population. There are no illegal means to success, and social controls are weak. The major behavioral reaction is one of violence—bopping, gang wars, etc. "Heart,"

---

[5]Martindale, Don: *The Nature and Types of Sociological Theory.* Boston, Houghton Mifflin, 1960, p. 476.

"guts," and "turf" are important concepts in the conflict subculture.

(3) The retreatist pattern also emerges in a disorganized area. The major response here is a retreat to "kicks" or "thrills," usually in the form of drugs. To become an addict one must have the right contacts with addicts. The retreatist pattern is characterized as "double failure"—failure at both legal and illegal means to success.

Glueck and Glueck

The most detailed and thorough analysis of delinquency yet made in America has been undertaken by Sheldon and Eleanor Glueck. Over the past twenty years, they have collected and analyzed data from 500 delinquents, the results of which have been published in three volumes to date.[6]

The Gluecks' methodology combines both clinical and statistical means for collecting data. They matched the 500 delinquents with 500 nondelinquents, in an effort to establish a control group. These two groups were matched for age, intellect, neighborhood, and ethnic background, on the assumption that such a technique would hold constant these several variables. This is an interesting procedure; but the basic assumption (that by using a matching technique these variables can be treated as constants) is erroneous on several points.

(1) The study attempted to exclude age, sex, ethnic background, and residence as variables in delinquent behavior, although these are significant factors and should be the object of analysis.

(2) The matching technique gives the investigator statistical control over the data—not experimental control. One cannot infer anything about the individual delinquent from a matched sample. For example, on the basis of group data the average

[6]Glueck, Sheldon, and Eleanor: *Unraveling Juvenile Delinquency*. New York, Commonwealth Fund, 1950; *Delinquents in the Making*. New York, Harper, 1952; *Physique and Delinquency*. New York, Harper, 1956; *Family Environment and Delinquency*. Boston, Houghton-Mifflin, 1962.

intelligence of delinquents is the same as for nondelinquents. On a statistical basis, one can rule out intelligence as a variable. On an individual basis, intelligence cannot be disregarded: whether John's IQ is 85 or 150 or 110 is significant in terms of the behavior he displays. If his IQ of 85 or 150 is averaged with 500 other IQ scores, the average of which is 100, we learn absolutely nothing about John or his delinquency.

The Gluecks used a combination of data-gathering techniques: somatotyping of body builds, clinical interviews, social case histories, Rorschach testing, Wechsler-Bellevue testing, and records from schools and courts. Thus the authors combined all the methodological difficulties of statistical analysis with those of clinical and test analysis.

The Gluecks concluded that delinquents differed from non-delinquents in that *physically*, they are mesomorphic; *temperamentally*, they are restless, impulsive, energetic, extroverted, aggressive, and destructive. In *attitude*, they are hostile, defiant, resentful, suspicious, stubborn, assertive, adventurous, unconventional, and nonsubmissive; *intellectually*, they are direct and concrete rather than abstract; and *socioculturally*, they have been reared in homes of little understanding, affection, stability, or moral fibre, under conditions unfavorable to the development of character and conscience.[7]

The ten most accurate predictors of delinquency listed by the Gluecks are: delinquent companions, truancy, school misbehavior, mother's discipline, supervision by mother, departure from home, gang companions, attitudes toward school, submissiveness, and father's discipline.[8] The five factors that are used as a scale to predict delinquency are:

(1) Discipline of boy by father.
(2) Supervision by mother.
(3) Affection by father.
(4) Affection by mother.
(5) Cohesiveness of family.

---

[7]Glueck and Glueck: *Delinquents in the Making. op. cit.*, p. 185.

[8]Glueck and Glueck: *Unraveling Juvenile Delinquency. op. cit.* p. 261 ff.

The Gluecks use correlational data from which to draw causal relationships. To quote from their writings:

> While recognizing the fundamental significance to the idea of cause-and-effect of *sequence in time*, we can rationally assume, further, that if such sequence occurs consistently in a definite order from the presence of a certain combination of factors to the presence of persistent delinquency, then these successive events not only *follow* but *follow from* one another. In other words, we can legitimately assume the existence of a system of cause-and-effect in the generally accepted sense. We can, moreover, test it by experiments designed to modify or eliminate the conditions that have been found to precede delinquency in one sample of cases so that we may check on whether or not the subsequent result in the new sample turns out to be delinquency or nondelinquency.[9]

The Gluecks claim to have had real success in predicting delinquent behavior.[10] In this connection, Sol Rubin has stated:

> The relatively successful prediction is not the feat it appears to be. It is not surprising that the examination of a great many possible correlations produces half a dozen which, taken together, have a rather accurate predictive result. . .[11]

If one masses hundreds of correlations, as the Gluecks have done, one will find, *by chance*, some very significant ones. By examining 1,000 bridge hands, or 1,000 horse races, one can produce some impressive statistics. Many fallacious conclusions have been reached in the past through this kind of data analysis.

A related problem lies in the Gluecks' practice of predicting future behavior on the basis of *past conditions*. The crucial

---

[9]Glueck and Glueck: *Delinquents in the Making. op. cit.,* pp. 165-66.

[10]Glueck, Sheldon, and Eleanor: *Predicting Delinquency and Crime.* Cambridge, Harvard University Press, 1959; Glueck, Eleanor: Toward improving the identification of delinquents. *Journal of Criminal Law, Criminology, and Police Science, Vol. 53,* (1962), pp. 164 ff.; Glueck, Sheldon: Ten years of unraveling juvenile delinquency: an examination of criticisms. *Journal of Criminal Law, Criminology, and Police Science, Vol. 51,* (1960), pp. 283 ff.

[11]Rubin, Sol: *Crime and Juvenile Delinquency.* New York, Ocean Publications, 1958, p. 232.

variables are those that exist *in the future*. This criticism can be made of all statistical prediction tables, including those on marital behavior and parole practices.

Despite the foregoing extensive critical analysis, it should be pointed out that the methodology used by the Gluecks in their works is standard for most sociologists and psychologists. The Gluecks are to be highly commended for maintaining and pursuing an interest in criminology research. They have been criticized for not producing a universal theory of criminal behavior, as did Sutherland. Sociological theory, however, is often used in lieu of good research. The Gluecks have made a much greater contribution to criminology through their extensive studies than had they spun some theories of behavior that were not based on research.

Statistical Analysis of Behavior

To a large extent, criminological research is based on a statistical analysis of criminals. Sutherland's theory is based on statistical evidence concerning age, sex, ethnic groups, delinquency areas, and migrations. As has been noted, the Gluecks' work is based on statistical analysis.

Statistical controls reveal correlations, not causal relationships. If A and B are related statistically, this means either that A causes B, B causes A, A and B are caused by C, or A and B are related by chance.

Correlation is not causation. For example, a statistical analysis of death will reveal that a given number of subjects in each age category will die of cancer in the coming year. Such predictions are accurate enough so that life insurance companies can write policies for large groups of individuals. An actuarial table, however, will not disclose the causes of cancer; not a single case of cancer has been detected, prevented, or cured by an actuarial table.

Statistically, cancer is related to smoking. Since this is not a cause-and-effect relationship, it is impossible to control cancer through statistical studies of the disease. People who smoke have cancer; so do people who do not smoke. People who do smoke don't have cancer, and people who don't smoke don't have cancer.

Although life insurance tables can be used to predict group characteristics, the whole point of life insurance is of course the very weakness of statistics—there can be no prediction regarding which individuals out of a group will die in any specified year. A life insurance table provides no control over the life-span of the individual, nor does it allow us to predict how long he will live. Increased longevity is the result of experimental laboratory data that enabled man to change his environment so as to reduce the death rate. Not by statistical methods but with a few cases of tuberculosis, Koch discovered the tubercle bacillus in a laboratory. Pasteur, also in his laboratory, discovered the role of microorganisms in disease. The knowledge thus gained saved the French silk industry and made possible the elimination of epidemic rabies. Pasteurization is now used to control typhoid and tuberculosis. Walter Reed, likewise experimenting with individual organisms, eventually related yellow fever to the bite of the mosquito.

Statistical controls are used in industry where it is necessary to control the quality of mass-produced items. A factory that produces 10,000 transistors a day can use a sampling technique in checking the product. In order to determine the quality of the items as a group, a test can be run on 100 transistors a day. As long as the general quality of the group is above an established level, it would be uneconomical to test each item individually. Since the transistors are sold at $2.75 each, it is cheaper to replace defective transistors, once they are sold to the consumer. The consequences of putting a defective transistor into a radio or a television set are not serious. If, however, this piece of equipment is to be part of a $50 million space capsule, the cost of replacing the transistor is not the important consideration, but in terms of space equipment and an astronaut's life, the cost of failure would be high. Under these conditions, the scientist does not use statistical controls. Before a launch into space is attempted, the item to be used specifically in the project is tested many times.

Rather than revealing or explaining variability, statistical averages will cover it up. An illustration of this problem is the old joke about the two soldiers at the front line: when one missed the target by a foot to the right, the other by a foot to the left, each shouted "Bullseye!" We would regard our space effort as less than successful if our experts were to send two astronauts to the moon, each in a separate missile, and one missed the target by 1,000 miles to the left, the other by 1,000 miles in the opposite direction. If a patient dies under the surgeon's knife because the incision was a fraction too far to the left, the next patient is not likely to survive either if the incision is too far to the right.

Reliability, or the ability to reproduce the results some time in the future, is handled statistically by a test of significance, based on the theory of a normal distribution of sampling errors or on a theory of chance.[12] If the observed results are likely to be due to chance one time out of a hundred, we say there is a high probability that the observed results were due to factors other than chance. Boring has observed that chance is a synonym for ignorance, a name for unknown variables.[13]

In respect to statistical correlations, Festinger and Katz have stated:

> The distinction between concomitant variation, dynamic interdependence, and causal relationships is a familiar one. The existence of correlation merely indicates that two or more events change together. It cannot be inferred from correlational evidence alone that variable are interrelated dynamically . . . Howland has discussed this problem, noting that the independent manipulation of two processes is often difficult, if not impossible. This is true especially when the variables involved are constructs *that must be inferred from their effects.* . . Specifically the question is: If you show movies depicting the British role in the war and find that

---

[12]Sidman, Murray: *Tactics of Scientific Research.* New York, Basic Books, 1961, p. 43.

[13]*Ibid.,* p. 45.

both motivation to go overseas and attitude toward the British change, is there any way to find out whether change in attitude has been responsible for change in motivation. Since correlation between variables is the only evidence, it is not clear whether motivation has been changed by the movies directly or by attitude change, or is it clear whether attitude affects motivation or motivation affects attitude, or whether they interact. To establish such relationships, control of the independent variable is necessary, and in this case impossible. In the absence of such controls, we can only surmise about the nature of the relationship. The problem is ubiquitous and familiar, but often overlooked.[14]

These authors also comment on the "ex post facto" design [used by the Gluecks]:

Greenwood defines the "ex post facto" experiment as one in which "we work backward by controlling after the stimulus has already operated, thereby reconstructing what might have been an experimental situation." This is to say that the stimulus is not controlled by the investigator. The nature of the experimental manipulations the investigator can make are strictly limited.[15]

Commenting on research of this sort, Eysenck noted that the following logic prevailed: Parents (P) practice early weaning (X); children (F) are aggressive (Y): therefore, early weaning causes aggression (X - - - Y). This argument has no logical validity, states Eysenck, because other alternative hypotheses are possible. For example, aggressive parents wean children early and children inherit aggression via the genes from parents. Or, aggressive children bite the mother's breast; the mother then weans them early. Eysenck states:

The facts offered are correlational. A certain type of behavior on the part of the parent is shown to be correlated with a certain type of behavior on the part of the child. This is

---

[14]Festinger, Leon, and Katz, Daniel: *Research Methods in the Behavioral Sciences.* New York, Dryden Press, 1953, pp. 278-79.

[15]*Ibid.,* p. 317.

almost universally interpreted as proof of causation by modern psychologists . . . but once it is realized we are simply dealing with correlation and nothing else, this assumption is immediately seen to be untenable. It is one of the first lessons a student of statistics learns, that *correlation does not imply direct causation* and must not under any circumstances be so interpreted *without additional experimental proof.*[16]

The following comments can be made concerning sociological research into the causes of crime:

(1) The relationships drawn are correlational, not causal. Statistical anlysis does not allow the investigator to specify the independent and the dependent variables. Sutherland's theory states that association with criminals causes criminality. It has been argued, however, that one can first become a criminal and then associate with other criminals. There are people who do associate with criminals yet who are not themselves engaged in crime; there are those who are criminals but have not associated with other criminals. There are also Negroes, young males, and people living in slum areas who do not commit crimes. Being a Negro or a young male, or living in a slum area, does not cause crime, although statistically these variables are important in the process of developing criminal behavior. Statistics on crime are usually expressed in the form of "some of X is correlated with crime"—not "X causes crime."

The Gluecks' analysis also fails to specify the dependent and independent variables. For example, mesomorphic build is associated with delinquency because more delinquents than nondelinquents are classified as mesomorphs. Does mesomorphy cause delinquency, or vice versa? The authors assume that body structure is the independent variable, but they do not design the study accordingly. They state that lack of affection on the part of a father causes a boy's delinquency. Is this true, or—using the same set of facts—can it be that the boy's delinquency causes the man to have less affection for his son? They state that

---

[16]Eysenck, H. J. (ed.): *Handbook of Abnormal Psychology.* New York, Basic Books, 1961, p. 8.

severe discipline by the father promotes delinquency. Or does the boy's delinquent behavior cause a father to be severe with his son?

(2) Inferences are drawn from the behavior observed; then these inferences are used as explanation of criminal behavior. From criminal behavior, Sutherland infers a criminal attitude or motive; he then uses attitudes to explain criminal behavior. From lower-class behavior, Cohen infers a reaction-formation to middle-class values. Cloward and Ohlin infer "goals," "means," and "norms" from delinquent behavior. The Gluecks infer affection and cohesiveness from the behavior they study.

(3) The procedures used afford the investigator no control over behavior. If an individual has a criminal attitude or associates with criminals, what can be done to bring about a change? How does an investigator establish good discipline or affection in a home? What makes for cohesiveness in a family, or inspires a father to love his son? How are acceptable behaviors developed in delinquents who lack opportunities, need more education or a better job? How do we keep them from dropping out of school or from failing academically? What motivates them to take advantage of opportunities made available to them by the community?

Without control, it is possible to predict the weather, a solar eclipse, the rates of death or cancer, etc. Control implies prediction; prediction does not imply control. Prediction without control provides no control over the future occurrence of these events: we do not change the weather, or the incidence of death or cancer, by prediction alone. Only if we control the relevant variables involved can we alter or control the future occurrence of events. Only by knowing the conditions that produce it can we control delinquency—not by predicting it.

Take, for example, the serious problem of the young driver. As reflected in the accident rate and in insurance tables, statistically the driver between ages sixteen and twenty-five is a high risk. Now we wish to engage in a campaign to reduce automobile accidents involving young drivers. The statistical picture reveals something of the magnitude and direction of our problem; it does not tell us how to reduce automobile accidents. What behaviors should be changed: Drinking? Knowledge of auto mechanics? Familiarity with traffic laws? Practice in driving a car? Respect for life and property? Awareness of the dangers involved in driving? How does the fact that teen-age drivers are involved in automobile accidents lead to knowledge about the relevant behavior? What can be done to change this behavior—that is, gain control over it? Not by averaging the driving habits of young people and arriving at some statistical answer. If we aim to reduce the accident rate, *each driver* must be dealt with in terms of his *specific behavior*. The traffic authorities do not average the scores on driving tests and eye examinations when they grant a driving license. If one driver has 20/20 vision and another has 200/20, we differentiate in terms of driving behavior. It is possible that altering the automobile and/or the highways would be simpler and more effective than altering the behavior of drivers in reducing accidents. This should be a consideration in any such program. The same can be said for dealing with delinquency.

(4) The sociologist often does not manipulate the variables with which he is concerned. He relies on naturalistic observation to study delinquent gangs, or he may use statistical measures of relationships. In neither case does he manipulate the independent variable in order to measure its effect on the dependent variable.

If he does manipulate the environment by the use of counseling, special educational programs, community service programs, gang work, or employment opportunities, he uses a statistical measure of change which does not reveal the independent and the dependent variables. He uses an experimental group and a control group, and measures changes in group performance. This means that many variables are left uncontrolled or unknown. If a hundred delinquents receive counseling or vocational training and sixty of them achieve some measure of improvement, the experimenter still does not know what actually happened to the sixty who changed or to the forty who did not. Because of differences in past conditioning and in present environment, each individual in the experimental group will respond differently to treatment. These crucial differences are hidden by the type of analysis undertaken. The dependent variable is the behavior of a hundred delinquents; the independent variable is the counseling or vocational training. The behavior, however, is under the control of variables other than training or therapy and, as a result, the behavior of each individual differs in many respects. The reaction of each subject to environmental change is never observed or measured. Since each individual reacts differently, the behavior must be analyzed in terms of the environment that produced it. This is not possible with a statistical design.

(5) Many sociological studies of behavior are made by indirect observation, based on interviews, questionnaires, and test scores. As Goldiamond and others have indicated,[17] these methods are no substitute for direct observation. The responses to interviews can be changed by altering the consequences attached to the answers given. A questionnaire concerning race prejudice will not reveal how a person will respond to a Negro in any given situation. Responses to questionnaires may be independent of the behavior under study. The answers given by a delinquent to a sociologist or a probation officer may not be related to the subject's actual behavior. Verbal behavior is under the control of environmental contingencies, as is delinquent behavior.

(6) The sociologist frequently uses an *ex post facto* design, as did the Gluecks in their studies. The sociologist studies the subject after he has become delinquent, then tries to relate the delinquency to poverty, slum areas, race, religion, home life, employment and medical records, and body build. Starting with the dependent variable (behavior), he looks for the independent variable in the environment. He does not know which if any of these environmental conditions is crucial, or in what direction. An investigator should never start his analysis with

---

[17]Azrin, N. H., Holz, W., and Goldiamond, I.: Response bias in questionnaire reports. *Journal of Consulting Psychology, Vol. 25* (1951), No. 4, pp. 324-26.

the dependent variable, yet in studies of delinquency, this is a common practice.

EXPERIMENTAL ANALYSIS OF BEHAVIOR

The second theory of behavior now available to behavioral scientists is based on experimental laboratory procedures. It is the youngest of the theories presented herein.

The experimental analysis of behavior is concerned with learning processes and learning theory. It emphasizes the interaction of organism and environment, the responses or behavior of the organism in a given stimulus situation or environment. The experimentalist deals with emotion, motivation, intent, will, desire, and need, in terms of their behavioral dimensions.

Experimental psychology also emphasizes the importance of environmental contingencies in behavioral control rather than psychic control over behavior. Behavior is controlled by environmental contingencies or stimuli. Stimuli that are present before a response occurs, and which control the response, are known as discriminative stimuli. This process is called stimulus control. Those stimuli which occur after the response and which are contingent on the response are known as reinforcing or aversive stimuli. A reinforcing stimulus strengthens or reinforces a response; an aversive stimulus weakens a response. The latter process is popularly referred to as punishment. Modern learning theory states that behavior is controlled by reward and punishment.

Many related processes are involved in operant conditioning: shaping of behavior, chaining of responses, satiation and variation, secondary reinforcement, generalization, avoidance and escape behavior, anxiety, self control, and schedules of reinforcement. Details concerning these procedures and methods of modern learning theory will be omitted here since they are available to the interested reader in textbooks and published articles.[18]

---

[18]For discussions of operant techniques, see Sidman: *op. cit.*, pp. 393 ff.;
Footnote continued on page 243

Experimental Method

The experimental anlysis of behavior is based on laboratory procedures. The formula used in $Y=f(X)$ under C. Y is the dependent variable; X is the independent variable; f is the functional relationship between X and Y; and C is the condition under which f occurs. If X is altered, then Y will be altered since the value of Y is dependent on X. If we know the value of X, we can state the value of Y; knowing the value of Y will tell us nothing about the value of X. In psychology, the response of the organism is Y, the dependent variable; and the environment (stimulus) is the independent variable: $R=f(S)$ under C.[19]

The goals of scientific procedure are prediction and control. Given X, we can predict Y. If the value of Y is not what was predicted, we then have a *negative* case and we must revise our procedures. Thus we make statements about behavior that can be proven or disproven.

The second goal of science is control. If we wish Y, we must then establish X under C. Prediction and control are thus identical procedures in science. If we have control over events, we can produce the event we wish, and we can reverse the procedure to eliminate the events by changing the value of X.

The experimental method differs from the clinical or statistical in several significant ways:

(1) The experimental method begins with the organism in its present state—as it is now behaving. The past conditioning of the organism is not known, and it can only be roughly—and

Ferster, C. B.: Essentials of a Science of Human Behavior in Nurnberger, John, Ferster, C. B., and Brady, John B., *An Introduction to a Science of Human Behavior.* New York, Appleton-Century-Crofts, 1963, pp. 199-345; Sidman, Murray: Operant Techniques in *Experimental Foundations of Clinical Psychology,* New York, Basic Books, 1962, pp. 17-210; Hill, Winfred F.: *Learning.* San Francisco, Chandler, 1963; Lawson, Reed: *Learning and Behavior.* New York, Macmillan, 1960.

[19]Goldiamond, Israel: *Dynamic Variables in the Maintenance and Controlled Alternation of Behavior.* Unpublished manuscript.

often erroneously—approximated by asking questions or giving examinations. Suppose, for example, a pigeon arrives at a laboratory in Arizona from a supply house in New Jersey. Every time an attendant in a red coat and white pants enters the room, the bird turns around three times, then pecks for food. Is this response due to the red coat, the white pants, the male figure, the buzzer on the door, the light turned on by the attendant—or what? One can assume that this pigeon was conditioned to associate food with some stimulus in his environment. But which one?

When Jane Doe, in a therapist's office, states that she is anxious, unhappy, and depressed, what is she saying? What does she mean by "depressed" or "anxious?" She is communicating with the therapist, but what stimulus makes her feel anxious or depressed? Case histories, the major technique of the clinician or the social worker, give clues about what to look for, but they do not indicate cause-and-effect relationships.

A response is always in relation to a stimulus situation existing in the present, although it may be based on past experiences. When a person eats a hamburger, it is because of the present situation—his food-deprivation level, the availability of the hamburger, etc. He has been conditioned in the past to eating in general, and to hamburgers specifically, but his present response can be understood only in terms of present conditions, not past conditions. A person can be conditioned to eating hamburgers, yet in the present situation, he may not eat because he is satiated or ill; or he may eat fish (he is a Catholic and it is Friday); or he may eat steak (he is dining with the boss or with his favorite lady-friend). The analytic approach tends to view behavior as determined by past conditioning, such as early childhood experiences. The behaviorist is also interested in past conditioning, but he is more interested in the stimulus situation to which the organism responds, and this situation exists only in the present.

(2) The experimenter starts with the organism responding in a given situation, which is called the *baseline;* then he manipu-

lates some aspect of the environment so as to observe the change in the response rate. The record indicates whether the response rate is increasing or decreasing in relation to a change in the environment. Each aspect of the situation is carefully controlled so that any change in response rate can be related to the one variable manipulated by the investigator. The weight of the organism, the type and amount of food used, the lights on or off, etc., are held constant.

This approach is unique in that the experimenter *manipulates the situation,* then under carefully controlled conditions, he observes the changes that occur. The clinical method and the statistical method are static in their anlysis; that is, the investigator studies by *naturalistic observation* an on-going process such as a gang war, a family dispute, a patient in a therapeutic setting, or a small group solving a problem in an observation room. Naturalistic observation is valuable as a source of data for further analysis, but *experimental analysis* is needed to establish cause-and-effect relationships.

(3) Experimental anlysis of behavior is single-organism research, not group research. Group data require statistical controls, and these do not give the experimenter control over the dependent variable. Statistical controls group together variations in individual subjects, thus hiding a major source of variation in results. For this reason, predictions are stated in terms of group performance rather than of individual behavior.

Sidman, an experimental psychologist, has noted the problems involved in group data:

> Whenever we are forced to use groups of subjects or large behavior samples from an individual subject in order to smooth the data, we are demonstrating a lack of experimental control over our subject matter.
>
> Group averages are contaminated by both intra- and inter-subject variability. Individual averages are free from the latter. Group data may often describe a process or a functional relation that has no validity for any individual. The validity of a behavioral description obtained from group data

will be related inversely to the amount of intersubject variability. But, most important of all, we often have no way of
evaluating whether or not a given example of group data
actually does provide a true picture of individual behavioral
processes.[20]

In an experimental situation reliability is demonstrated by
either (1) repeating the experiment and getting the same results,
or (2) reversing the results by removing the variable that
produced them. If X produces Y, a repetition of the experiment
next week should again show that X produces Y. If X produces
Y, and X is removed, then Y should change. Goldiamond
reduced or eliminated stuttering in subjects by the use of
operant techniques; he also produced stuttering in normal subjects by such techniques.[21] The ability to produce a response
and to reverse it is the ultimate in reliability.

(4) Experimental analysis relates changes in behavior to
changes in the environment—that is, observable events. These
include changes in the subject's physiological condition (such as
may be induced by drugs, electric stimulation, or lack of sleep)
as well as changes in his external environment. Inferential or
hypothetical concepts are eliminated or kept at a minimum.

> The basic notion of the school of psychological thought called
> behaviorism is that the raw data of psychological research
> must be the observable actions of an organism (which are
> called responses) that occur in the presence of observable
> environmental changes (which are called stimuli). . . My
> usage of stimulus-response terminology is intended for one
> purpose only—to emphasize that the facts of science must refer
> to observable events.[22]

(5) Experimental anlysis is concerned with the direct observation of behavior. Questionnaires and interviews are used as
examples of verbal or test behavior, not as samples of the

---

[20]Sidman, Murray: *op. cit.*, p. 16, p. 274.

[21]Goldiamond, Israel: Maintenance of ongoing fluent speech and stuttering.
Journal of Mathetics, January, 1962.

[22]Lawson, Reed: *Learning and Behavior*. New York, Macmillan, 1960, pp. 8-11.

behavior discussed during an interview session.

(6) Experimental analysis yields a high degree of control over behavior. Once a functional relationship is established between a response and the variables controlling it, the response can be controlled by systematically altering these variables. It is possible to predict and control behavior when the variables are known and the conditions are under experimental control. Some examples of the application of conditioning procedures will be given in the next section.

Application of Conditioning Procedures

Such procedures as mentioned above have been used successfully in psychopharmacology to study the effect of drugs on behavior. Drug manufacturers use operant techniques as a routine aspect of testing programs.[23] Several applications in the area of emotional problems have been made. Hysterical blindness has been treated in this manner.[24] A patient was placed in an experimental situation in which a visual stimulus was discriminative stimulus for reinforcement. Since the subject was under stimulus control, the experimenter could state that he had vision, though the patient behaved in other situations as if he were blind and reported verbally that he could not see. Speech defects such as stuttering have been produced and eliminated in experiments by Goldiamond and others.[25] Verbal behavior was restored in a psychotic patient who had been mute for nineteen years.[26] This was accomplished by holding up a piece

[23]Dews, P. B.: Psychopharmacology in Bachrach, A. J. (ed.): *Experimental Foundations of Clinical Psychology.* New York, Basic Books, 1962, pp. 423-41.

[24]Brady, J. P., and Lind, D. L.: Experimental analysis of hysterical blindness. *Archives of General Psychiatry*, April, 1961, pp. 331 ff.

[25]Flanagan, Bruce, Goldiamond, Israel, and Azrin, Nathan: Operant stuttering: the control of stuttering through response contingent consequences. *Journal of Experimental Analysis of Behavior, Vol. 1*, April, 1958, pp. 173-77.

[26]Isaacs, Wayne, Thomas, James, and Goldiamond, Israel: Application of operant conditioning to reinstate verbal behavior in psychotics. *Journal of Speech and Hearing Disorders*, February, 1960, pp. 8-12.

of chewing gum and, through the technique of successive approximation, reinforcing any movement of the lips until finally the patient spoke the word "gum." In the area of psychosomatic medicine, stomach ulcers have been produced by operant techniques.[27]

At the Metropolitan State Hospital in Massachusetts, O. R. Lindsley has been studying psychotic behavior by the use of operant techniques.[28] Bijou has used such techniques to develop normal behaviors in a group of retarded children.[29] Ferster has analyzed the behavior of autistic children in this manner, and by reinforcing normal behavior in these children he was able to obtain normal responses from them.[30]

In a special ward at Anna State Hospital, Anna, Illinois, operant techniques have been successfully used for the treatment of mental patients.[31] Bachrach has reported the successful treatment of a case of anorexia (voluntary starvation through the loss of appetite). In order to get the patient to eat, Bachrach made other reinforcers (talking to people, reading, listening to a radio) contingent upon eating behavior.[32] Ferster has used conditioning principles in the treatment of obesity in a group

---

[27]Brady, J. V.: Ulcers in executive monkeys. *Scientific American*, October, 1958.

[28]Lindsley, O. R.: Characteristics of the behavior of chronic psychotics as revealed by free operant conditioning methods. *Disease of the Nervous System, Vol. 21*; Lindsley, O. R.: Operant conditioning methods applied to research in chronic schizophrenia. *Psychiatric Research Reports, Vol. 5.*

[29]Bijou, S. W., and Sturgess, P. T.: Positive reinforcers for experimental studies with children. *Child Development, Vol. 30*, 1959, pp. 151-70; Orlando, R., Bijou, S. W.: Single and multiple schedules of reinforcement in developmentally retarded children. *Journal of the Experimental Analysis of Behavior, Vol. 3*, 1960, pp. 339-48.

[30]Ferster, C. B.: Positive Reinforcement and Behavioral Deficits of Autistic Children. *Child Development, Vol. 32*, 1961, pp. 437-56.

[31]Ayllon, Teodoro, and Michael, Jack: The psychiatric nurse as a behavorial engineer. *Journal of the Experimental Analysis of Behavior, Vol. 2*, October, 1959, pp. 323-33.

[32]Personal correspondence with A. J. Bachrach, Chairman, Department of Psychology, Arizona State University.

of nurses.[33] Enos and Ham, the astrochimps, were trained by this method to operate space capsules so as to control the flight and relay information from outer space to scientists on earth. Findley, in the ECHO project (Environmental Control of a Human Organism), has worked with a human subject in an environment wherein every response was carefully controlled and recorded. The subject was isolated in the test chamber for over five months.[34]

In the field of education, programmed instructional materials have been developed whereby a student is immediately reinforced for a correct answer, and he is not allowed to proceed to the next stage until he has mastered the earlier materials.[35] Under our present educational system, we pass students from one grade level to another even though they lack the prerequisite skills. Students enter high school or college without adequate mastery of English, history, science, or mathematics. For this reason, they are unable to do satisfactory academic work, become discouraged, and drop out of school.

Another basic assumption of our educational system is that if a student fails, it is his own fault and not the fault of the school. He is said to lack ability or motivation. One is reminded of the freshman girl who complained to her psychology laboratory instructor that she had a feeble-minded rat that could not learn. When it was given to another student, the animal suddenly developed a normal IQ and learned the proper responses. A great majority of students can perform adequately if given the proper environment. Our system of education does not provide strong reinforcers for good academic achievement. Scholastic grades are weak reinforcers because they have little prestige or economic value in our society. The student who works hard is regarded as a bookworm, a brain, a maladjusted personality. Our culture reinforces social conformity, mediocrity, and popularity.

---

[33]Ferster, C. B., Nurnberger, J. I., and Levitt, E. B.: The control of eating. *Journal of Mathetics, Vol. 1,* pp. 1-18.

[34]Long voyage in inner space. *Life,* May 17, 1963, p. 119.

[35]Skinner, B. F.: Teaching machines. *Scientific American,* November, 1961.

A girl is rewarded for being a popular date or a campus queen; a boy is rewarded for being a football star or for driving a sportscar. In such an environment, it is a wonder we ever produce scientists, engineers, physicians, educators, or social workers. We do not provide reinforcement for dedication to a career in teaching or research. We pay baseball stars $80,000 for hitting a ball over a fence; we pay our teachers and professors $5,000 to $8,000 a year for passing on to our young our heritage of knowledge and art. We ask our students to prepare themselves for useful careers in the service of humanity, and then they observe that one can make more money in one evening singing rock-and-roll than can be earned in a year as a nurse, a teacher, or a social worker.

By using operant techniques, Moore has taught three-year-olds to read by means of a typewriter that is used as a teaching-machine.[36] Slack and Schwitzgebel used reinforcement principles in order to get delinquents into psychotherapy by paying them to talk to the experimenter.[37] Jessor has recently recommended that learning principles be applied to the problem of delinquency.[38]

One of the most fascinating developments has been that involving electrical stimulation of the brain. Olds and Milner discovered quite by accident that if an electrode is implanted in a given area of the brain, a rat will press a lever at a high rate whereby part of the brain receives electric stimulation.[39] This is now known as the "pleasure center" of the brain. It is now possible to map the various functions of the brain by use of electric stimulation, which has been found to produce many

[36]Pines, Maya: How three-year-olds teach themselves to read—and love it. *Harpers,* May, 1963.

[37]Kids in trouble. *Look,* December 4, 1962; Slack, C. W.: Experimenter-Subject psychotherapy. *Mental Hygiene, Vol. 44,* 1960, pp. 238-56.

[38]Jessor, Richard: A behavioral science view of the correctional officer. *Federal Probation,* March, 1963, pp. 6-10.

[39]Olds, J., and Milner, P.: Positive reinforcement produced by electrical stimulation of septol area and other regions of rat brain. *Journal of Comp. Physiological Psychiatry, Vol. 47,* 1954, pp. 419-27.

of the responses produced by external stimuli. For example, depending on what area of the brain is involved, people will hear or see things, or recall past events, or experience the pleasure of eating a good meal. Motor activity, such as the movement of an arm or a leg, can be directed by brain stimulation. Emotions such as fear or rage can thus be produced; likewise, eating behavior can be increased or decreased, depending on where the stimulation is delivered.

Abnormal or pathological behavior has been produced by use of conditioning techniques. In a paper entitled *The Normal Sources of Pathological Behavior,*[40] Sidman discusses one of the conditioning processes by which pathological behavior is produced. In this experiment, a monkey used a lever-press as an avoidance response to shock. A clicker was a signal for an unavoidable shock. The response rate goes up for both the clicker period and the silent period, since the avoidance response is not controlled by the clicker. When the avoidable shocks are removed, lever-pressing occurs only during the clicker period, but the rate increases as the time approaches for the shock. This is the opposite of *conditioned suppression,* and Sidman labels it *conditioned facilitation.* The response has no adaptive value, yet it increases. At one time, this response postponed an avoidable shock. The contingencies changed but the response continued. The monkey had no way of learning that his response did not postpone the shock. The lever-press continued because the shock reinforced the lever-press—the response which, in the past, postponed the shock.

In another experiment, a chain-pulling response was reinforced by food; a lever-press by the postponement of a shock. The chain-pulling response continued at a high rate even though the food chamber was disconnected. It decreased when *shock* was disconnected, indicating that chain-pulling was maintained by shock, although there was no relationship between the response and the contingency.

---

[40]Sidman, Murray: The normal sources of pathological behavior. *Science,* July 8, 1960.

This type of conditioning is referred to as accidental contingencies or superstitious behavior.[41] A person who calls "seven-eleven" when he throws dice is occasionally reinforced by a seven or an eleven, although these contingencies bear no relationship to the verbal behavior.

Behavioral Scientists in Court

Expert testimony concerning mental disease and crime as introduced in our courtrooms is of one kind. A majority of these experts have been physicians, usually psychiatrists. The assumption is made that physicians are experts on behavior, crime, and social problems. The logic is simple: crime is a disease, criminals are sick, physicians treat disease; therefore, physicians treat crime.[42] In this way, deviant behavior has come to be classified as illness to be treated by medical means. Alcoholism, drug addiction, and sociopathic behavior are now regarded as illnesses. Such a view of behavior ignores the social factors responsible for criminal behavior.

The only theory of behavior studied by lawyers is the Freudian theory. The *Durham* decision reflects the influence of Freudian psychology upon the law. The *Harvard University Law School Bulletin* describes the course in law and psychiatry as "a critical survey of one particular theory of behavior, psychoanalytic." Many law schools offer courses in law and psychiatry, while paying too little attention to sociology and experimental psychology. The most successful treatment methods have come from learning therapy, based upon modern sociology and psychology.

In the discussion of the *Jenkins* case, it was noted in the language of the Court of Appeals that a Ph.D. in clinical psychology was required if a psychologist was to qualify to

---

41Skinner, B. F.: *Cumulative Record.* New York, Appleton-Century-Crofts, Inc., 1959, pp. 404 ff.

42Szasz, Thomas S.: *The Myth of Mental Illness.* New York, Hoeber-Harper, 1961; *Law, Liberty and Psychiatry.* New York, Macmillan, 1963.

testify about behavioral disorders. In the language of the dissenting opinion:

> It is sheer folly to attribute to a lay psychologist, who admittedly is not a doctor of medicine, such presumptive medical knowledge and diagnostic acuity as to entitle him to wear in a criminal courtroom the badge of an expert witness with respect to the existence of the elusive *medical* condition known as mental disease or defect. [Jenkins vs. United States, No. 16,306, United States Court of Appeals for the District of Columbia.]

Judges and lawyers are most reluctant to accept psychologists as expert witnesses.[43] Professor David Louisell has noted the dearth of materials and the paucity of cases involving the psychologist as an expert witness,[44] despite the fact that Wigmore wrote, "Judicial practice is entitled and bound to resort to all truths of human nature established by science and to employ all methods recognized by scientists."[45] Louisell cites only two cases in which psychologists presented expert testimony other than that of a clinical nature, and both involved public opinion surveys.

In a Michigan case, *People vs. Hawthorne*, 291 N.W. 205 (1940), an opinion of three judges of the Supreme Court stated:

> Insanity is held to be a disease . . . and, therefore, comes within the realm of medical science, which comprises the study and treatment of disease. Only physicians can qualify to answer hypothetical questions as experts in such science.

In a contrary opinion, five judges stated:

> I do not think that the psychologist's ability to detect insanity is inferior to that of a medical man whose experience along such lines is not so intensive. . . No case has been called to my

---

[43]Scheflen, Norma A.: The psychiatrist as a witness. *Pennsylvania Bar Association Quarterly*, June, 1961, pp. 329-34.

[44]Louisell, David: The psychologist in today's legal world. *Minnesota Law Review*, (February, 1955), pp. 236 ff.

[45]*Ibid.*, p. 237.

attention where a general medical training has been held to be the *sine qua non* of the competence of a trained specialist to advise on the matter of insanity.

Sociologists have testified in desegregation cases, such as *Brown vs. Board of Education,* 347 U.S. 483 (1954). To this writer's knowledge, no sociologist or experimental psychologist has ever testified in court concerning the issue of criminal behavior. Criminology is traditionally taught in sociology departments, and sociologists have done extensive research in this area. Experimental psychologists have developed techniques and concepts concerning behavior which are often quite at variance with those used in clinical psychiatry and psychology. Nowhere in the criminal trial are such data utilized by our legal experts in tackling the problem of crime and mental disease.

Eysenck notes that in the field of psychology, it is assumed by the layman that he knows why people behave as they do, whereas the layman does not challenge the physicist or neurosurgeon in the same way. "There are few people who in their hearts do not resent the assumption of superior knowledge about human behavior, who do not feel that they know far more about people than any scientific textbook can tell them. . ."[46] "Psychoanalysis in my view is trying to *understand,* rather than to *explain;* that consequently it is essentially nonscientific and to be judged in terms of belief and faith, rather than in terms of proof and verification; and that its great popularity among nonscientists derives precisely from its nonscientific nature, which makes it intelligible and immediately applicable to problems of understanding other people."[47]

Eysenck's statement is borne out by examination of court records wherein are contained statements by judges and lawyers as to why people behave as they do. One of the major difficulties encountered by this writer in discussing the insanity issue with lawyers is that many of them accept psychoanalysis,

---

[46]Eysenck, H. J.: *Uses and Abuses of Psychology.* Baltimore, Penquin Books, 1953, p. 15.

[47]*Ibid.,* p. 226.

or if they reject psychoanalysis, they do so on the basis of a theory of behavior which is even more suspect and less scientific than psychoanalysis.

Psychoanalytic concepts have been picked up by clinical psychologists, sociologists, social workers, educators, lawyers, counsellors, and others, and today it is not too unusual to find a psychiatrist doing research on human behavior which is not Freudian-oriented, whereas the chief proponents of the anal or oral stages of development are sometimes nonpsychiatric people.

The lawyer has selected the most prestigeful profession from which to get help and with which to interact, namely, medicine. Studies of human interaction reveal that people will interact with those who possess similar prestige and social status. However, the high status of medicine in general in our society is no reason why we should assume that physicians are experts in all areas, including social problems and behavior.

It is also relevant that the *helping* and service professions—psychiatry, clinical psychology, and social work, have been the least involved in basic research activities. The research in human behavior has been carried on for the most part by nonservice professions—experimental psychology, sociology, and anthropology.

Experimental research is now underway in psychiatry, and we can anticipate some major changes in psychiatry in the near future.

Failures at Delinquency Control

Why have we failed to control delinquency in this country? The conclusion drawn from the Cambridge-Somerville project was that the delinquency prevention program appears not only to be negative but paradoxical.[48] In a review of the results of the Midcity Project (a total community delinquency-control project

---

[48]Powers, Edwin, and Witmer, Helen: *An Experiment in the Prevention of Delinquency*. New York, Columbia University Press, 1951.

in Boston), Miller concluded that the project had a "negligible inhibition on delinquent behavior."[49]

As sociologists have long pointed out, most delinquents come from minority groups and broken homes, and live in poverty in deteriorated neighborhoods. Delinquency prevention projects emphasize total community programs by which the environment wherein the delinquent resides is changed. Experimental psychology also emphasizes the importance of environmental conditions. Poverty, deprivation, alienation, anomie, unemployment, and family disorganization are contingencies controlling the behavior of delinquents.

A statistical approach to criminal behavior gives the investigator a picture of the average delinquent. In clinical practice, however, it is the individual subject who must be dealt with, not the average. The procedures used in behavioral psychology are designed to be applied to individual subjects. Such an approach supplements and complements the total community approach (now in operation in delinquency control programs in many American cities) by focusing attention on individual responses to specific environmental settings. Criminal behavior involves both an environment and the response of an individual to his environment. We now know a great deal about the environment from which the delinquent comes. We know little about the variables controlling the behavior of individuals in this environment. We need more knowledge about the principles governing the specific responses of delinquents to specific environmental conditions, and to gain from this the specific procedures which can be used to alter antisocial behavior.

Demonstration projects have not isolated the variables that control the responses of individual delinquents to their environment. Cause-and-effect statements cannot be made concerning delinquency. A combination sociology-experimental psychology project, wherein behavior is analyzed more systematically through the use of conditioning procedures, seems to be worthy

---

[49]Miller, Walter: The impact of total community delinquency control project. *Social Problems*, Fall, 1962, p. 190.

of consideration. Such a program would make use of environmental contingencies and group processes in an effort to control juvenile delinquency.

SUMMARY

Sociological and experimental data concerning criminal behavior support the thesis that behavior is learned in a given type of environment. The group to which one belongs is important in this learning process.

This evidence indicates quite clearly that mental illness is not an important aspect of the process by which criminality is acquired. Such data focus attention not on personality disorders but upon social disorganization and upon environmental contingencies that may govern behavior.

Clinical data as introduced into the courtroom present a picture of the criminal as he has reacted to interviews and tests. Behavioral science data from sociology and experimental psychology are not used by lawyers in their evaluation of criminal behavior.

Chapter 14

CONCLUSIONS

MENTAL DISEASE AND CRIME

THE DURHAM test of criminal responsibility is based on what must appear to the lawyer as the most logical ground in the world, that is, if a criminal act is produced by mental disease, there can be no responsibility according to the basic moral premise of Western philosophy. The rule in operation has encountered several problems some of which are discussed in this report.

The term "mental disease" is not a scientific term concerning which there is anything approaching agreement in the professional community. The term "mental disease" refers to a classification of behaviors for which we regard treatment rather than punishment as the proper response of the community through its legal institutions. In the same way, "criminal behavior" refers to a classification of behaviors for which we regard punishment as the proper response of the community. Therefore, whether we regard a given type of behavior as mental disease or crime depends upon our social policy at any given point in history, and not upon our scientific knowledge of behavior.

Mental disease refers to behavior for which we do not find a reward or gain. If a man steals money, we say he is sane. If he steals money and talks to God, we say he is insane. A woman who kills her four children to protect them from the devil is regarded as mentally ill, because we can find no reward. A woman who kills her husband so she can be with her lover is regarded as sane, because we can see the consequences.

Psychiatrists disagree as to the meaning of mental disease because they disagree as to social policy concerning the treatment of behavioral problems in our society. The lawyer insists that it is the proper function of the courts to decide social policy, and therefore lawyers will challenge in court psychiatric statements concerning human behavior.

Though the *Durham* test was put forth in an effort to allow psychiatrists to testify in medical rather than legal terms, the courts are now faced with the situation in which the medical terms are social policy concepts rather than scientific concepts, and, as is always the case, people disagree as to policy issues. If the treatment of criminals is to remain a policy issue, then the lawyer is as well equipped as anyone else to decide such policy issues.

However, there are behavioral experts in our society, as there are experts on law, economics, glass making, and highway construction. Such expert testimony is not introduced into our courtrooms because such issues are treated as policy issues rather than scientific issues.

The *Durham* rule does not tell either the lawyer or the psychiatrist which behaviors are to be included in or excluded from the term "mental disease." The defense lawyer's job is to fit a psychiatric label into a legal definition. The issue is left to a jury, a body of laymen, to decide. The rule does not solve the problem of conflicting psychiatric testimony given within an adversary setting, or the problem of the indigent defendant who cannot afford to have psychiatric aid.

It is therefore recommended that the insanity plea be re-evaluated in the light of new knowledge of behavior based on scientific analysis. Further, it is recommended that experts from the fields of sociology and experimental psychology be allowed to testify as experts on criminal behavior. As stated by Freud, Szasz, and others, it is unfortunate that behavioral problems have come to be regarded as "illness" and therefore considered the proper province of the medical profession. At present, psychiatrists are recognized by the courts as experts on the diagnosis and treatment of behavioral disorders and criminality. This is because behavioral disorders are defined as insanity, which is a mental disease, and only physicians are qualified to treat disease.

Alternative explanations of behavior are not now available to lawyers in their effort to handle the problem of crime. Sociological and experimental psychological data indicate that the problem of behavioral control is located in the interaction of the organism and environment, rather than in internal psychic controls involving the mind in interaction with behavior. Criminal behavior is learned behavior, and therefore it might be appropriate to apply learning theory to the problem of insanity and crime.

CAUSATION AND SCIENTIFIC METHOD

The legal view of causation is that the behavior of the accused must be related to the harm which the criminal law has prescribed as illegal and harmful. To be guilty of murder, a man must have behaved in such a way as to cause death of another human being. This view of causation is a common sense view, and it does not conflict with the scientific view of causation.

The scientific view of causation states that event Y is caused by event X under given conditions. The term "function" is often used to express the relationship between X and Y, and here the term "function" is used in a mathematical sense, i.e., a change in X will produce a change in Y of a certain magnitude and in a given direction. The terms "independent" and "dependent" variables are often used in place of cause and effect; the independent variable is the variable controlled by the experimenter, and the dependent variable is the variable in which change is observed by the experimenter in relation to the change in the independent variable.

The law must deal in probabilities of less than 100 per cent. It may be that a preponderance of the evidence satisfied the court, which might mean that a 51 per cent probability of A causing B satisfies the court. On the other hand, the law may require that A caused B "beyond a reasonable doubt," which is to say that if there is any doubt that A caused B, then the decision must be that A did not cause B. This view of causation approaches the probability level of 100 per cent. In a murder case, if there is any possibility that B rather than A killed Smith, then A must be acquitted, even if the probability is 99 per cent that A did in fact kill B.

The lawyer cannot go into the laboratory and reconstruct the events in order to observe the results, as can the scientist. Whether or not A killed Smith is a matter that can be decided only on a probability basis, since we are dealing with past events which are not under the control of the observer. There is, however, a difference between deciding if A murdered Smith, and deciding if A should be executed, sent to prison, or sent to a mental hospital. The variables involved in disposing of a case are under the control of the investigator, and the results of various dispositions upon the behavior of the defendant can be observed. Though the lawyer must deal with probability in determining the issue of guilt or inocence, he need not deal with probability in dealing with punishment and treatment.

Another crucial difference between legal procedures and scientific procedures is that the lawyer uses past precedent as a justification for action. If a scientist asks a lawyer what is meant by murder, intent, *mens rea*, punishment, or mental illness, the lawyer will respond by citing past legal decisions and statutes. The scientist does not rely upon past precedent for establishing the validity of a concept, whereas the lawyer does. The lawyer looks to the past for answers, whereas the scientist looks to the future for answers. The scientist assumes that procedures must be established whereby concepts are tested as valid or invalid before a statement is accepted as true.

Legal laws and scientific laws can be in conflict for this reason. The legal principles were established at a time and under conditions when scientific knowledge was not available. Today new scientific knowledge is available. The lawyer is not likely to find fault with natural science findings, though he will disagree with behavioral science principles. This is due in large part to the fact that many statements made about behavior are not of a scientific nature, and the scientific approach to behavior is only now starting to emerge in sciology and psychology. The legal view of treatment, punishment, mental illness, and so forth, can be re-evaluated in the light of new experimental findings concerning human behavior. The *Durham* decision was attempt to bring the law of insanity and criminal responsibility up-to-date, but the *Durham* decision was based upon an 1871 New Hampshire decision.

The attempt to find a causal relationship between mental illness and crime has been futile. Psychotics constitute about 1 per cent of the criminal population, and there are more neurotics in the normal population than in the criminal population. This leaves only one major psychiatric classification for criminal, the class of personality disorders. The personality disorders include personality pattern disturbance, personality trait disturbance, sociopathic personality, alcoholism, sexual deviancy, and drug addiction. These individuals are poorly adjusted individuals, and by definition criminals have personality disorders since criminals are antisocial individuals.

The Model Penal Code excludes as evidence of mental illness any abnormality manifested only by repeated antisocial conduct. In the District of Columbia, sociopaths were not included in the category of mentally ill until the *Leach* case where, by administrative decision, the staff of Saint Elizabeths Hospital decided to declare that psychopaths are mentally ill.

By extending the concept of mental illness to include sex deviancy, sociopathy, alcoholism, and drug addiction, all behavioral problems are now viewed by some as mental diseases. In the District of Columbia, there is an effort to have both addicts and alcoholics defined as mentally ill. In *California vs. Robinson*, 82 S. C., 417, the United States Supreme Court held that addiction was not a crime, and addiction must therefore be treated and not punished.

The *Durham* rule requires that the mental disease or defect "produce" the criminal act. According to the *Carter* case, the criminal act would not have occured "except for, but for, because of, effect of, results of, or caused by" mental disease or defect. The "but for" test is the *sine qua non* test, it looks for prior events which caused the event under consideration. This often involves the fallacy of *post hoc, ergo propter hoc,* after this, therefore, on account of it. Two independent events which occur in a temporal sequence need not be causally related, though this is often viewed as a causal sequence. Mental illness and criminal behavior can coexist in the same person without the two conditions being related to each other, as can smoking and mental illness, or smoking and criminal behavior. Mental illness is an effect, not a cause. Crime is behavior; mental illness is behavior. Behavior does not cause behavior.

DUE PROCESS

As may be seen in the case of *Lynch,* the insanity defense raises serious questions concerning due process. The difficulty is that, once the issue of insanity is raised in a trial, there is no longer a question of guilt or innocense as concerns the criminal act: the insanity defense is tantamount to admitting the facts of the indictment. *Mens rea* is still an issue, however. In the *Kent* case, for example, the defense did not raise the question whether Kent actually raped two women. The danger lies in the possibility that an innocent man might be found not guilty by reason of insanity and thereupon sent to a mental institution.

Criminal proceedings are designed to discover whether or not the defendant committed the act alleged, and this can be done by the court better than by any existing institutional system. The court system is not, however, the place to decide why men behave as they do, or what should be done to rehabilitate them. The tremendous antagonism and hostility between lawyer and psychiatrist is a result of using the adversary system in this manner.

The problem is complicated when defense lawyers file petitions for the release of criminals from Saint Elizabeths, once they have been found not guilty by reason of insanity. Thus a criminal may escape both punishment and treatment. Some defense lawyers are unable to see why many judges and a large segment of the population are opposed to the insanity defense. If a defendant uses the insanity defense, the public has a right to expect that he will be institutionalized. The defense lawyer can argue that he is a hired advocate, and his job is to defend his client by any means available. This philosophy makes sense when dealing with the question, "Did the defendant commit this act?" A defendant has a right to the best legal defense available. When, however, the lawyer states that this client is insane but is being unfairly detained in a mental hospital because, for example, fellow patients froth at the mouth or smear themselves with feces, he is opening the doors for a potentially dangerous man to walk the streets. Commitment to a mental institution is often much more damaging to an individual than is a prison sentence or probation. Nevertheless, the judicial process is not set up for the advantage of either defendants or defense attorneys. The rights of the victim and of the general public must also be considered.

It can be said that, in many instances, the insanity defense operates to the disadvantage of the defendant. The insanity defense did not help Kent, for even if he is released as cured from Saint Elizabeths, he now faces ninety years in prison. The insanity defense was not helpful to Lynch; he committed suicide. Horton, another casualty of the insanity defense, has been released without treatment or cure. Tremblay was not helped by the insanity defense; she also committed suicide.

The *purpose* of the insanity defense, in so far as many defense attorneys are concerned, is to secure the *freedom* of the defendant regardless of his behavioral problems. The insanity defense is used to secure the freedom of defendants, *not* to *treat* or *rehabilitate* them.

Commitment procedures for the mentally ill are filled with dangerous practices. Professor Sulzer has pinpointed these difficulties when he states:

> I personally cannot accept commitment on psychiatric grounds as a legitimate undertaking. As Szasz has so well illustrated, "mental illness" is no more than the expression of a particular social, ethical, or moral point of view. More than any single event known to me, the *Durham* decision allows, nay, encourages, further inroads upon personal freedom by permit-

ting involuntary institutionalization of the accused citizen without his being given the opportunity to defend himself against a criminal charge.

Can one defend himself against the charge of "mental illness"? This is almost impossible as there is no accepted standard to measure someone against except the personal viewpoint of the psychiatrist . . . Either adult citizens are uniformly "responsible" for their behavior or no one is. To say that some behavior derives from a "mental illness" is to replicate the thinking of the Middle Ages. At that time, some behavior was the result of being "possessed by the devil." There were specialists (the Inquisitors) who could detect the phenomenon. Today we have replaced the devil with a pseudo-scientific construct called "illness" and have appointed psychiatrists and psychologists to tell us when it is present.[1]

Some people may feel that Sulzer overstates his case, but there is substance to the comment that it is difficult to defend oneself against such a charge. A paper on the institutionalization of the mentally ill, written by Professor Sulzer, is reproduced in the appendix.

Professor Thomas Scheff has just completed a research project on Decision Making in the Hospitalization and Release of Mental Patients,[2] in which he concludes that judges very often decide whether or not a person needs to be institutionalized. These judges ask the accused such questions as "Who is President?"; "Where are you?"; and "How are you feeling?" These hearings last only a few minutes, with little regard for safeguarding the rights of the accused. On the other hand, psychiatrists seek to obtain medical control of commitments, without legal safeguards. The medical examiners often ask such questions as "Who is President?" These medical interviews also are hasty—a mere

---

[1]Personal correspondence with Doctor Edward Sulzer, Division of Clinical Psychology, University of Minnesota Medical School.

[2]Scheff, Thomas: Decision Making in the Hospital and Release of Mental Patients. Unpublished manuscript to be published in future, Department of Sociology, University of Wisconsin.

formality—and not particularly sophisticated. The general assumption is that the defendant would be better off in a mental hospital than at large in the community.

Release procedures are based on concepts of treatment and cure. Unless there is treatment and cure for mental illness, there is no advantage in sending a man to a hospital. The evidence shows that the recovery rate is the same, whether or not psychotherapy is used. The facilities available for the treatment of the mentally ill (behaviorally disturbed) are inadequate and grossly underfinanced and understaffed. Unless there are experts who can work with behavioral problems, and unless there are adequate treatment facilities, a mental hospital tends to be a custodial institution rather than a treatment center.

STATISTICS ON DURHAM

One of the major objections to the *Durham* rule stems form the charge that too often it enables a criminal to go free. Recently, it was blamed for the increase of crime in the District of Columbia. In an effort to curb the high rate of crime in the Capital, the House District Subcommittee has recommended legislation that would re-establish the right-and-wrong test in the District of Columbia, and that would require "substantial evidence" in order for the insanity issue to be raised as a defense.[3]

The statistics on the post-*Durham* situation are contradictory and confusing. One report indicates that the number of acquittals by reason of insanity has increased from .49 per cent in 1954 to 2.5 per cent in 1959.[4] Another study, sponsored by the Committee on the District of Columbia for the House of Representatives, states that there has been an increase from 1.5 per cent in 1957 to 25.0 per cent in February 1961.[5] The big shift occurred after the *Leach* case in 1957, in which sociopaths

---

[3]*Washington Post,* May 2, 1963; July 12, 1963.

[4]Donnelly, Richard C., Goldstein, Joseph, and Schwartz, Richard D: *Criminal Law.* New York, Free Press of Glencoe, 1962, p. 810.
[5]*Ibid.,* p. 840.

were classified as mentally diseased. In his article, United States Attorney Acheson quotes figures indicating a change from 29 per cent in 1953 to 13.0 per cent in 1962.[6] Both proponents and opponents of *Durham* find comfort in these figures, depending on which ones are quoted. The number of acquittals by reason of insanity has increased five times, according to the conservative figures (.49 per cent to 2.5 per cent). These is no doubt that the number of cases involving the insanity defense has increased in the District, regardless of which statistics are examined. This is however, quite different from saying that the *Durham* decision has a bearing on the over-all increase in the D. C. crime rate. Certainly the men released from prison each year, on parole or on probation, are responsible for more of the crimes committed than those who are acquitted by reason of insanity. The United States Attorney's office recently released figures showing a general decrease in insanity acquittals since the *McDonald* decision: from sixty-seven cases in fiscal year 1962 to fifty cases in fiscal year 1963. This has been interpreted to mean the *McDonald* case reaffirmed the position that the jury, not the psychiatrist, has the responsibility for determing criminal responsibility.[7]

It is the individual case, however, that impresses the public. In May of 1963, three inmates of Saint Elizabeths were arrested in connection with the murder of a jewelry salesman.[8] Eugene Rollins, the man charged with the murder, had been committed to the hospital in 1956 on charges of breaking and entering. In April, 1963, he walked away from the hospital, where he had been given ground privileges. As a consequence of this crime, a survey of Saint Elizabeths was made, revealing that, at that time, seventy-six escapees from the hospital were still at large, thirty-nine of whom had been committed after being acquitted of crimes. On this occasion, Doctor Winfred Overholser, former

----

[6]Acheson, David C.: McDonald v. United States; the Durham rule redefined. *Georgetown Law Journal*, Spring, 1963, p. 589.

[7]*Washington Post*, July 14, 1963.

[8]*Washington Post*, May 12, 1963.

Superintendent of Saint Elizabeths and a leading forensic psychiatrist, stated, "When I hear of a hospital that has no elopements, I feel it is being run as a prison." Hospital Superintendent Doctor Dale Cameron said, "In my opinion, many of the crimes committed by those who elope have nothing to do with their illness." Both of these statements are correct, yet neither meets the problem of protecting the public from dangerous criminals.

On August 8, 1963, an escapee from Saint Elizabeths terrorized and raped a woman in her apartment in Washington. This man had been sent to the hospital after acquittal by reason of insanity of charges of house breaking and attempted rape. On August 17, 1963, six inmates of Saint Elizabeths, all committed under criminal proceedings, escaped from the hospital. Included in the offenses for which these men had been charged were murder, armed robbery, and assault with a dangerous weapon.[9] The conclusion may be drawn that the insanity defense protects the public no more than it protects or reforms the individual criminal.

PUNISHMENT vs. TREATMENT

The criminal law has been justified in terms of several theoretical systems—retribution, deterrence, treatment, and the protection of society. The theory of retribution will be dismissed for purposes of this paper, since most criminologists today deny that revenge is a satisfactory justification for criminal justice.

The distinction between revenge and deterrence is one that must be drawn in terms of a temporal sequence. Revenge is punishment used because a person deserves it.[10] Deterrence is punishment used to change future behavior. Revenge as a concept applies to behavior which has occurred; deterrence refers to behavior which may occur in the future. A science of behavior can deal with the future occurence of behavior; it cannot deal with past behavior. The concept of revenge, therefore, has no application in a science of criminology.

---

[9]*Washington Post*, August 9, 1963; *Washington Star*, August 18, 1963.

[10]Lewis, C. S.: The humanitarian theory of punishment. 6 Res Judicatae, 224.

Deterrence, treatment, and protection of society are not contradictory goals and aims, but are the same argument in different forms. If one deters criminal behavior, then one protects society and reforms criminals. Likewise, if one reforms criminals or protects society, then one must deter criminal behavior.

The major argument revolves around the use of punishment. The Classical School (Bentham, Beccaria) argued that punishment should fit the crime, not the criminal. The Classical School favored fixed sentences for each crime. The Positive School (Lombroo, Garofalo, Ferri) was opposed to fixed sentences, and it advocated indefinite sentences based on a philosophy of treatment. The Positive School rejected the notion that legal measures could deter criminal behavior, and in the place of punishment they placed therapeutic efforts at rehabilitation.

One of the major difficulties in this argument between the Positive School and the Classical School is that each school is looking at criminal behavior from a different perspective. The Classical School is looking at deterrence, the ability of punishment to prevent criminal acts from occurring. This is the control of behavior *before* the criminal act has occurred. The Positive School is looking at the rehabilitation of criminals *after* the criminal act has occurred. In the one case, we are dealing with punishment as a means of preventing behavior from occurring, and in the other case, we are looking at the individuals for whom punishment has not worked and who have committed criminal acts in spite of the legal system of punishment.

One of the major conclusions reached by modern criminologists who reject the deterrence theory of the Classical School is that *punishment does not deter.*[11] The death penalty is often used as evidence of this fact. The notion that punishment does not deter, and that therefore legal controls and sanctions are meaningless, is a misinterpretation of the data. Laboratory studies demonstrate that punishment does deter when it is used properly. The problem is that punishment must be contingent upon the

[11]Allen, Francis A.: Criminal justice, legal values, and the rehabilitative ideal. 50 *Journal of Criminal Law, Criminology, and Police Science,* 226 (1959).

behavior to be controlled, and punishment must follow the behavior in time in such a way as to influence the behavior.

The legal use of punishment is inadequate for several reasons: (1) Many offenders are never detected, convicted, and/or punished. The rate of execution for capital offenses is about 1 per cent of those who commit such offenses. (2) The punishment that follows the criminal behavior is too remote in time. When two stimuli or contingencies are presented to the actor, both dependent on the same response (robbery), the first contingency (money) will control the response, rather than the second contingency (punishment). (3) Punishment shapes avoidance and escape behavior. After a robbery, the criminal will try to avoid detection, will lie to the police, will hire a lawyer, will tell a certain type of story to the probation officer, will plead insanity, and so forth in order to avoid the punishing consequences of his act. The threat of punishment does not prevent the robbery response, but it does create other behaviors which are designed to avoid punishment. Thus, the criminal law often creates new behavior rather than preventing illegal behavior. Any punitive situation will create avoidance and escape behaviors. (4) Behavior which is paired with a reinforcing consequence (food, sex, money) as well as with punishment will be maintained by the reinforcing consequence in many cases since the individual will take a chance that punishment will not be forthcoming, or he will accept the punishment as a cost of the food or money. Thus, a person who is hungry will risk punishment in order to get food. We can see this relationship by posing the following two situations: In one case, we make available to the subject a penny which he can steal, and for this behavior we set the punishment at thirty years in prison; in the other case, we make available to the subject one million dollars and make the punishment ten days in jail. It is obvious under these two situations which response the punishment will control, and which response it will not control.

The way to weaken a response by the use of punishment is to reward an alternative response. If the subject is trained in two responses which lead to food, one of which is punished, the other which is not, the subject will rapidly learn to respond to food in the nonpunished manner. The trouble with our present system for punishing criminals is that our society often does not provide these alternative responses. A delinquent youth who is a high school drop-out without education and work skills has no choice but to steal money and cars. The answer to criminal behavior is a retraining program whereby such individuals are provided with legal responses for gaining economic and social status. Punishment of criminals would be more successful if these individuals were provided with alternative responses.

According to the procedures used under the *Durham* rule, a kleptomaniac (a person who is a compulsive thief) is sent to a mental hospital rather than a prison. A psychiatrist would in such a case testify that the defendant steals useless items, shoes or purses, because the stolen item has symbolic meaning and is related to psychic conflict from which the defendant suffers. The decision to send the defendant to a mental hospital is not based on his lack of guilt (he stole the item and he intended to steal the item) but is based upon the supposition that kleptomaniacs belong in hospitals and not in prisons. Such a decision as to the disposition of the case is not related to the issue before the court, i.e., is the defendant guilty. A defendant can be found guilty and sent to a special institution without the use of the insanity plea.

If the purpose of the *Durham* rule is to place defendants in mental instituions rather than prisons, then the advocates of the rule must show (1) it is only through an insanity plea that criminals can be treated rather than punished, and (2) psychiatrists and mental institutions are the proper people and facilities to carry out the treatment of behavioral disorders. This writer would argue that one need not classify people as insane in order to treat behavioral disorders, and there are behavioral techniques available which are superior to psychiatric techniques for the treatment and prevention of antisocial behavior.

In the *Durham* decision, we have the argument presented

that for the mentally ill we have treatment, for the criminal we have punishment. This argument is fallacious on several scores:

(1) The notion that criminals ought to be punished and not treated is outmoded. Most criminological thinking emphasizes deterrence, rehabilitation, and protection of society. Even the criminal law emphasizes this point of view, as seen in *California vs. Robinson*, 82 S. Ct., 1417. (2) Treatment can be punitive. Institutionalization in a mental hospital or in an institution for youthful offenders can be as punitive as institutionalization in a prison. (3) Punishment can be used for treatment purposes, as was indicated above in the discussion of punishment.

One major fallacy of the legal approach is that it uses punishment to control behavior once the behavior has occurred. This creates many problems, such as those involving constitutional issues surrounding the concepts of due process and civil rights. If a person is *prevented* from behaving in a criminal manner, rather than treated after he behaves as a criminal, then the issue of civil rights disappears. If an individual never commits a crime, then we need not be concerned with illegal arrests, illegal search and seizure, the first or fifth amendment, coerced confessions, undue delay in arraignment, assignment of counsel to indigent defendants, and so forth. Punishment must be used as a preventive measure. We do not have successful treatment measures for antisocial behavior. The future of criminology rests upon prevention programs, not treatment programs. The analogy might be made to cancer. If a person enters a clinic for treatment of cancer, the chances are good he will not be treatable, since by the time the cancer is detected, it often is too late to institute successful treatment. If cancer is prevented, however, no treatment is needed. That is why the emphasis today is upon preventing cancer, not upon treatment. Likewise, we must prevent crime, not treat it. By the time a man is sentenced to prison, it is too late to rehabilitate him in many cases. It is like operating on a cancer patient and finding that the cancer is so widespread that no treatment is possible.

CRIMINAL INTENT

The criminal law requires a criminal intent or evil purpose

as well as an overt act. This intent is a mental state whereby the actor intended to produce a given event. The law assumes that a man intends the natural and probable consequences of his action. Intent is known by inference: it is inferred from the behavior. Mental states are never directly observed. They cannot be subjected to scientific analysis; one cannot study how a person "feels or thinks" since such terms refer to subjective states. A person may say how he feels or thinks, and thus communicate with others concerning his subjective mental states, but this is not the same as studying the subjective mental states. The investigator has no proof of the existence of mental states; he only has verbal behavior in this case.

If one looks at the problem of intent in the law, however, one observes several interesting situations. Intent to commit an act is inferred from the act; if a man commits robbery, it is assumed he intended to commit robbery. The behavioral scientist should have no problem with this proposition, since it is a basic learning principle that behavior is governed by its consequences. This is usually stated in terms of a response being controlled by a contingent stimulus; when a lawyer states that the defendant who stole a watch intended to steal the watch, he means that the stimulus controlling the response (stealing) was a watch. So long as the lawyer views behavior in terms of its objective consequences, such as possession of money, or killing a person, the concept of intent is not in conflict with the scientific view of behavior. The only thing the behavioral scientist insists upon is an objective environmental variable which he can measure and relate to the behavior of the defendant.

The legal purpose of intent is to exclude from punishment and moral sanction these acts which are not of an immoral nature. The law of murder is designed to control accidental killings of human beings. The law recognizes that homicide can occur quite by accident. A man can be chopping wood and the ax can slip out of his hands and strike another, thereby inflicting upon the bystander a mortal wound. The law does not wish to punish wood chopping, for the consequences of chopping wood are socially desirable. If a man kills another while in the performance of a legal act, carried out in a reasonable and responsible manner, then no crime has been committed. Again, to use psychological terms, the stimulus controlling the behavior was wood, and not a human being. The stimulus controlling murder is the death of another human being, not wood. It is obvious to a behavioral expert that these two events are not the same and so must be differentiated. When we punish murder, we control the responses of human beings to other human beings; we do not control the responses of human beings to wood. Punishing murder does not control wood chopping.

The concept of intent is extended to include reckless behavior, but the relationship between the behavior and its consequences is still clear and observable. Reckless driving can have as its consequence the injury of another person or property. The object of the law is to control behavior, and by making reckless driving an offense, it brings reckless driving under the control of the law. This is good behavioral psychology. The law wishes to shape good driving behavior, and to eliminate or weaken reckless driving behavior.

The usual legal defenses—infancy, coercion and necessity, accident, and mistake of fact—have one thing in common: they take into account the fact that behavior is related to the environment in which it occurs, and that behavior is governed by the consequence occurring in that environment. When a man commits murder, the act is related to an environmental contingency; the same is true when a man steals at watch.

A child of five is not an adult; this is so obvious that no psychologist or sociologist would dispute the issue. A child does not know the consequences of his action, since only through experience does learning occur. Accidental consequences do occur as a result of behavior. It is also recognized that coercion and necessity exist. To use the famous cases of *Regina vs. Dudley and Stephens*, 14 Q.B.D. 273 and *United States vs. Holmes*, 26 Fed. Cases 360, a ship-wrecked sailor will commit murder and cannibalism if the alternative is starving to death. Men in concentration camps will eat rats and commit homosexual acts, which they do not commit when they have access to beefsteak and females. The element of coercion is an obvious and observable environmental event.

Similarly, a mistake of fact is possible. A man may pick up a watch belonging to someone else thinking that it is his own. Again, the law is designed to punish stealing, and not the taking of one's own watch. The law does not wish to control the taking of one's own watch, since such behavior is not socially harmful.

The insanity defense raises some different issues, however. For one thing, the other legal defenses free the individual of criminal responsibility; in the case of the insanity defense, the defendant is not freed but is often committed to a mental institution. The distinction is thus not whether the individual intended to commit a crime, but whether he is sent to an electric chair or to shock therapy.

Another related distinction is that in the insanity defense, the defendant admits that he committed the act, that is, he killed a man. If a defendant is chopping wood and kills someone, the behavior which is involved is wood chopping. In the case of murder by the insane defendant, the behavior is not wood chopping but killing an individual. One might argue that the insane defendant is under a hallucination and thought he was killing someone else, as M'Naghten thought he was killing Sir Robert and not Drummond; however, the fact remains that M'Naghten intended to kill a human being. The fact that M'Naghten felt he was being persecuted by his enemies is not really relevant, since even if his delusions were correct, he still does not have the privilege of killing his enemy. One can question the meaning of hallucinations and delusions. There is evidence that schizophrenics are aware of environmental contingencies. They respond to reward and punishment. This often leads to the "remission of symptoms" problem, periods of behaving in a normal manner. Given certain environmental contingencies, the psychotic will respond in a normal manner; given other environmental contingencies, he will respond in a bizarre manner. From the legal point of view, insanity is a defense because it negates *mens rea*. According to the *M'Naghten* rule, intent is negated by the absence of cognition; according to the irrestible impulse test, intent is negated by the absence of volition; according to the *Durham* rule, intent is negated by mental disease and productivity.

The assumption is made that mental illness negates intent. There is no psychological evidence that individuals who behave in a bizarre manner are not responding to the environment. Even insane individuals intend the consequences of their behavior, e.g., act as to gain pleasure and avoid pain. A person can behave as a schizophrenic and still possess volition and cognition. It is often assumed that mentally ill persons see and hear things that do not exist; however, as was stated above, there is no evidence that the cognitive processes of schizophrenics are unusual or abnormal. Though the lawyer uses the insanity defense as a means of negating intent, there is no psychological evidence to support this assumption.

A person can hear voices and have periods of depression and still intend the consequences of his behavior. If he did not intend certain consequences, he would not behave. There is no evidence presented in the *Kent* case, to take an example, that the defendant did not intend to rape and steal. It may be assumed from psychological principles that when Kent raped he did so for sexual gratification, as any normal man, and when he robbed he did so for money, as any normal man. The fact that Kent responded to test questions in a given manner, or had a history of bizarre behavior, does not prove that he did not intend either the consequences of his criminal acts or his schizophrenic behavior. All behavior is intended to produce consequences in the environment in which it occurs, be it criminal behavior or schizophrenic behavior. The environmental conditions controlling murder or rape may be the same for both the sane and the insane. The schizophrenic is responding to his environment so as to gain reward and avoid punishment. A great deal of what is called mental disease is behavior designed to avoid punishment. Behavior is natural, that is, it is appropriate to the environment in which it occurs. If a person behaves in a bizarre and abnormal manner, it is because he is in a bizarre and abnormal environment.

It has been argued that punishment will not deter a psychotic patient. Psychotic patients do respond to punishment, as is seen in the mental hospital in regards to the use of shock therapy.

The crucial and important difference between the insanity defense and other defenses is that the insanity defense is not based upon an observable environmental event. The age of a person (infancy) or the presence of necessity and coercion can be established as observable events. A man who takes a watch which he believes is his is under the control of environmental contingencies. The man who eats his shipmate to avoid starvation is under environmental control. On the other hand, insanity or mental illness is not an observable event. Behavior of a bizarre nature is observable, but this is behavior, not illness. Mental illness is inferred from the behavior. Mental illness is then used to explain behavior. The criminal act is thus explained as a reaction to a subjective mental state, and not an observable environmental state. One cannot observe schizophrenia as one observes coercion or accidents. Behavior which is labeled schizophrenic can be observed, but it is this behavior that we are attempting to explain. However, in the insanity defense this behavior is used as an explanation of the criminal behavior. Behavior does not cause behavior. A man can talk to God and kill another human being. Both of these behaviors are caused by environmental forces; both are effects and not causes. To say that talking to God caused Schmidt to commit murder is the type of statement that can never be proven. Schmidt intended to kill a human being, and this remains a basic fact regardless of whether he rationalized it on the basis of a command from God or because he wanted to rob his victim or get rid of an enemy. The intent to kill remained, even though the motive for the crime might be different.

If we are right in stating that behavior is controlled by reward and punishment, then we can state that the insanity defense is a contingency which the defendant wishes to occur, since it is less punishing to be sent to a mental hospital than to the electric chair. For this reason, the insanity plea is usually used for

CRIMINAL RESPONSIBILITY AND MENTAL DISEASE

serious cases involving capital offenses, and not for minor offenses. A defendant would rather be placed on probation or sent to prison for a year than be sent to a mental institution for an indefinite period, perhaps for life.

The issue of intent, when anlyzed in terms of the environmental contingencies controlling behavior, reveals a major difference in the causal process involved in the insanity defense. The other legal defenses deal with environmental events which are directly related to the criminal behavior. However, in the case of insanity, the events under discussion are not part of the behavioral act for which the defendant is before the court. The issue of insanity is proven by showing that in the past the defendant behaved in a strange and bizarre manner. He may have talked to God or smeared feces on himself. These behaviors, however, are not related to the situation which produced the criminal behavior. The lawyer now must examine not the immediate situation which produces the murder, but must look at past behavior. The lawyer now searches for insanity, not an environmental contingency related to the crime.

The behavior which the criminal law is interested in controlling is not bizarre behavior of the schizophrenic, but the criminal behavior, such as stealing and murdering. The law is not interested in controlling talking to God, but murder.

If free will is the crucial issue in the insanity plea, then one must point out that mental disease does not negate free will, the ability to make choices based upon the consequences of behavior. If the argument is that certain persons are exempted from responsibility because they behave in a bizarre manner and therefore they cannot control their behavior, then it must be noted that behavior is also determined by slum areas, poverty, racial discrimination, and other sociological variables. Why does the lawyer believe in *psychic determinism* as put forth by the psychiatrist, and not believe in environmental determinism as put forth by sociologists and experimental psychologists?

The only reason one can find for stating that we punish criminals and treat the mentally ill is that we regard it as a moral obligation to treat mental illness but not crime. This is not only poor science; it is poor ethics.

FREE WILL vs. DETERMINISM

The law postulates a doctrine of free will, as seen in the Model Penal Code and in the *Durham* decision. The scientist talks about determinism.

By free will we mean choice, the ability to behave in alternative ways in order to produce different results. If a person behaves one way, then consequence A is produced; if he behaves in a different way, a different consequence is produced. The doctrine of free will holds that a person is able to behave so as to produce consequence A and not B. The actor is a causal agent in the determination of events. We say he is responsible for his behavior because of a causal relationship attributable to him. If a man commits murder, the death of a human being is attributable to the actor. The reason we hold the actor responsible is because behavior is determined. The free will doctrine assumes that the behavior of the individual can be determined by reward and punishment.

Individuals do make choices based upon the probable consequences of their behavior. The law recognizes this as a basic fact of behavior as does the behavioral scientist. For this reason, the law adds a new contingency (punishment) to the behavior in order to control the behavior.

The law must assume that behavior is determined, since the law applies consequences to behavior in order to change behavior. Why punish or treat offenders if these consequences do not alter future behavior? Why does the Catholic Church excommunicate members if such contingencies do not control religious behavior?

RESPONSIBILITY

Does determinism eliminate responsibility? The assumption now made is that if behavior is determined, there can be no responsibility. The insanity plea is based on this proposition. By this time, the reader may have concluded that the behavioral scientist is in favor of completely negating responsibility. This is not the case. A. J. Bachrach, an experimental psychologist who is chairman of the Department of Psychology at Arizona State University, noted recently that the most damaging aspect of the

Durham decision was the idea that people are not responsible for their behavior.[12] He cited the example of the honor system at the University of Virginia, which worked until psychotherapy entered the picture. Before psychotherapy, a student who violated the code was required to leave the campus within twenty-four hours. Once students began bringing letters from the psychology clinic stating, for example, that "this student is under great emotional stress because of his parents" or "this student is emotionally unstable and immature," there was no longer an honor system. Students could now "plead insanity." We have already argued that the insanity defense produces the psychotic symptoms it is supposed to treat. What Bachrach is saying is that, in order to control behavior, we must attach contingencies to it. If we allow students who cheat to go to the psychology clinic rather than expelling them from school, we can expect them to cheat. Major Lewis Kurke, an Army psychiatrist, has discussed this problem in relation to the treatment of Army neuropsychiatric casualties.[13] If men are kept in the situation that produced the behavioral disorder, they are restored to duty within a few days, and few of them need permanent hospitalization. If, however, such casualties are sent to a hospital miles removed from the action, 90 to 95 per cent of them never return to active military duty. The consequences of the latter treatment are favorable (warm food, clean bed, nice nurse, and no one shooting at you), which explains why most of these men did not return to active duty.

Responsibility means response (ability)—the ability to make a response. To a behaviorist this means creating the condition under which a response will occur. If a response does occur, the actor has the ability to make it; otherwise he does not. If a person makes a response not acceptable to society, he must be held responsible. The only way to control behavior is to control the variables producing the behavior. This control is called

---

[12]*Arizona Republic*, April 16, 1963, p. 16.

[13]Personal correspondence with Major Lewis Kurke, Institute of Research, Walter Reed Army Medical Center.

responsibility. The difficulty with the system now in operation is that we apply the concept unsuccessfully. The legal system is quite right in maintaining a concept of responsibility. The crucial issue is, of course, how this concept is applied. We now blame individuals for their behavior, assuming they could have behaved otherwise. Once we understand that contingencies controlling behavior, however, we can control these contingencies so as to alter the behavior. We hold people responsible for their behavior not because of free will but because, when we attach contingencies, we control the behavior. When students who cheat are dismissed from school, we are controlling their behavior; we do this by holding these students responsible. We should examine the consequences of behavior, not probe the mind, to understand the problem of responsibility.

A criminal act having occurred, the law is psychologically sound in administering punishment to decrease the likelihood that the act will be repeated. This is in accord with learning procedures. The issue is not a philosophical but an empirical one: namely, is the applied punishment effective in safeguarding society and decreasing the likelihood of an act? The critical issue, then, becomes not one of determinism versus responsibility but the responsible use of punishment by society to safeguard itself. Such use involves applying the knowledge of what variables maintain behavior.

ALTERNATIVE RECOMMENDATIONS

The American Law Institute Model Penal Code provides that "a person is not responsible for criminal conduct if at the time of such conduct, as a result of mental disease or defect, he lacks substantial capacity either to appreciate the criminality of his conduct or to conform his conduct to the requirements of the law."[14]

In a recent case, *United States vs. Currens*, 290 F. 2d 751 (3rd Cir. 1961), Chief Judge Biggs made use of the following formula

---

[14]Donnelly, *et al.*: *op. cit.*, p. 831.

from a modified version of the Code:

> The jury must be satisfied that at the time of committing the prohibited act the defendant, as a result of mental disease or defect, lacked substantial capacity to conform his conduct to the requirements of the law which he is alleged to have violated.

The *Currens* doctrine omits the phrase "appreciate the criminality of his conduct" that is contained in the *Model Penal Code* because it would over-emphasize the cognitive element in criminal responsibility.[15]

In 1963, the State of Missouri passed a new criminal responsibility bill[16] in which the test of responsibility is that:

> . . . a person is not responsible for criminal conduct if at the time of such conduct, as a result of mental disease or defect, he did not know or appreciate the nature, quality, or wrongfulness of his conduct or was incapable of conforming his conduct to the requirement of the law.

The proposed New York Code[17] states that a person is not criminally responsible for conduct if at the time of such conduct as a result of mental disease or defect, he lacks substantial capacity to know or appreciate either, (a) The nature and consequences of such conduct; or (b) That such conduct was wrong.

Two distinguished law professors, Jerome Hall and Gerhard O. W. Mueller, have defended the *M'Naghten* rule as against the *Durham* rule, the *Currens* rule, or the Model Penal Code.[18]

---

[15]*Ibid.*, p. 838, note 32.

[16]Senate Bill No. 143, 72nd General Assembly of the State of Missouri. See also, Mueller, Gerhard, O.W.: A commentary on Missouri's new mental responsibility bill. *Missouri Bar Journal*, October, 1963.

[17]Hall, Jerome, and Mueller, Gerhard, O.W.: *Criminal Law and Procedure.* 2nd ed., Indianapolis, Bobbs-Merrill, 1965.

[18]Hall, Jerome: Mental disease and criminal responsibility—M'Naghten versus Durham and the American Law Institute's tentative draft. *Indiana Law Journal*, Winter, 1958, pp. 212-25; Mueller, Gerhard, O.W.: M'Naghten remains irreplaceable: recent events in the law of incapacity. *Georgetown Law Journal*, Fall, 1961, pp. 105-19.

They object to the rejection of rationality (cognition) in *Durham* and *Currens,* and the use of the irrestible-impulse test (volition) in the Model Penal Code. Hall and Mueller point out that cognition is an important aspect of an integrated personality system (cognition, emotion, and volition), and that a criminal act cannot occur on the basis of disturbed or sick emotions or volition unless cognition also is impaired. The irrestible-impulse test, the *Durham* rule, and the *Currens* rule recognize the psychiatric argument that the volitional or emotional aspects of behavior can be sick or disturbed while at the same time the cognitive aspects remain whole or intact. The *M'Naghten* rule has been attacked because of its emphasis on cognition.

Professor Mueller argues that the insanity defense has been misinterpreted by the courts. The *M'Naghten* rule, according to Mueller, recognizes two essential elements of any crime: *actus reus* and *mens rea.* The "nature and quality of the act" refers to *actus reus,* and "to know right from wrong" refers to *mens rea.* Accordingly, the purpose of the insanity defense is to establish the absence of a necessary element of a crime, *actus reus* and/or *mens rea.*

> The only legal meaning of insanity, as far as the criminal law is concerned, must be that of an absence of *mens rea* or an absence of *actus reus* by reason of a medical condition, whether we call it a mental disease or a mental illness, or madness, foolishness, or lunacy. . . The *M'Naghten* test is simply a no-crime test; it negates crime by virtue of opposing medical factors which cancel out the existence of some or all of the elements of the crime charged.[19]

This view makes it possible to eliminate the insanity plea, since it is possible to ask whether or not the necessary *actus reus* and *mens rea* are present without resorting to the insanity defense. According to Mueller, one of the basic purposes of the insanity defense is to secure hospitalization for a mentally ill person, and this can be accomplished through civil commitment procedures.

---

[19]Mueller: *Ibid.,* pp. 110-11.

It must be noted, however, that the *Durham* test places the insanity issue not on the elements necessary for a criminal act but on the question whether mental disease existed *as a fact* in the defendant, and whether this mental disease produced the alleged criminal act *as a fact*. Both of these are scientific, not legal or moral issues; and the task then becomes one of verifying the facts concerning mental disease and productivity. This, however, is left to the jury to decide—not to the behavioral expert. As Mueller comments, this is like asking the jury to decide what an elephant is, rather than asking a zoologist for an acceptable definition of an elephant.

A second approach makes use of the concept of diminished responsibility, which is a legal doctrine in Scotland. In 1957, England adopted a diminished responsibility test for homicide. The British Homicide Act provides for a reduced sentence if the court finds that the defendant was not insane but that there were mitigating circumstances in the criminal act. The courts also use a similar concept of partial responsibility whereby, because of the defendant's mental condition, one of the elements of a crime is lacking, usually *mens rea*. For example, if the defendant is intoxicated, he may be found incapable of forming the necessary intent for murder in the first degree, though he may be guilty of second-degree murder or manslaughter. In *Fisher vs. United States*, 149 F. 2d 28 (1945) (not to be confused with *Cameron vs. Fisher*, 328 U.S. 463 (1946)), the Court of Appeals for the District of Columbia refused to recognize the doctrine of diminished responsibility. Fisher was charged with first-degree murder, a capital offense, and he faced possible execution. He was diagnosed as a person of low-grade mentality and a psychopathic personality of an aggressive type. The defense urged that the jury be allowed to convict Fisher for second-degree murder if they found he lacked "sound memory and discretion." The court rejected this argument. [See also *Stewart vs. United States*, 214 F. 2d 879 (1954), where the same argument was again rejected.]

Professor Sheldon Glueck has recently attempted to solve the riddle of determinism versus free will by means of the concept of reduced responsibility.[20]

He begins by quoting from a Kansas case in which the court announced:

> It may be noted that Freudian psychiatrists tend to discount the existence of the capacity in the individual to exercise free will. . . We can only wish all of these learned men success in their quest for knowledge in a new field. But, the law has always insisted upon an exercise of will.[21]

Professor Glueck concludes that "freedom of will is a cherished concept in law."[22] However, he also notes that law must meet the challenge of scientific determinism.

> Looked at individually, men are both free and determined, but the proportions of creative choice and shackled conditioning vary among them on the basis of original endowment, chance influences, and sociocultural impacts. . .[23]

He therefore recommends a mid-verdict of partial or diminished responsibility.

> The provision of a verdict of partial responsibility not only takes account of the inherent difficulty of proof of specific connection between the mental aberration and the crime, but is based on the recognition that a complex problem of degree is involved. The mid-verdict provides for treatment, supervision, and correction of the mentally ill, yet protects society. . .[24]

The concept of reduced responsibility offers nothing new in legal doctrine and it perpetuates the myth that a man is half free and half slave—one part free will, one part determined. If behavior is partially determined, then we must deal with those determinants of behavior in order to prevent crimes or other criminal behavior. We cannot control or predict behavior on

---

[20]Glueck, Sheldon: *Law and Psychiatry*. Baltimore, John Hopkins Press, 1963.

[21]*Ibid.*, p. 10

[22]*Ibid.*, p. 11.

[23]*Ibid.*, p. 14.

[24]*Ibid.*, p. 111.

the basis of free will, so we are obliged to control and predict on the basis of the variables we can manipulate.

The law already uses the partial-responsibility doctrine, although in terms of the *Fisher* decision, it is technically unacceptable. The law assumes that behavior is both free and determined, the problem being to decide in court whether the act in question was free or determined. This position asserts that all behavior involves partial responsibility. As Professor Glueck has argued, the issue is to determine the degree of determinism. Under the *Durham* decision, all behavioral disorders—including personality disorders, alcoholism, and drug addiction—have been labeled "mental disease." Certainly this is an acceptance of the doctrine of partial responsibility in that it states that men should be excused from full responsibility if their behavior is to some degree determined . . . there is less than a psychotic condition present. The *Durham* decision does extend the concept of nonresponsibility to cases less than psychotic.

It should be noted that Glueck's recommendation differs from the *Fisher* decision in one very important respect: according to Glueck, the criminal who received a mid-verdict would be given psychiatric treatment; whereas, in the *Fisher* case, the concept of diminished responsibility was used in an attempt to save the defendant from the electric chair. Even under a second-degree murder verdict, Fisher would have been in a prison, not a hospital. Glueck uses the mid-verdict as a vehicle for treating criminals. One need not resort to concepts such as "mental disease" or "free will" in order to treat criminals; one need only be scientific.

SPECIFIC RECOMMENDATIONS

The specific recommendation for criminal responsibility put forth by this writer is as follows:

(1) Did the defendant engage in behavior which produced consequences which are defined as unlawful?

(2) Did the defendant intend the consequences of the action? Were the consequences of the act the natural and probable

consequences of the act, i.e., did the defendant act so as to gain reward or avoid pain?

(3) Did the defendant know that he could be punished for behaving as he did?

This is essentially the *M'Naghten* Rule in modern psychological terms. The phrase "natural and probable consequences" refers to environmental conditions. Did the defendant know when he pulled the trigger a human being would be killed? Under normal conditions, murder is a natural consequence of shooting at a person, or rape is a natural consequence of sexually assaulting a female. Shooting at a deer and killing a person is not the natural consequence of the act. An infant does not know the consequences. An infants will touch a hot stove until he learns from experience the consequences of his behavior.

Mental disease is a defense only if the defense establishes the fact that mental disease eliminated the intent to commit the crime. As Professor Mueller has noted, the insanity defense is not needed because if a person did not intend the consequences of his behavior, he does not have the prerequisite *actus reus* and *mens rea*.

This is a rule which can be understood by a jury of laymen, and it avoids the confusion of psychiatric jargon. The test of intent is basically the environmental conditions surrounding the criminal act. If modern psychology is right in holding that behavior is governed by its consequences, then one must judge the criminal act in terms of its consequences. If a man robs an airlines office (the *Campbell* case) or flees from the police (the *Watson* case), then it can be assumed he intended to steal money or to escape from the police. If the defense can show that when the defendant robbed the airlines office, he did so under the illusion he was talking to God rather than stealing money, then the defense of insanity is established.

Is there a mental illness which makes it impossible for a person to know the consequences of his action? There is no case cited in this study wherein evidence was introduced that the defendant did not realize the natural consequences of his act. In the *Kent* case, the diagnosis was schizophrenia, though there was no evidence that Kent did not intend to rape and steal. In the Ray case there was evidence that the defendant had delusions of persecution. There was no evidence that Ray did not intend to commit forgery, larceny, or housebreaking. Similarly, in all cases discussed no evidence exists that mental disease eliminated intent.

The only possible mental disease which eliminates intent is schizophrenia involving hallucinations or delusions, and these must apply to the criminal situation, not to some other situation; for example, a man who hears voices or talks to God and robs a liquor store or murders his wife is presumed to have intended his acts unless the jury believes that he did not realize he was killing or stealing. His hallucinations or delusions must be of such a nature as to make it impossible for the defendant to know the consequences of his act. As yet, no psychological evidence exists that such psychophysical distortions of perceptual processes do as a fact exist.

SCIENCE, LAW, AND THE FUTURE

I am not an advocate for frequent changes in laws and institutions. But laws and institutions must go hand in hand with the progress of the human mind. As that becomes more developed, more enlightened, as new discoveries are made, new truths discovered and manners and opinions change, with the change of circumstances, institutions must advance also to keep pace with the times. We might as well require a man to wear still the coat which fitted him when a boy as civilized society to remain ever under the regimen of their barbarous ancestors.   THOMAS JEFFERSON

The advances in science over the past twenty years have been staggering. At this time, the application of science to behavior is in its infancy. A major break-through in this area is now occurring. Recent developments indicate that experimental procedures are being applied to clinical problems. *Life* magazine recently featured a series on the Control of the Brain, in which the advances made in electrical stimulation of the brain (ESB) were described.[25] B. F. Skinner is quoted therein as stating, "Science is steadily increasing our power to influence, change, mold—in a word, control—human behavior." Robert Morison, medical director at Rockefeller Foundation, comments:

> Knowledge of human behavior is becoming organized and accumulative. . . It is becoming scientific. . . It is not too early to prepare ourselves for the day when there will be a behavioral science which will make possible the control of human behavior with a high degree of precision.

Carl Rogers, the founder of nondirective therapy, states:

> We have in the making . . . a science of enormous potential importance, and instrumentality whose social power will make atomic energy seem feeble by comparison.

Robert Felix, the former director of the Institute of Mental Health, has stated:

> In the field of brain physiology I think it (ESB) is the most exciting single discovery. . . I am almost frightened to say what might come of this in terms of the treatment of the mentally ill. If we can, by knowing what elements in the environment produce electrical or chemical changes in the brain, cause this particular circuit, or others which we may find, to function differently than they do in so-called normal individuals, thus altering emotional states, I don't know where we will go. . . We are just on the threshold and where we will go—I don't know. But it is so far, so fast, that our wildest dreams are likely to be ultraconservative.[26]

Man's knowledge of and control over his environment has doubled in the last forty years; since 1920, man has added as much to his knowledge as he possessed and accumulated from the beginning of time to 1920. It is possible that man will double his present knowledge of behavioral technology in the next twenty years.

Scientific analysis of behavior is now far beyond the statements

---

[25]*Life*, March 8 and 15, 1963.

[26]*Life*, March 8, 1963.

made in court concerning human behavior. There is a gap of thirty to fifty years between legal concepts and what is being published in scientific journals in 1966 concerning behavior.

Scientific analysis involves (1) systematic public observation, (2) deterministic principles, and (3) a skepticism of authority, dogma, and tradition.[37] In the courtroom, statements made concerning human behavior are based upon legal precedent, that is, the authority of an earlier decision. It should be noted in this connection that the *Durham* decision the purpose of which was to bring legal concepts into line with modern psychiatric concepts, is based on decisions put forth in *State vs. Pike* in 1870 and *State vs. Jones* in 1871. The lawyer assumes the answers to problems lie in the past, whereas the scientist assumes the answers lie in research yet to be undertaken. This difference is at the core of the conflict between law and behavioral science.

In 1870, Freud's writings were not yet published; his major impact on behavioral science was made in the 1920's and 1930's. Skinner's experimental analysis of behavior began in the 1930's and reached a climax after 1945. Starting with Sutherland, sociological research in criminal behavior has developed over the past thirty or forty years.

It should be noted that the law reifies the opinions of laymen concerning why people behave as they do, for even under the *Durham* rule, the jury must decide what is or is not a mental disease, and whether or not mental disease produces criminal behavior. The writer is all too much aware of the dilemma here: If behavioral experts are allowed to make these decisions, then one must recognize the fact that much of what passes for science in psychiatry, psychology, and sociology is not science but unverified opinion.

If, on the other hand, judges, lawyers, and jurors are allowed to make these decisions, then we are not utilizing to the best of our ability the knowledge we now possess concerning human behavior. In any society as complex as ours, there must be

---

[37]Staats, Arthur W., and Carolyn K.: *Complex Human Behavior.* New York, Holt, Rinehart and Winston, 1963, p. 257.

specialization and expertness. A man would be a fool to be his own lawyer or physician, and we must look to the experts for answers. Where are the experts in behavioral science? We are in our infancy in behavioral science, and the best conclusion this writer is able to come to concerning why men are criminals is "we don't really know." What is needed is basic research (of a scientific kind) in this area. Perhaps one of the difficulties of the *Durham* rule is that it assumes we know when men are mentally ill, or why they are mentally ill, or why they commit crimes.

The extension of scientific knowledge into applied areas is always a difficult task at best. This fact ought to be recognized by both lawyers and scientist. Lawson has summarized this problem when he writes:

> The scientist must be willing to accept practical results as a reasonable objective toward which to apply his methods. The layman, in turn, must be prepared to alter markedly his ways of thinking about whatever phenomena may be involved in the problems that he has asked the scientist to help him solve.[28]

In his article, Krash states that the *Durham* rule has reduced the tension between law and psychiatry.[29] Glueck states that the *Durham* rule resolves the major issues between law and psychiatry.[30] The research project on which this report is based does not indicate any reduction in tension nor any resolution of conflict. If anything, the *Durham* decision has focused attention on the basic conflict between law and science. As a result of the experiences involving the *Durham* rule in the District of Columbia, it is hoped that the issue of crime and mental illness will be given a second look.

The *M'Naghten* rule raised the issue of mental disease and its relation to criminality, an issue that was hidden in such phrases

---

[28]Lawson, Reed: *Learning and Behavior*. New York, Macmillan, 1960, p. 366.

[29]Krash, Abe.: The Durham rule and judicial administration of the insanity defense in the District of Columbia. *Yale Law Journal*, May, 1961, p. 951.

[30]Glueck: *op. cit.*, p. 94.

as "nature and quality of his act" and "know right from wrong." The *Durham* rule made specific the issue involved: mental disease and productivity in relation to criminality. It is now possible to raise questions concerning the insanity plea, because a scientist can now ask, "What is mental disease?" and "How does mental disease produce criminality?" The *Durham* decision brought out into the open questions for which answers can be found. This is the real contribution of the *Durham* decision to law and psychiatry.

In his Law Day address,[31] Judge David L. Bazelon quoted Justice Cardozo, and it seems appropriate to end this report with the quoted remarks:

> If insanity is not to be a defense, let us say so frankly and even brutally, but let us not mock ourselves with a definition that palters with reality. Such a method is neither good moral nor good science nor good law.

The *Durham* decision was put forth as the response of the law to the progress achieved in the field of psychiatry. Psychiatrists regard the *Durham* rule as the Magna Carta of the law-psychiatry field. Yet most courts have rejected the *Durham* decision. [See *Sauer vs. United States,* 241 F. 2d 640.]

The following general conclusions can be noted in respect to the operation of the *Durham* decision.

(1) Rather than resolving the philosophical notion of free will versus the scientific notion of determinism, the *Durham* rule perpetuates this dualistic and conflicting system.

(2) Expert testimony concerning mental disease and criminal behavior is often less than scientific, since it is based on other than scientific procedures.

(3) An acceptable definition of mental disease has not been put forth at this time by psychiatrists or psychologists.

(4) Techniques and facilities for treating behavioral problems, be they labeled "mental disease" or "crime" or both, do not exist at this time. We do not know how to cure or treat antisocial behavior, though the *Durham* rule assumes that such knowledge

---

[31]*Washington Post,* May 5, 1963.

exists. The *Durham* rule does not reform the criminal nor protect society.

(5) The *Durham* rule does not resolve the ancient issue of punishment versus treatment, since it allows both. Treatment can be provided to criminals without labeling them mentally ill. Punishment can be used for rehabilitative purposes. Incarceration in a mental hospital can be punitive.

(6) The criminal law requires criminal intent as an element of a crime. Mental disease does not negate intent, either in the form of cognition or volition. People who are classified as mentally ill respond to reward and punishment. Intent can be defined as objective behavior rather than as a subjective mental state.

(7) A defendant found to be mentally ill under the *Durham* rule is found to be not guilty by reason of insanity. This is in fact an illusion since the nonguilty defendant is deprived of his freedom and incarcerated in an institution. Serious due process issues are raised by the *Durham* rule.

(8) The insanity defense defines crime as a *medical* problem; it therefore ignores the fact that crime is a *social* problem, not a *medical* problem. Experts on criminal behavior from sociology and experimental psychology are not called upon to testify in criminal trials. For this reason, the evidence introduced is often out-of-date, and a lag between scientific knowledge about criminal behavior and courtroom testimony exists which makes it almost impossible at times for the behavioral expert to communicate with the legal expert. This gap in communication must be overcome before any legal definition of criminal responsibility can be created which will make sense to both the scientific community and the legal community.

APPENDICES

Appendix A

LAWYER'S INTERVIEW SCHEDULE

1. What is the present proportion of criminal to civil work that you do? (Has there been any change in this in recent years?)
2. How much of your criminal work involves assigned cases?
3. In your criminal case load, what is the proportion which received psychiatric and/or neurological examinations in the last five years?

........a. More than 75 per cent ....d. 25 per cent

........b. 75 per cent ....e. 10 per cent

........c. 50 per cent ....f. 5 per cent

........g. less than 5 per cent

4. Does this constitute a rise or fall in the incidence of mental examinations and the insanity defense in your practice, proportionately speaking, since *Durham?*
5. What is the proportion of insanity defenses to straight defenses you have propounded in cases of:
   a. Narcotics violations involving drug addicts? ....
   b. Pedophilic crimes and crimes characterized by other sexual deviations? ....
   c. Crimes committed by chronic alcoholics with and without manifestations of delirium tremens? ....
   4. Crimes committed by apparently compulsive recidivists? ....
6. What was the most serious and what was the least serious crime for which the insanity defense was used?
7. What is your conception of the nature of a causal relationship between crime and psychopathology which entitles a defendant to acquittal?
8. Do you think the causal relationship must be direct or can it be indirect? Why?

9. What are your criteria of direct relationship? Indirect relationship?

10. Could you give me a typical example from your own experience of circumstances which have led you to propounding an insanity defense?

11. How about a less typical example?

12. Usually we understand a client to be competent to stand trial when he understands the charges, is capable of conferring with counsel and intelligently participating in his defense. Is there anything in addition to intellectual understanding which you might consider essential to competency?

13. It has occasionally been asserted that 90 per cent of the patients at Saint Elizabeths are "competent to stand trial." Do you agree?

14. What is your conception of the philosophy underlying the *Durham* decision?

15. What meaning do you attach to the terms "mental disease" and "mental defect" as used in the first *Durham* decision?

16. Which of the Court of Appeals decisions, dealing with insanity since the first Durham case, have you found particularly significant? [If the respondent does not provide a rationale, then] Why do those cases stand out in your mind?

17. Have you heard of the *Carter* case?

18. Do you think that an insanity defense should be based solely upon a psychiatric disorder of some severity or do you think that a minor or any minor psychiatric disorder will do? [If the respondent says severe] What are your standards for a severe psychiatric disorder? [If the respondent says *slight*] Would you believe the mental disease or defect requirement of an insanity defense to be satisfied on practical as well as legal grounds in the following:

    a. A client who is an alcoholic?

    b. A client who is a drug addict?

    c. A client who is a homosexual?

    d. A client who has been diagnosed as having a passive-aggressive personality disorder?

    e. A client who has been diagnosed as having an obsessive-compulsive personality disorder?

    f. A client who has had a clearly defined psychotic reaction but is presently clear of psychotic disorder?

    g. A client who is viewed by the examining psychiatrist as
    "ill primarily in terms of society and of conformity with
    the prevailing cultural milieu?"

19. What is the minimum evidence of psychopathology upon which
you would base (a) a request for private psychiatric consultation;
(b) a motion for mental examination; (c) an insanity defense?

20. How seriously would you be inclined to consider an insanity
defense in a misdemeanor case involving a relatively mild mental
disorder—say a neurosis or personality disturbance—and subject
to a maximum penalty of six months?

21. Can you visualize any state of mental disease or defect con-
current with the commission of a crime in which the crime is
not the product of the mental disease or defect?

22. Are the following considerations likely to affect your deciding
on an insanity defense on practical as well as legal grounds:
    a. The financial resources of your client and his family?
    b. The legal limits of the penalty which may be imposed in
    the event of a verdict of guilty?
    c. The nature of the diagnostic facilities made available under
    court auspices?
    d. The character of the crime?
    e. The cultural and/or subcultural background of your client?
    f. Your estimate of the therapeutic facilities at Saint Eliza-
    beth's.
    g. The stigma of insanity or mental illness?
    h. The lack of any other legal defense? Can you think of any
    instances where this was the case?

23. In the event that you decide to proceed with the insanity defense,
what, in brief, is your general *modus operandi?*

24. In presenting an insanity defense, do you have any preference for
either trial by the court or a jury trial? What is the basis for
your preference?

25. What has been your experience with regard to judicial attitudes
to the insanity defense?

26. To what extent, if any, do you consider yourself handicapped
in offering relevant psychiatric data by your witness as a result
of the existing rules of evidence?

27. Can you give us an idea of the proposed instructions that you
have most frequently submitted to the trial court on the issue
of the insanity defense?

28. In choosing a jury on *voir dire* for an insanity case—what specific individuals [in terms of (a) class, (b) race, (c) ethnic and cultural background, (d) education, (e) occupation, (f) sex, (g) age, (h) political affiliation and perspective, (i) religion, (k) any other criteria] do you tend to welcome or reject? Why? Specifically on the basis of what experience and what expectations?

29. What alerts you to look for mental disorder in a client?

30. Do you usually conduct a systematic interview to determine the mental state of a client charged with a crime? [If yes] What form does the interview take? [If no] Then do you inquire as to prior mental hospitalization, attempts at suicide, rejection or discharge from service on mental grounds, marital incompatibility, scolastic and/or occupational failure, drinking, narcotic addiction, etc.?

31. How do you select a private psychiatric consultant for courtroom use?

32. What are the important considerations in making the selection?

33. How do you get a line on prospective psychiatric witnesses?

34. How many different private psychiatric consultants have you used? Who were they?

35. What are the usual arrangements by which their services have been secured?

36. You are undoubtedly familiar with the legal use of medical specialists in personal injury litigation. Lawyers cultivate and train doctors to prepare satisfactory reports, i.e., reports essentially slanted to highlight the case of the hiring party. We have been accustomed to think of plaintiffs' doctors and defendants' doctors in this connection. Would you agree that this state of affairs is duplicated in the lawyers' use of psychiatrists for the insanity defense?

37. I would like to get as clear a picture as possible of how you use private psychiatric experts. Could you, therefore, give me a concise description of how you use your expert in preparing a case? [If the respondent either needs prompting or fails to cover the topic, use the following questions]:

   a. Do you consult with him prior to his contact with the patient?

   b. To what extent do you provide him with instructions to guide him in his examination?

    c. Do you instruct him as to your conception of mental disease or defect or your criteria of causal relationship between crime and mental disorder?

    d. Do you make information available to him which you have gathered?

    e. To what extent do you check on the thoroughness of his examination?

    f. What is your conception of diagnostic adequacy? Do you have any specific criteria of diagnostic adequacy?

    g. Do you insist on a detailed written psychiatric report to you in advance of trial? If no, why not? If yes, what are your standards of adequacy for psychiatric reporting?

38. In the case of a client committed to (a) Saint Elizabeths, (b) D.C. General, and then certified as "sane, competent, and capable of standing trial and free of mental disorder at the time of the crime charged in the indictment" would you:

    a. Accept the report and try the case on its merits?

    b. Seek individual consultation with hospital doctors and check on hospital records?

    c. Seek further consultation? And, if so, by what means in the case of:

        (1) a paying client?

        (2) an indigent one?

39. What kind of psychiatric testimony are you after?

40. What do you understand by a psychodynamic explanation of the criminal act?

41. What psychiatric texts do you use to brief yourself for the handling of an insanity defense and which do you favor in the cross-examination of adversary psychiatric witnesses?

42. Do you give any instructions to psychiatrists on the subject of causation?

43. Do you think that psychiatrists on the witness stand are easy to communicate with? [If negative] What accounts for the difficulty [If technical language not mentioned] Does psychiatric terminology present a problem in communication?

44. Would you ask your psychiatric witness on direct examination to specify the detailed basis upon which he rests his opinion, or would you ask him to state his general findings? If you should insist upon the detailed basis, would you ask him to report on:

    a. What he was told by the defendant?

    b. What he was told by the friends or relatives of the defendant?

    c. What he was told by the police?

    d. The opinion expressed by another examining psychiatrist?

    e. The data gleaned from a social worker's investigation?

    f. The decision of a diagnostic staff conference?

    g. The content of a psychological report, based on the results of the Wechsler-Bellevue, Rorschach, and other psychological tests?

    h. The data gleaned from a gross neurological examination, carried out by another specialist?

    i. His study of the hospital records and the data contained therein?

    j. The results of (1) an electroencephalogram ⎤ obtained by
                   (2) a pneumoencephalogram ⎦ a neurologist?

    k. The criminal record of the defendant?

45. What has been your experience in securing unpaid psychiatric volunteers to aid in the defense of an indigent client?

46. What has been your experience in securing the oppointment of psychiatric witnesses in your behalf under Rule 28, F.R.Cr. P.?

47. The Court of Appeals has spoken in the *Winn* and *Calloway* cases of the need for a full and thorough mental examination when the insanity defense is interposed. Do you think such examinations are obtained by (a) the indigent, (b) the private client?

48. Can you tell me/us your impressions of:

    a. Legal Psychiatric Service?

    b. D. C. General Hospital Psychiatric Division?

    c. Saint Elizabeths Hospital

        (1) its diagnostic,

        (2) its therapeutic effectiveness?

49. What is your general impression of the caliber of the psychiatric testimony obtainable from these three services?

50. To what extent, if any, does your evaluation of these services tend to affect your pretrial and trial tactics in the insanity defense?

51. Would you be willing to use the insanity defense more often if Saint Elizabeths had better treatment facilities?

52. How would you rate the adequacy of psychiatric services obtainable for courtroom use on a private level?

53. Have you ever had occasion to object to a governmental attempt to secure the mental examination of your client, and, if so, on what grounds? Can you visualize a situation in which you might be inclined to interpose such an objection?

54. Have you found it possible or desirable to prepare an insanity defense without allowing the Government to learn about your plans and then "spring" it as a surprise?
    Have you ever done this, and, if so, with what results?

55. What are your personal impressions of the reasons for the success of the insanity defense?
    [Then] What are the chief causes of its failure?

APPENDIX B

PSYCHIATRIST'S INTERVIEW SCHEDULE

1. How many times have you examined a defendant accused of crime for (a) a defense lawyer, (b) the United States Attorney's Office, (c) the Court? [If the psychiatrist has worked with the defense, then the next question should be]: What defense lawyers?
2. What is your conception of the nature of that causal relationship between crime and psychopathology which entitles an accused to acquittal by reason of insanity or requires you to say that the crime was a product of mental illness?
3. Do you view the causal relationship between crime and mental disease or defect as predominantly a legal or a psychiatric problem? Why?
4. Do you think the causal relationship must be direct or proximate to secure an acquitttal by reason of insanity or to enable you to say that the crime was a product of mental illness?
5. What are your own criteria for determining whether an adequate causal relationship between mental disorder and crime has existed, i.e., to determine whether the accused has acted because of mental disorder.
6. Have you received any instructions from lawyers on the subject of causation? Have you given any instructions to the lawyers on the subject of causation?
7. Would you give me two or three typical examples in your experience in which the causation requirement was satisfied in your opinion? How about a few typical ones?
8. Is your attitude toward causation likely to be affected by the treatability of the defendant and his co-operation with you?
9. Do you ever use the terms "insane," "of unsound mind," "incompetency"? If so, what generic or other kind of meaning do you assign to these terms in general or in any specific context? To what extent, if any, do you equate those terms with psychosis?

304

10. What do you understand by the statement that the defendant is not competent to stand trial? What is your view of the degree or character of disability which he must represent to qualify under this heading? Are you concerned primarily with cognition in this context?

11. What do you consider to be the philosophy underlying the *Durham* Rule?

12. What meaning do you attach to the terms "mental disease" and "mental defect" within the *Durham* frame of reference? Do you think it is essential that you have a definite conception on the subject as an expert witness?

13. Do you think present law requires an insanity defense to be based upon a mental disorder of some severity or do you think that any mental disorder will do?

    [If respondent says *severe*]

    What are your standards for a severe mental disorder?

    [If respondent says *any*]

    Would you believe the mental disease or defect requirements of an insanity defense to be satisfied on legal as well as medical grounds in the case of any of the psychoneurotic and personality disorders, including those involving only mild impairment, listed in the *Diagnostic and Statistical Manual* of the APA? On what do you base your assumption? And, what specific advice would you give the lawyer who solicited your guidance?

14. Do you think the term "insanity" in the insanity defense might tend to predispose psychiatrists to assume some severity of psychopathology is needed for a valid insanity defense?

15. Suppose you diagnose a person as in need of psychotherapy. Would that diagnostic judgment, without more, be sufficient in your opinion to justify the assumption that he was suffering from mental disease or defect in the context of the *Durham* Rule? More specifically, would you testify that he was not suffering from mental disease or defect if he manifested only a mild degree of impairment caused by a minor personality disorder?

16. What advice would you be prepared to give a defense lawyer under the following circumstances: His client is charged with a simple assault involving a maximum penalty of one year's imprisonment. His chances for probation appear good. Your diagnosis of the client is that he suffers from a passive-aggressive

personality disorder. Would your advice vary if you diagnosed the client as (a) a sociopath, (b) a paranoid personality, (c) a neurotic, (d) a victim of a transitory psychotic reaction?

17. What was the nature of the arrangements by which your services have been generally procured for the mental examination of a patient in a court case? When selected by the lawyer, have you maintained a more or less continuing relationship with the lawyer who selected you in other court cases? If so, what has been the nature of this relationship, e.g., have you generally been available to testify on psychiatric issues in negligence, as well as criminal cases? What fee arrangements have been generally made in such a context? Have you received referrals of patients or cases from lawyers you have worked with?

18. Have you ever been invited to participate in an insanity defense on a gratuitous basis? If so, what has been your response?

19. Do you expect to receive instructions from the lawyer to guide you in your examination? How often have you received such instructions? What type? On *legally* relevant areas of inquiry? Form of testimony?

20. What problems do you generally encounter in communicating your professional opinion to laymen in the legal arena?

21. What kind of guidance do you give the lawyer as to the best means of eliciting your expert opinion?

22. How soon after arrest do you usually see the defendant? What has been the effect of the time lapse upon your examination?

23. How often have you felt that your final diagnosis, given from the witness stand, might have been different if you could have made a more exacting study of the defendant?

24. What, if any, is the role of empathy in the diagnostic determination of mental illness and its relationship to the crime charged in the indictment?

25. To what extent have you found that you had or lacked empathy in your work with defendants awaiting trial?

26. What is the realistic chance of finding a psychiatrist who can have empathy in the routine case? How about a case involving sociopathic or other personality disorders?

27. What, if any, has been the difference in your diagnostic practice and testimony since *Durham*?

28. Could you tell us briefly your impressions of:
    a. Legal Psychiatric Service?

    b. Saint Elizabeths:
          (1) its diagnostic,
          (2) its therapeutic effectiveness?
    c. D. C. General Hospital Psychiatric Division?

29. To what extent, if any, does your evaluation of these services tend to affect your pretrial tactics in the insanity defense?

30. Do any of the following considerations affect your examination of the defendant or your courtroom testimony?
    a. The severity of the punishment.
    b. The defendant's motivation for treatment.
    c. The merits of jail as punishment.
    d. Community treatment facilities.
    e. Saint Elizabeths treatment facilities.
    f. The defendant's public dangerousness.
    g. The prognosis.
    h. Public opinion and community attitudes.

31. Have you ever presented the court with a psychodynamic interpretation of a crime? [If not] Why not? [If yes] How was it received?

32. What aspects of psychiatric interpretation have you found unacceptable to the jury? [Then] Why?

33. Have you ever adjusted or omitted material which may have been important because you felt that it might have been misinterpreted by the court or jurors?

34. Have you ever felt that the judge was unfriendly to your testimony? [If yes] How did he express his attitude?

35. Have you felt that the judge succeeded in communicating such an unfriendly attitude to the jury?

36. To what extent, if any, have you felt handicapped by restrictive evidentiary rules?

37. Have your experiences in forensic psychiatry made you more or less willing to participate in the insanity defense?

38. What are your impressions of the chief causes of the success of the insanity defense?
    [Then]
How about the failures?

39. What do you consider to be the major problems of the insanity defense?

40. What is your theoretical persuasion in the field of psychiatry?

INVOLUNTARY INSTITUTIONALIZATION: SOME LEGAL, ETHICAL, AND SOCIAL IMPLICATIONS[1]

EDWARD S. SULZER

University of Minnesota

Those aspects of science and medicine which are often introduced in procedures leading to the involuntary institutionalization of an individual are usually not pertinent to the basic question. People committed to institutions against their wishes are committed there primarily on social grounds. I suggest that mental illness (and its many synonyms and euphemisms) is neither illness nor mental. In the first place, mental illness is not mental; it is a problem of human behavior. In the second place, it is not an illness; it is essentially socially unacceptable behavior—behavior which, from the point of view of other people, is undesirable; behavior which is irritating, annoying, unpleasant, or in some cases simply different. I will try to give several examples of this later on. You may have noticed that my title did not include the scientific aspects of involuntary institutionalization but was restricted to the social, the ethical, and the legal. The reason is that, as a scientist, I do not view the problems that we generally deal with in the treatment of the psychiatric patient, or the so-called mentally ill individual, as essentially scientific today. These problems are questions of ethics, morals, social and societal values, and law. Very often activities in the legal or social arenas are alleged to be scientific or the products of some part of science. I suggest that the allegation is false insofar as our treatment of the involuntary psychiatric patient is concerned. What we do in the name of science is sometimes not scientific and, in fact, goes against the relevant evidence we find on the subject. Usually, in science, we expect that the criteria for the labeling of anything or any person will allow us to differentiate the thing or person from anything else we deal with. In the field of mental illness, or the mentally disabled, this is not the case. The evidence today is that there is a very low degree of concordance among psychiatrists, psychologists, psychiatric social workers, and other people working in the field of mental health. What is mental illness for one person in one society at one time is often not mental illness for another person in another society, despite the fact that the behavior of the two individuals is highly similar or identical.

A recent case in one of our southern states is a good example. A young Negro man who was applying to the law school at one of our southern state universities was apprehended by the state police on the grounds that he was mentally ill. He felt that Negroes in his state should be treated as fairly as white people. This became the criterion for mental illness in the situation. In a recent, fairly well publicized case in the city of Chicago, two people, a married couple, immigrants to this country from Poland, refugees from Nazi persecution, were institutionalized, partly because they could not speak English very well.[2] They had few friends in this country and did not understand, nor was it explained to them, what they were doing in a courtroom. They were not provided with sufficient information about what was happening to them. They were institutionalized against their will and, unfortunately, in this particular situation, institutionalization led to the death of the husband. There are other examples that could be offered to demonstrate the fact that what we have today is not a system based upon science, but a system based on certain social and ethical viewpoints. Some of these viewpoints have been established in our laws so that they have become statutory or have become part of our common law or have become part of administrative procedure.

In a recent volume, Professor Thomas Szasz examines the problem of how mental illness became illness.[3] That is, what brought it

---

[1]Excerpts of an address before the National Convention of Therapeutic Self Help Clubs, Minneapolis, June, 1962. While the original talk is presented here only in part, an attempt has been made to retain the flavor of the oral presentation.

[2]American Civil Liberties Union, Illinois Division. *The Duzinski Case;* Chicago, Author, 1962.

[3]Szasz, T. S.: *The Myth of Mental Illness.* New York, Hoeper-Harper, 1961.

under the purview of medicine and, most particularly, psychiatry. In effect, he demonstrates how, to a large extent, this was a historical development based on the alteration of moral and ethical values held by authority figures. It could very well have become a matter of theological and religious concern as it was in the Middle Ages. Then a person was not mentally ill but was possesed by the devil. Historically, neurologists became interested in problems of behavioral deviation and in people whose behavior was not socially accepted. Thus, it became a medical problem, particularly when a leading specialist of the time decided that behavioral deviation was an illness. This was a medical decision, insofar as the decision was made by physicians. Society at that time, particularly French and Austrian-German society, adopted the medical point of view. Some behaviors are sick and therefore the province of the physician. From that acceptance into medicine developed the present-day specialty of psychiatry.

I also believe mental illness is an ethical problem and for many people, particularly clergymen, a moral or religious problem. In our society, as well as in other societies, we have developed ethical and moral codes which deem certain behavior desirable or good and other behaviors as undesirable, bad, or evil. In our society there are many features of a person's behavior which are viewed as undesirable. When a person's behavior is so viewed and when people in his surroundings find it difficult to explain why this person's behavior is what it is, he is very likely to end up with the label "mentally ill." These two characteristics are generally required: first, the behavior is viewed by some person or persons as undesirable; and, second, it is difficult to understand. A recent case in New York City demonstrates this. A lady attacked the Reverend Martin Luther King, the leader of a movement to increase the speed of integration. This lady was a Negro. When she attacked the Reverend Mr. King, she was immediately apprehended, accused, and later "convicted" of having a mental illness. Let us assume, however, for the moment a hypothetical case in which she wasn't Negro and that it was a Southern white woman who had attacked King. Would she have also been considered mentally ill? I doubt it. I think this would have been seen as politically or socially motivated action which was criminal in its intention and treated as a crime. But since it became difficult for people to understand why a Negro woman should attack a Negro minister who had been so important in the Negro's effort to obtain integration and equality in the South, people said, "This must be a crazy act. How else can we explain it." Therefore, this woman was sent to Bellevue Hospital in New York and it was alleged that she was mentally ill.

Now, one might ask, is it not better for a person to be thought of as mentally ill in our society than to be thought of as a criminal? I would raise very serious doubts about that. In criminal law in this country, there are many safeguards afforded the individual who is accused of committing a crime. On the whole, the very same safeguards are *not* afforded to the person accused of being mentally ill. In our criminal courts, a person is generally deemed to be innocent until proven guilty. When a person is accused of being mentally ill, the situation is reversed. Generally, rather than the burden of evidence falling on other people to demonstrate the presence or probable presence of something, it becomes the burden of the person to demonstrate that he is innocent of the charge of mental illness. Since this question cannot be answered in a scientific sense, it falls into the legal, social, and ethical area for demonstration of the absence or presence of something called mental illness. This is not a scientific enterprise.

Let me demonstrate the lack of provisions made to safeguard individuals who are accused—and I use the word accused in a highly emotional fashion—of being mentally ill. What happens when a person is so accused and how does this compare to the situation in which the same person might be accused of a criminal act?

We find that thirty-seven of our fifty states require or have some form of judicial hospitalization.[4] On what basis may the court decide which "mentally ill" person may be institutionalized involuntarily? In five states, the sole criterion in the law is that a person is dangerous to himself or others. The prediction of this, scientifically, is a most awkward business. When we look at the data, we find that one cannot successfully predict either for individuals or for groups whether he will be a danger to himself or to others. If anything, a psychiatric patient (as defined in the research literature) is less dangerous to himself and to society than members of other groups which are not psychiatrically labeled.

Twelve states provide that a person may be institutionalized if

4Lindman, F. T., and McIntyre, D. M., Jr. (eds.): *The Mentally Disabled and the Law. Chicago*, Univ. of Chicago Press, 1961.

he is a danger to himself or to others and also needs treatment. Presumably we have forms of treatment which are efficacious for the psychiatric patient who is ill. Again, the scientific literature lends little support to this conclusion. If anything, the institutions to which people are committed involuntarily probably do not "help" the persons any more than were he not hospitalized. In fact, the evidence suggests that a person is often better off outside an institution than he is inside the institution, if the criterion is eventual adjustment to a life outside of an institution.

Seven states in our country have only the requirement that the person require treatment to be hospitalized. He does not have to be dangerous to himself or others. In one state, we have a most honest even though strange statute regarding hospitalization. The state is Massachusetts. The state says, essentially, in its statutes, that social nonconformiy may lead to involuntary institutionalization and this can be the only basis. This is an honest statute because it recognizes what is implicit in the statutes of all other states, i.e., that social nonconformity brings people into the court and later into a hospital against their will.

In five states, there are no statutory requirements; that is, it is entirely up to the judge in the particular court to decide himself without the guide of statutory law if the person should be institutionalized. This summarizes what we call judicial hospitalization. But there are also other forms—administrative and medical. In nineteen states, any citizen of the state may initiate proceedings in a court to get any other citizen of that state involuntarily institutionalized. In other words, if your neighbor or friend, relative, spouse, child, or parent wishes to institute proceedings he may do so. It does not require any demonstration on his part of the presence or absence of any phenomenon called mental illness. It also does not require that he demonstrate that he will not benefit from the person's institutionalization. In many cases, the spouse, parent, or child unquestionably benefits from the hospitalization of the relative. In eleven states, when a person applies for the commitment of another citizen, a physician must be brought into the affair. A physician must certify that, in his opinion, such an action is called for. In four additional states, two physicians must be called into action to bring the person into the hospital against his will.

What happens after a person is accused of being mentally ill and requiring hospitalization? I take a general case here that differs slightly from state to state. Ordinarily in criminal law, were a person accused of committing a crime he would immediately have the right to communicate with counsel, an attorney of his own choice, or, if he were indigent, of having an attorney probably assigned by the court. What happens to the person accused of being psychiatrically or mentally ill? In only *seven* of our fifty states does a person accused of being mentally ill have the unrestricted right to counsel and to communicate freely with counsel. Forty-three states do *not* provide this safeguard. In only nineteen states is it required to give notice to the person who is accused of being mentally ill that he is so accused, that there will be a hearing, that there may be physicians involved, that there will be a judicial determination of his status, and that he might end up in a hospital against his will for an indeterminate period.

One would imagine, if someone's life is going to be dealt with in this fashion, that not only should he know about it but also that he should be present when these decisions are being made. It is traditional in Anglo-Saxon countries that a person be present if he is being charged with and tried for a crime. In only ten states of the United States is the prospective patient required to be in attendance. To repeat, nineteen states require that he be told, and of those nineteen, only ten require that he be there. Twelve states permit the patient into the hearing *if* he demands it and *if* the court accepts the demand as reasonable. Only half of the states require that the proceedings take place in a courtroom or in any other location that is usually used for judicial hearings or judicial decisions. Twenty-five states authorize that a hearing may be held outside of a courtroom in any informal situation as may be deemed desirable by the court. Hearings have been held in everything, including—in one case—a lavatory. Often there is little legal record kept of the proceedings. A judgment may be entered, with appeal made difficult because of the absence of a stenographic record. The problems that arise and that are dealt with in a criminal proceeding by an open evaluation of the problems cannot be accomplished in such an informal procedure.

One might expect, if social nonconformity is the reason people get institutionalized, that a group of a person's peers should have some evaluative role in determining whether a behavior is truly nonconforming or nonacceptable to the public. In criminal trials, we accept the idea that a jury of a man's peers may be introduced. No state in this country requires a jury trial for a person accused of mental illness. Ten states permit it on the demand of the patient and, of those ten, three require that the court agree to it. The courts have ruled that the United States Constitution does not guarantee the right of trial by jury in state courts in civil trials. This includes the adjudication of mental illness, insanity, or involuntary institutionalization. Some state constitutions do require trial by jury even though it has not always been interpreted to be applicable to the psychiatric patient. In some states' constitutions, the right to trial by jury in a civil case is guaranteed *except* if one is accused of mental illness. In that case, he is deprived of this right.

Now, suppose a person doesn't have very much money and is accused of committing a crime. In most jurisdictions, he will be offered the opportunity to have an attorney represent him. What happens if he is accused of mental illness? Seventeen states provide that counsel may be supplied to someone having none. In most other states, this is done only if the judge deems it appropriate!

If he has no money, only fifteen states provide that the attorney assigned be compensated by the state or by the county. In some states, an assigned attorney may not be legally compensated for his actions on behalf of someone accused of mental illness. In two states, the statutes define how much money the attorney can get when he is to be paid. In one case, the maximum is $10 a day. In other cases, it is $25 a day. One wonders how many attorneys look forward to receiving these cases on assignment by the court. Finally, in twelve states, no legal adjudication in a courtroom need take place not in fact need a judge be involved. All commitment requires is a physician or psychiatrist or in some cases two physicians or two psychiatrists.

So far, I have dealt with the problem of how did one get into this institution that he didn't want to get into in the first place. What happens afterwards? Suppose he wants to get out, communicate with his family or friends, communicate with the judge who sent him there, or the physicians who were instrumental in getting him there. He may want to communicate with the governor of the state, or with the responsible agency in the state. Again, we might look at the criminal who does have, in most cases, the opportunity to contact his attorney throughout his incarceration. Compare him to the person in the hospital. Eight states have statutory provisions permitting a psychiatric patient to communicate with his attorney.

In most jurisdictions, the superintendent of the institution is given responsibility for determining whether a person may or may not communicate with people on the outside.

Remember, he is supposed to be in there because he needed treatment. Treatment may be the use of mechanical restraints, the use of chemical restraints, electroconvulsive therapy, insulin coma therapy, brain surgery, or it can be psychotherapy. It can be many things, including the loss of the opportunity to communicate with the outside.

Late in the nineteenth century, word began getting out to the public as to what may happen to people in state and other mental hospitals. Miss Dorothea L. Dix and other reformers began investigating. Laws were passed by state legislators who had heard of obvious examples of mistreatment or maltreatment. However, there are only twelve states that went so far and still have on their law books any regulation for the use of mechanical restraint on a patient. Mechanical restraints may mean different things: cuffs, muffs, restraining jackets, and so forth.

While one is in the state institution or other hospital involuntarily, what safeguards are afforded? In not a single state does the patient have an effective right to object if the staff of the institution wants him to submit to brain surgery, electroconvulsive therapy; to insulin coma therapy or to psychotherapy. In only two states is approval by a nonstaff member required. In these two cases, the responsible person may be the superintendent of the institution, or a relative of the patient. If a husband had his wife institutionalized, he may be asked, "May we treat your wife in such a manner?" Of course, he will very often give his permission. He would assume, usually in all honesty on his part, that the staff of the institution is doing what is best for his wife. The evidence, however, leaves much to be desired in terms of what positive effects it has on human beings to have the brain operated on.

Let us look at another possibility. The psychiatric patient believes while in the institution or after he is discharged that he was negligently treated while in the institution. Suppose he feels that he should not have been given electroconvulsive therapy, or should not have had his brain operated upon. Suppose he comes out of one of these procedures deformed or damaged. One would imagine that in most cases of negligence he could sue the person or persons responsible. Here you discover a very interesting fact.

No psychiatric patient has ever won a case of negligence against a physician because of electroconvulsive therapy of psychosurgery despite the frequent occurrence of death and injury. This fact has led to vigorous dissents in various courts of appeal. A case occurred in the State of California some years ago. A woman had been grossly deformed as a result of electroconvulsive therapy, ending up with broken legs and a deformed hip, leaving her almost incapable of walking. The majority, on appeal, affirmed a lower court decision saying that the woman could not even enter the case against the physicians and other staff people responsible for her condition because she was not competent to bring suit on her own behalf.[5]

Suppose one is in an institution, wants to leave, and hasn't been able to communicate with people on the outside. The patient wishes to be re-examined by the staff of the institution so that he may know whether they believe he ought to be released. Only eleven of our states require periodic examinations and, of those, four do not specify frequency. No state details the scope or procedure to be employed in the examination. The "Hello, how are you feeling?" form of examination has been accepted in some jurisdictions.

Further discussion of current procedures could be developed, but it seems appropriate now to examine what may be the concepts and assumptions that appear to furnish the background for the procedures. Perhaps the most pervasive concept, often unstated, is the assumption that some group in society possesses the means to detect "evil" (mental illness)[6] and also may have the means to purge it. Physicians have legally achieved the position of wise men who are responsible to society for the detection of possible danger and to remove the danger. Further, they are assumed to have this superior wisdom on the basis of their education and experience.[7] Without going into the substantive issues, one wonders what in medical training provides the physician with the presumably necessary background to be the judge of his fellow citizens' behavior. Apparently we have relieved ourselves of the responsibility of answering the question by deciding that unpopular behavior is illness or a product

[5]*Farber vs. Olkon*, 40 Cal. 2d 503, 510, 511. 254 P. 2d 520, 527, 528 (1953).

[6]Szasz, T. S.: Bootlegging humanistic values through psychiatry. *Antioch Review*, 1962, 341-49.

[7]Szasz, T. S.: Scientific method and social role in medicine and psychiatry. *AMA Arch., Int. Med., 101*: 228-38, 1958.

thereof. The philosophers, judges, and theologians have been excused from their historical position as the arbiters of social behavior. The physician, particularly the psychiatrist, is now pre-eminent in the field and his tools (words) are not the "evil" or "virtue" of the past but the "sick" or "healthy" of the present. As the priest was relieved of having to deal with the substance of the reformer's position by the Inquisition, the public is relieved of having to deal with the behavior and statements of the unacceptable person by the physician and his paramedical and legal colleagues.

The concept of the rule of law (as against the rule of man) has been considered one of the foundations of the "open society."[8] We have deemed it wise to prevent the assumption of excessive authority by a group or individual through a system of checks and balances. Yet we find the psychiatric patient neither protected by checks and balances nor by the opportunity to rely on legal processes that are equal to the task. We have permitted a relatively small group of specialists to be the accusers, judges, and wardens of those *they* elect to choose as "sick." Outside of the psychiatric realm, the assumption of such authority by physicians or other professional groups is unthinkable and were it proposed, would probably lead to a hue and cry of considerable proportion. The details of apprehension and prosecution of the criminal have been worked over to develop a fairly detailed, elaborate, and systematic procedure. Such has not seriously been attempted to any large degree in the case of the psychiatric patient.[9]

Comparison is invited between the specificity of the criminal act and its punishment and the totally open-ended quality of "sick" behavior and its penalty. We have assumed that the "open society" requires the explication of offenses and the punishment. Yet we find the person who is only a "little" mentally ill open to a life sentence to a state or veterans' hospital. The "very" mentally ill may pay only a small penalty. The threat of a life sentence for a psychiatric patient is not a mere possibility. In 1956, 36 per cent of all men admitted for the first time to a psychiatric institution died in that insitution within three years. Thirty-three per cent of women ad-

[8] Popper, K.: *The Open Society and Its Enemies.* Princeton, N. J., Princeton Univ. Press, 1950.

[9] Ross, H. A.: Commitment of the mentally ill: problems of law and policy. *Michigan Law Rev.*, 57: 945-1018, 1959.

mitted died within the institution within three years. In 1956, almost one out of every five in-patients were separated from a psychiatric institution by death. Life sentences for the psychiatric patient are everyday occurrences.

At this point, let me propose an alternative solution to our problem. Any involuntary institutionalization of a person on the grounds that he is mentally ill is unacceptable—unacceptable because our present system assumes that some group in society has superior wisdom about the rightness and wrongness ("sickness and health") of behavior; unacceptable because we create a class of second-class citizens whose rights and liberties are taken away under the guise of treatment and protection; unacceptable because of the toll of human misery and horror it charges.

Science does not dictate ethical or value positions. The alleged scientific bases for institutionalization should be suspect when proposed. Let us not accept either the pretensions to superior wisdom made by scientists *qua* scientists or the pretensions of others under any label. Rather, let us examine what we currently maintain and what we would view as desirable for an open society based on the freedom of the individual. We may find much that needs change and we should work for it rather than have others impose their wishes on us.

We should not be misled by what professionals *say* they do. Look at what in fact they *are* doing. If you examine the language that is employed and what the person does, you will find quite different phenomena involved. We ought to undertake a very careful and intensive examination of what our ultra-first-class citizens, the psychiatrists, psychologists, social workers, and attorneys, are doing to the second-class citizen, the psychiatric patient.

INDEX OF AUTHORS

INDEX OF CASES

INDEX OF SUBJECTS